Christmas
1990

THE BIG FAT BUNTER BOOK

THE BIG FAT BUNTER BOOK

CREATED BY
FRANK RICHARDS

INTRODUCED BY
MARY CADOGAN

DESIGNED & COMPILED BY
MIKE HIGGS

HAWK
BOOKS

GRATEFUL ACKNOWLEDGEMENTS TO MARY CADOGAN
AND NORMAN WRIGHT FOR MANY OF THE ITEMS USED TO
ILLUSTRATE THIS BOOK. SOME ILLUSTRATIONS COURTESY
OF THE CHARLES HAMILTON MUSEUM, MAIDSTONE, KENT.

THE BIG FAT BUNTER BOOK
ISBN 0 948248 02 5

PUBLISHED BY
**HAWK BOOKS LIMITED
SUITE 309
CANALOT STUDIOS
222 KENSAL ROAD
LONDON W10 5BN
ENGLAND**

DESIGN: MIKE HIGGS GRAPHICS

PRINTED IN FINLAND

FOREVER BUNTER!

By Mary Cadogan

When Billy Bunter rolled off his creator's Remington in 1908 no-one could have dreamed that he was set for literary immortality. The first mention of him in *Magnet* No. 1 conveys only a hint of the lurid and inflated character that he was to become. He rushes and blunders and sprawls on the floor because he is too short-sighted to see more than a foot in front of him, but he is hardly the stuff of which resilient anti-heroes are made. He doesn't even utter his famous 'Yarooh!' which was soon to be established as his very own ejaculation whenever Mr. Quelch, his form-master, gave him six of the best on his bags, or when Herbert Vernon-Smith, the Bounder of the Remove, kicked him for pinching his jam tarts.

Charles Hamilton, using his most famous pen-name of Frank Richards, tells us that Billy Bunter is 'a somewhat stout junior, with a broad, pleasant face and an enormous pair of spectacles'. The broad face was soon to become knowing, smug or arrogant rather than pleasant; the *Magnet* began to ring with his wheedled, whined or imperiously delivered catch-phrase, 'I say, you fellows!', and his buffoonery began to be Falstaffian and immensely intriguing to a wide range of readers. Hutton Mitchell, who illustrated the paper from No, 1 to No. 39, conveys Bunter as a plump faced, bespectacled but unremarkable schoolboy. It was not until Charles Henry Chapman took over the pictures in 1911 that Bunter developed his larger-than-life 'Fat Owl' appearance. Chapman was something of a caricaturist, and he drew as zestfully as Frank Richards wrote. The gleefully grinning Bunter, overflowing his loudly checked trousers and even the *Magnet* itself, became a familiar, almost an archetypal image. Billy Bunter emerged from the halfpenny *Magnet* as one of the first popular anti-heroes of juvenile fiction, famous not only in Britain and throughout the Empire (at a time when the sun really *didn't* ever set on it) but elsewhere. His name quickly entered the English language as a synonym for someone who was gluttonous and obese, and it even insinuated itself into other tongues in phrases such as 'Gros comme le Buntair'.

Bunter by turns was stupid, unscrupulous, cunning, arrogant, snobbish, racist and xenophobic. He was jammy and sticky and sweaty and scruffy; he washed as little as possible, 'frowsted' in front of the common room or study fire while healthy, decent fellows like Harry Wharton, the Captain of the Remove, played footer or cricket, went for bracing walks over the downs, or rode their 'jiggers' to the point of exhaustion. He lied unashamedly and extravagantly; he spied and eavesdropped, and, of course, anyone's—even the masters'—tuck was a target for his pilfering. Nevertheless, he was appealing! Readers enjoyed his clowning, his conceit and grandiose ideas. He was a truly comic character, blest with so many blind spots that he sincerely believed he was no end of a good chap—'kindest friend, noblest foe', as he liked to describe himself.

In the heyday of the *Magnet* stories, he provides the comic relief that high drama demands, as surely as the grave-digger in Hamlet or the porter in Macbeth. But, more importantly, he manages to bring out the best in his school-mates who, though recognizing in his weaknesses, are surprisingly protective and refuse to let him be bullied. They find 'that piffling, potty, pilfering porker' infuriating, they are frequently goaded into walloping him with a cricket stump or well and truly bumping him, but no manly and upright Greyfriars junior ever really fights Bunter, because the Fat Owl's stupidity would then rub off on his attacker. On the whole everyone shares Harry Wharton's view that Bunter is 'a born fool' and simply doesn't understand the seriousness of what he's been doing. In essence, Bunter commands our affections because he is in almost every way the underdog, yet he manages constantly to come out on top of the heap!

As George Orwell commented in his intriguing 'Boys Weeklies' essay, he is without doubt 'a first class character'. Bunter starred in the *Magnet* until its demise in the wartime pulp paper shortages of 1940. He has been celebrated in several other story-papers, annuals, hard-back novels, in pastiches, on the stage, and in radio and T.V. presentations. He has actually never been out of print, in some shape or other, since he first bounced onto the sub-literary scene in 1908. It is, however, in strip form and not in the *Magnet* that Bunter has enjoyed his longest life. He cavorted through the story-paper for 32 years, and through the *Knockout, Comet* and *Valiant* comics for 37.) It is good that we now have a large selection of these strips in the form of a collected, permanent edition, which enables us not only to laugh at the antics of 'The Fattest Schoolboy on Earth', but to trace his development in the hands of successive artists.

"Well, here's a bit of luck," said Billy Bunter, as he espied a lonely little horseshoe lying on the road. And he bent down to pick it up. Being short-sighted, of course, he did not see that that horseshoe had been left by some practical joker in the manner illustrated above.

"If you throw it over your shoulder," said Billy, picking up the discarded portion of iron, "it'll bring you luck. Well, let's try it." So he gave an artful flick of the hand, and the horseshoe sailed over his head.

But as that shoe was tied by string to the tree-stump, it came back like a boomerang and hit Billy just behind the ear. Whack! "Hi, who did that!" roared Billy Bunter. "Ow!" I fancy Billy did not call that a bit of luck, anyway.

But William was a determined fellow. When he saw the string on the horseshoe he frowned and untied it. "I'll try my luck again," he muttered. "And I'll make sure it won't come back again this time. Away, thou saucy varlet!"

And he tossed that luck-giving horseshoe, yet again, behind him. It was at that moment that the figure of Sammy Bunter loomed on the horizon. The horseshoe sailed merrily through the air—straight at the oncoming figure.

Crash! Biff! Whoooop! "Ow!" Sammy Bunter was awakened from his day-dreams with a jump as that lump of iron hit him a nasty one in the optic. "Yarooooop!" howled the injured Sammy. "The irony of fate!" murmured Billy, and he beat a hasty retreat.

EARLY BUNTER STRIP FROM MAGNET.

Impersonating Billy Bunter

By GERALD CAMPION

A new series about Billy Bunter of Greyfriars School begins in television on Saturday

AFTER playing Bunter for so long I get hazy about who was in which series, and when a bearded man accosts me in the street booming, 'Campion—remember me? I played Nugent (Cherry, Wharton, Mauleverer) in 1953' I shake the extended leg-of-mutton hand, wondering if he was the one I tripped up (deliberately) in the study scene.

I must say I'm absolutely delighted with my new body, which I collected from the theatrical costumiers the other day for the new series. I'd had the old one for a long time, and it had been bashed about a lot and had got lumpy in places. But the new one is a great improvement; it's made of some light wadding instead of kapok, which is a good thing as I must confess the old one used to make me a bit edgy when the studio got hot and stuffy, or when we were on location in midsummer.

Like Wearing Three Overcoats

Playing Bunter my Eton collar gets scratchy, the stud digs into me, and with the old padding I used to feel as if I was wearing three overcoats. I get a sort of closed-in sensation and have the idea that everyone's against me—until I remember how very kind everyone is, especially the make-up department and the stage- and floor-managers, who all seem to realise how uncomfortable I can get and do their best to help.

The lines are very difficult to learn as they are so repetitious. I remember one episode in which Bunter was evilly pretending that his mother was ill so that he could go home, and had to say the broken line: 'But sir—my mother—' eighteen times during the half-hour. Kynaston Reeves and I went nearly mad trying to learn this, and I ended up saying 'But sir—my mother' in the most unlikely places.

I have never been able to discover how the various producers who work on *Bunter* feel about it. They are all delightful, of course, and remain (I hope) my friends, but I have a sneaking feeling that the job is given to them as a sort of punishment. Shaun Sutton, who once produced six

' I say, you fellows, what about some grub? '

Bunters, has never quite got over it. Whenever I see him in BBC corridors or in the restaurant he greets me with whoops and yells. ' Yarooh ! ' he shrieks wildly at me. I call back ' Beast ! ' in order to humour him. ' I say, you fellows ! ' he counters, and is delighted with my reply, ' Go and eat coke ! '

He actually produced my favourite episode, in which I played both William George Bunter and his studious, athletic cousin Sammy Bunter. This was managed by exposing only one side of the film while I, dressed as Sammy, played the scene, leaving pauses for Billy's dialogue. I then changed clothes, the film was re-wound, and then the other strip was exposed with me, as Billy, answering Sammy's questions.

We did it in one go and congratulated ourselves, as a slip on anyone's part would have meant starting all over again.

Bunter is greedy, dishonest, grubby, and untruthful. He is disloyal, boastful, and cowardly, obese, rude, and stupid. He is also cunning and unscrupulous, which is, I suppose, the secret of his success. You are all better than Bunter, and of course Mr. Frank Richards with concealed craft has tucked away somewhere beneath the mountains of flesh, a little charm—the sort of charm possessed by the old lag who successfully taps you for half a crown on Derby Day.

Well, I must swab the jam off this impot and take it to Mr. Jack Melford (the *nouveau* Quelch). I hope he accepts it because I don't wear padding at rehearsals. ' Wretched boy ! Bend over.' ' Oh, but sir ! I didn't, I never, I wasn't ...'

Oh well, here we go again.

Gerald Campion—without the Eton collar

A PAGE FROM RADIO TIMES CONCERNING THE BUNTER T.V. SHOW.

C.H. Chapman, the *Magnet* illustrator, had drawn several Bunter strips for the *Magnet* and the *Popular* before the *Knockout* strip was launched in 1939. His flair for caricature and his long and skilful manipulation of the character made him an obvious choice as the illustrator of the Bunter sets. Chapman set to work with his usual flair, and produced picture-stories which were faithful to the traditional image of Greyfriars School as it was portrayed in the *Magnet* (where his illustrations to Frank Richard's stories were still continuing). He conveyed incidents that might well have come from the authentic stories, and the characters of Bunter, Mr. Quelch and other popular Greyfriars personalities seemed to have been picked directly off the pages of the *Magnet*.

Chapman drew only the first nine of the *Knockout* strips. he found it hard going to produce these as well as providing pictures for the weekly *Magnet* stories (by this time, he shared that task with Leonard Shields). Consequently he gave up the *Knockout* commission – something which he probably regretted as the *Magnet* was to fold soon afterwards (in the May 1940), and the regular income that he had received for so long for his part in the production of Bunter was to come to an end.

Several other illustrators were tried out, but no-one seemed quite appropriate to carry on the traditional Fat Owl pictures. The *Knockout* editors decided at this point to create a new image. Bunter was to be set in the slapstick, comic-paper mould. There is no doubt that the character was eminently suitable for development in this direction, although, of course, long-standing *Magnet* readers tended to find it unacceptable. Frank Minnitt, who had been working on comics like *The Butterfly, Illustrated Chips* and *The Joker* since 1927, was given the assignment (mainly, it seems, because he happened to turn up at the editorial office at the right moment). His robustly engaging style was just right for the beaming, bouncy Bunter, and, after keeping at first fairly closely for continuity, to Chapman's image, he began gradually to broaden the humour of the strip.

Minnitt's Bunter became the authentic one for several generations of child readers. It is an interesting

TWO EARLY ILLUSTRATIONS OF BUNTER.

fact that when the *Knockout* officially incorporated the *Magnet* (15th June 1940) the story-paper had a circulation of some 83,000, while the *Knockout's* was several times that figure. This suggests that more readers over the years must have become familiar with the comic strip Bunter than the one who inspired so many stories in the *Magnet*.

Minnitt gradually dropped Harry Wharton, Bob Cherry, Frank Nugent, Johnny Bull and Hurree Jamset Ram Singh from his strips. These Greyfriars heroes were replaced by the diminutive Jones Minor, who was the antithesis of Billy Bunter, and a perfect foil and sidekick for him. Jones minor was a swot, while the Fat Owl was dim; he was a conformist, and Bunter was anarchic; he was physically wispy while his chum, of course, was gargantuan. Minnitt stripped Mr. Quelch of much of his dignity. He changed from Olympian augustness to allowing the most retarded member of his form (Bunter) to address him constantly as 'Quelchy'. The brilliant classicist teacher of the *Magnet* started to use more simple phrases and to become involved in knockabout farce.

Bunter changed too. He retained some of his native cunning, but was a touch more genial than in the *Magnet* stories. He tangled consistently with Quelch, but often managed to avoid retribution for his misdoings because of flukes which enabled him to foil Tough Ted the footpad, who was after Quelchy's real gold 'ticker'. Percy the Pot-pincher (a burglar in drag), and other refarious denizens of Bunter's world.

Once the new pattern was established Bunter went from strength to strength. Frank Minnitt continued to produce the strip until he died in 1958, without any lessening of verve in his drawings. There was, however, editorial help from time to time with his plots. The now almost legendary figure of Leonard Mathews, for example, contributed ideas, and had some involvement in the creation of Jones Minor. For most of its run the strip occupied two pages which allowed reasonable scope for the development of the storyline.

Minnitt's comic strip character became so popular with readers that the yearly Annual from 1940 (dated

BILLY BUNTER'S CIRCUS

1. Wednesday afternoon is a half holiday at Greyfriars, so you can guess how excited the boys were when they discovered that Tomsonio's Circus had come to Courtfield on Wednesday morning. The circus procession passed the gates of Greyfriars and the juniors came running out to watch it go by. They learned then that the first show was to be that very afternoon. The whole school made up its mind to be there.

2. As luck would have it, poor old Bunter chose that very morning to upset old Quelch, his Form-master. Whilst Quelch was out of the Form room Bunter pranced up to the blackboard and scribbled "Broot" in big letters. Unfortunately for Bunter, all the rest of the boys in the Form spelled "Broot" b-r-u-t-e, so when Quelchy saw the bad spelling, he instantly twigged who had done it, and Bunter was kept in.

3. But Billy Bunter was determined to see the circus even if it meant trouble afterwards. He saw all the fellows going off to enjoy the show, and in no time at all he had made up his mind that he would get there, too—even though Harry Wharton and his chums told him he would catch it hot. It was just like Bunter that he never stopped to think what might happen later.

4. So off sneaked Bunter to see the circus, and the first person he bumped into was Quelch, his Form-master. He really did bump into him. As Bunter rounded a corner at full pelt—zonk!—he hit Quelchy so hard that he knocked him down. "I command you to stop, Bunter!" roared Quelch. But there was no stopping Billy. On he pranced like a baby elephant out for exercise.

5. "I'll have to disguise myself," thought Bunter as he pounded on. And he was lucky. It so happened that as he passed the river that flowed through Courtfield Common he came upon a heap of clothes. There was even a wig and false whiskers that belonged to a man who was having a swim. Bunter rubbed his eyes to make sure it was true. It was! "He, he, he!" chortled Bunter. "This is my lucky day!"

6. Bunter bagged the disguise and toddled off. Surely nobody would recognise him now? thought he, and he was right. A few minutes later he met up with Quelch again. "Excuse me," said Quelch, "but have you seen a fat and clumsy schoolboy lurking in this wood?" "Certainly not!" cried Bunter. But he was glad to get away for he felt that his fat sides would burst with the laughter he was holding back.

CHAPMAN'S BUNTER STRIP FROM 'KNOCKOUT.'

7. So away went Billy Bunter to the circus. He was wondering how he was going to get in, seeing that he had no money, but to his amazement he was saluted by the man at the gate. What Bunter didn't realise was that the disguise he had pinched belonged to Mr. Tomsonio, the owner of the circus. It looked like being Bunter's lucky day, all right!

8. To Billy Bunter's astonishment he was shown into the best seat in the place, and no sooner had he seated himself than the ringmaster came up and asked him if the show could start. So great was his surprise that the fat boy very nearly gave himself away, but by now it was beginning to dawn on him what had happened.

9. Then Billy Bunter spotted a bunch of Greyfriars boys quite close to him, and he was just wondering whether they would twig his disguise when the ringmaster told him there was trouble outside. Billy was glad to escape. He fairly leapt at the chance of getting away even though it meant missing a free show. Hurriedly he followed the ringmaster out of the big circus tent.

10. Once outside he was met by the manager of the circus. "The men are going on strike for double wages, guv'nor," explained the manager. Billy didn't care a jot. "Give 'em what they want!" he said. You see, it wasn't his money he was spending, anyway, so why should he worry? The ringmaster hurried away, leaving the fat boy holding his sides as he roared with laughter.

11. Billy Bunter's next move was to make himself comfy in the circus-owner's caravan. Thought he, if they take me for the owner I can do just what I like. What a chance for a free feed! "Listen, fellow!" cried he to the manager. "Bring me two dozen cream puffs, a bag of doughnuts, six bottles of ginger-pop, and anything else you can scrounge."

12. Of course, the circus hands were delighted. They had had their wages doubled. And Billy Bunter was delighted, too—he had a giant free feed all to himself. He didn't stop to think what was likely to happen next. He quite failed to realise that Quelch was still on his trail. But he will find out all about that next week, you bet.

1941) to 1961 (dated 1962) nearly always included three or four Bunter strips. After Minnitt's death in 1958, some of these Annual strips were reprints of his work. In the comic, he was succeeded as the regular Bunter artist by Reg Parlett, another great illustrator – whose work in British comics had been well known since the 1930's. Parlett gave new gusto to the strip, and made Bunter and his associates more cartoon-like than before. His strips continued until the *Knockout* end in 1961. They were then transferred to *Valiant* where they ran until 1976 when, after capering across comic paper pages for nearly forty years, Billy Bunter went into at least temporary retirement. (Frank Richard's original story-paper character, however, was then still very much in business through the Howard Baker facsimile *Magnet* reprint series, which began in 1969).

Three years after Minnitt's death, the *Knockout* was renamed *Billy Bunter's Knockout,* which was surely not only a tribute to the character's resilience but to Minnitt's work over so many years, and the vitality of Parlett's continuation of this. The linking of Bunter's name with the paper's title echoed the frequent use by the *Magnet* on its cover of the phrase *Billy Bunter's Own Paper.*

As mentioned earlier, Bunter ran for thirty-seven years in *Knockout* and *Valiant,* longer than his thirty-two year spell in *Magnet.* His creator, Frank Richards, was paid an honorarium of £5 a week (for the use in the comics of his most famous character) and this payment continued until he died in 1961. It was well deserved, but it meant that during the early years of the *Knockout* strip, Frank Richards was receiving more for it than Minnitt.

The Greyfriars author took little interest in the comic strip representation of his celebrated Fat Owl. Stunned by the sudden demise of the *Magnet* in 1940, he nevertheless went on producing stories about other schoolboy characters than the Greyfriars juniors throughout the war, although, with the then acute paper shortages, he had no immediate prospect of seeing them published. He just had to go on writing. In 1947 the first of his hardback Bunter books was published by Charles Skilton. The series ran to thirty-eight titles, and was to consume Frank's main writing energies during the post-war period. Apart, of course, from receiving his honorarium, he felt little involvement in Bunter's irrepressible antics in the *Knockout.*

By any standards, Billy Bunter's creator was a phenonmenon. The most prolific published writer in the English language, Charles Harold St. John Hamilton (to give him his full name) used more than twenty

ALL THREE BUNTERS IN THIS ILLUSTRATION BY C.H. CHAPMAN.

pseudonyms, created almost a hundred fictional schools and published well over seventy-two million words of fiction. When one considers that this is roughly the equivalent of a thousand novels this staggering output can be appreciated. (His word-count leaves other prolific popular authors – John Creasey, Barbara Cartland and Enid Blyton, for example – far behind). Charles Hamilton is best known to the world as Frank Richards, the pen-name he adopted when writing about Greyfriars School, Billy Bunter and its other imperishable inmates. He created St. Jim's as 'Martin Clifford' and Rookwoods School as 'Owen Conquest'. Both of these pen-names became famous in the weekly *Gem* and *Boy's Friend* respectively, but the *Magnet* pen-name was the one he cherished most. 'Frank Richards' became much more to him than a mere pen-name: it was an *alter ego*. The fact that he thought and wrote of himself as Frank Richards is well demonstrated in his many letters to his fans, and in the author's autobiography which Skilton published in 1952.

Frank Richards was born in Ealing on 8th August 1876; he died on Christmas Eve in 1961, by which time he had truly become a legendary figure. It is no exaggeration to say that he set his stamp on a generation, and that his influence is still strongly felt today. Over a quarter of a century after Frank's death, his stories of Greyfriars and St. Jim's are being regularly reprinted, and enthusiasts of his work range from nine-year-olds to nonagenarians.

As well as Bunter, the clowning fatty who has become a cult figure, Frank provided heroes and role models for countless readers. These include Harry Wharton and Tom Merry, the born leaders of Greyfrairs and St. Jim's, 'ordinary' but immensely appealing boys such as the sporting Bob Cherry and quiet 'backer-upper', Frank Nugent (based on Frank Richards himself) and a wonderful variety of showy sophisticates like Herbert Vernon Smith, the Bounder of the Greyfriars Remove, or the mocking and fastidious Ralph Reckness Cardew of St. Jim's. The list is endless: week after week, and decade after decade, Frank transported hundreds of thousands of children (and lots of adults too!) into the magical worlds of his charismatic characters. He had been condemned by misguided critics as an escapist writer, but, like all superb story-spinners, he realized that the greatest gift an author can give his readers is that of total absorption in a book or tale. Asked once whether he would like to have written 'something better' then stories for boys' weeklies,

BUNTER *NOT* GETTING ON WITH THE GIRLS.

13

Frank firmly replied that there *was* nothing better then writing for young people. He entertained; he educated and uplifted without ever appearing to 'preach'; he provided a yardstick for fair-minded behaviour – and even if some readers found his assumptions about adolescent honour and decency and cleanmindedness somewhat inflated, they couldn't fail to respond to his irresistible enthusiasm and stylishness. Above all, he wrote about friendship. He possessed the extremely rare ability to put across without sentimentality the intensity of schoolboy loyalities and chumminess.

Greyfriars and Frank's other schools represented both the real world in microcosm and the fantasy adventure, with boys taking responsibilities for their own destinies, looking to wonderfully broad horizons and also learning to function with *esprit de corps*. With Bunter and other humorous characters, Frank gave his readers a lot of laughs, but there was always something satisfyingly deeper, too. In his survey of Salford life in the early part of this century Professor Robert Roberts acknowledges this by stating that the stories…

Set ideals and standards. This our own tutors, religous and secular, had signally failed to do. In the final

THE GREYFRIARS GALLERY.

No. 31.—SAMMY BUNTER.

THE most charitable thing one can find to say about Sammy Bunter is that he is not old enough to know better. Unfortunately, this excuse has the drawback of being doubtfully true.

One is not at all sure that Sammy does not know better. If there is any difference worth mentioning between him and Billy, one is inclined to fancy that it lies in the fact that Sammy is slightly the less obtuse of the two.

They are alike in their greed and their lack of scruples, in their grubbiness and their ignorance. They are quite wonderfully alike in person. Sammy is simply a smaller edition of the egregious William George.

When Billy Bunter heard that his minor was to come to Greyfriars, he announced the fact as if it were really important.

"Sammy's coming!" he told the Remove, and promptly rolled away to blue the remittance which Aunt Peggy had forwarded to him to make smooth the way of Sammy.

Dicky Nugent and Gatty and Hop Hi met Sammy at the station, and were not pleased with him. Frankly, one may say that from the outset Sammy revealed himself as the perfect little beast he is.

His fat, discontented face impressed the fags unfavourably. His reply to the Formmaster when told that his hands were not clean had the same effect upon Mr. Kelly, then in charge of the Second.

"I washed them this morning!" grunted Sammy, which was at one and the same time a rude answer and a revelation of his low standard of cleanliness.

Nugent minor had promised Wingate to look after Bunter minor during his first day. It was no easy task, especially as the other fags were eager to give Sammy the licking which he asked for—though not in words—at least every five minutes.

Lonzy was in his bath when Skinner put Sammy in the bath-room. Sammy was very rude and rough to the gentle Alonzo, who wished nothing but his good, and directed his conversation to that end. Sammy ducked Lonzy's head under water, and held it down. But the Famous Five came in and rescued Lonzy from the ferocious fag. And Sammy was rude to them, but repented when he knew who they were. For it was firmly fixed in the mind of Sammy that Harry Wharton was brother Billy's best chum, and that Frank Nugent was horribly jealous because Wharton held that august position!

Perhaps disillusionment on that score tended to make Sammy morose. Anyway, the Second found him quite insufferable, and Dicky Nugent had his work cut out to protect him—hating the job with all his heart meanwhile.

Sammy perambulated trying to collect cash from fellows who, so he had been told, owed it to Billy. He was ready to believe things of this sort, though he had no faith what ever in his major's word when the matter concerned himself. He had discovered that Billy had embezzled Aunt Peggy's remit-

Samuel Bunter

tance, and made his senior uneasy by threats of informing. But Billy got his promise—for what it was worth—not to tell by refusing to cut him down when, hanged until he gave that promise.

Coker had hanged Sammy—but not by the neck; only by means of a rope under his armpits.

Wingate interrupted a dormitory ragging due to Sammy's obstinate determination to go to the Head and sneak about what had been done to him; and the skipper aroused the resentment of Sammy by not punishing anyone for the ragging. Furious, Sammy knocked Dicky Nugent down by an unexpected blow; and it was hard for Dicky to keep his promise then. But he kept it like a man!

The obnoxious new junior escaped, and on his way to the Head ran into Mr. Kelly and Wingate. An appeal to the Head could not be refused by any master, and Mr. Kelly took him along. Sammy got no change out of it; the Head caned him.

Back in the dormitory, Sammy threw his boot at Dicky's head. Nugent minor waited till next day, and then gave him what he had been asking for.

Between Billy and Sammy the relations are scarcely brotherly at the best of times—more like armed neutrality, as a rule. It is true that when Bunter got up a team to play for the Coker Cup he included Sammy, and put him in goal. Sammy was a frost in goal, but he was one of the only two left on the field—Alonzo the other—with their noble skipper soon after it had become plain that Dick Nugent and his men of the Second would be all over them. Probably Sammy had not noticed the others sneaking off.

He will back up Billy in any lie if only a share of the plunder be secured to him. He did not believe that Billy had lost his memory when the Owl succeeded in spoofing everyone else; and the Cliff House girls thought the affection between the two, when they were regaled with good things by Marjorie & Co., quite pathetic—though they would hardly have continued to do so if they had heard the asides between them!

Sammy, after being cuffed by Loder, had a shot at the lost memory dodge himself. But Hop Hi tripped him up. The little Chinee talked of a registered letter for Bunter minor, and Sammy forgot to remember that he had forgotten his name. So he did not profit as Billy had profited.

He played up to his scheming major when "Captain Bunter" appeared in the casualty list, and Billy claimed him as an uncle. Sammy boo-hooed in the most lifelike manner when the list was shown him, and made some of the fellows feel quite repentant—so much so that they were ready to comfort Sammy with such grub as his soul yearned after. But Sammy had seen the paper earlier without a breakdown, and "Bunter" turned out to be only a misprint for "Hunter" after all!

He is a blackmailer, in an infantile way, maybe, but up to the limits of his ability. He blackmailed Billy over the loss of memory trick, and added insult to injury by telling the girls that Billy and he might be taken for twins if only Billy were a bit better-looking!

He is meanly greedy. When Dicky Nugent was captured by Mr. Quelch and haled off, Dicky shed biscuits from a paper bag as he went, and Sammy walked behind him picking them up and popping them in his mouth. The other fags were worried about Dicky's fate; but not so Sammy. To him only the biscuits mattered.

"There's another bisker, Sammy," said Gatty.

Sammy stooped, and Gatty took a running kick. Served Sammy right!

When Cousin Wally took Billy's place at Greyfriars for a week or so, and the school was astounded by Bunter's supposed bucking-up, Sammy twigged, and Wally had to pay blackmail. But Billy refused to continue the subsidy, and Sammy let the cat out of the bag.

Sammy shared his major's captivity in the vaults of the ruined Priory, when the supposed archæologists were so liberal with their banknotes—made on the premises—to Billy, and Sammy wanted a share of the plunder. They were too pressing, and they had seen too much, so they were tied up and left there while the rascals made themselves scarce.

Once Sammy showed human feeling. Wun Lung was supposed to have been drowned. Hop Hi seemed inconsolable. Sammy tried to console him with a chunk of toffee—Sammy's own, too!

Let it count to his credit, small thing though it be.

SAMMY BUNTER. A PROFILE ON BILLY'S YOUNGER BROTHER FROM MAGNET 495 (1917).

estimate it may well be found that Frank Richards during the first quarter of the twentieth century had more influence on the mind and outlook of young working-class England than any other single person, not excluding Baden-Powell.

And this influence has not been confined just to one class of readers, or to one portion of the century.

Girls read the *Magnet* almost as avidly as their brothers, and they were not neglected in the stories. As well as producing Bessie Bunter of Cliff House School, who was in many ways a skirted version of her incorrigible brother Billy, Frank created absolute stunners like her chum Marjorie Hazeldene, who inspired undying (if unconsummated) passion in the rugged breasts of Bob Cherry and Harry Wharton (and many of the *Magnet's* boy audience).

So real were Franks characters in their heyday that the *Magnet's* editor often received letters from readers

THE GREYFRIARS GALLERY.

No. 69.—WALTER BUNTER.

WALLY BUNTER is "the other Bunter."

He does not belong to Greyfriars, but he does to the stories; and, though he has very seldom come into them, I know that many of my readers remember him with strong liking.

It is an interesting problem, this of two fellows almost exactly alike outwardly, but inwardly as dissimilar as fellows can be. Many a novelist has used it. And it has been used more than once in our papers. There was the case of Tom Merry and his double, the rascally Clavering. And there was that of Alonzo and Peter Todd, good fellows both, but as curiously unlike inside as they are curiously alike outwardly. Peter is as shrewd as boys are made, with a touch of sarcasm, of which the guileless Alonzo is absolutely innocent. Peter is strong just where Alonzo is weak. But get down to bed-rock, and you find the likeness after all—the likeness due to the fact that both are good, straight fellows.

Here the Bunter case differs. There are some readers who have developed something like an affection for the ineffable William George. They are ready to credit him with good qualities which, if he possesses them, are wonderfully concealed. I cannot see that Bunter had anything that could be classed as a positive good quality.

It is far otherwise with his Cousin Wally. Here is a fellow who knows how to play the game, and plays it. He has a wonderful appetite, and he carries no end of flesh; but he is not a pig. He resembles Fatty Wynn in character far more than he does his cousin. Wally is a good comrade, a cheery soul, the sort of fellow who would make no end of friends at a school like Greyfriars.

Billy Bunter did not know much of his cousin in their early days. Wally's people belonged to a branch of them that was rather looked down upon by the Bunter family to which Billy and Sammy belong, as not being well off. As a matter of fact, the Billy Bunters, so to call them, are not specially well off. But Mr. Samuel Bunter has had his days of prosperity in the City, and has doubtless swanked there, as his hopeful son swanked at Greyfriars when the big remittances came.

Wally had to go to a small school, and to take his seat on an office stool before he was fifteen. And that was a real pity, for Wally would have been a tower of strength to his Form at a public school. He is a fine cricketer, and, in spite of the weight he has to carry, can no doubt put up a good show on the footer-field. He might be a goalkeeper of the dear old Fatty Wynn type; but I don't think it at all out of the question that he should be a centre-forward of ability, or a good half, for he has learned to carry his burden of flesh more effectively than his cousin ever did; and it is not all fat, either. Under the adipose is a lot of good, honest muscle.

It was at Billy's suggestion that Wally masqueraded at Greyfriars as W. G. B. Billy had gone over to Margate to see Wally, who was then on holiday. Billy felt that he wanted a holiday, too. He could not quite understand why Wally should think him so lucky for being at school.

The affair was arranged. They changed clothes, and the change was enough. Perhaps Billy's mother might have known the difference. It is hardly likely anyone else would have done.

And, of course, Wally had the advantage of tips from Billy about the school and the fellows there. They did not amount to very much, for in this, as in everything except eating and prying, W. G. B. was lazy. But his cousin has a quicker brain than he, and the few hints were enough to give him a start.

So Billy stayed at Margate, to play the nut on the front, and Wally went to Greyfriars.

No one suspected anything at first. How should they, when they did not even know of the double's existence?

But they wondered. Billy Bunter seemed transformed.

He saved Marjorie and Clara from real danger, and he was quite modest about it. He would not ventriloquise at Cliff House, and that was not like Billy. But Wally wouldn't because he couldn't, which was an excellent reason, you must allow.

Frank Nugent alarmed Wally by saying he had changed. But Frank made it clear that he did not mean in appearance, only that Bunter had improved. Bunter must have improved when he gave away a huge chunk of cake to a man who seemed hungry, Frank thought. Only it wasn't Bunter, you see, and such a good-natured act came quite easily to the cheery and open-hearted Wally.

To overcome Skinner was nothing for Wally, either; but it would have been something astonishing, though not quite impossible, for the Owl. To make quite a good show at mathematics was easy enough for the other Bunter; but Mr. Lascelles was surprised, for W. G. B. had never made even a moderate show in any subject. Study No. 7 was almost thunderstricken when Wally, serving pie, took the smallest helping for himself. Temple & Co. were surprised when Bunter showed form at cricket that made them glad to include him in the Fourth Eleven against the Remove, Wharton and the rest really assenting to the arrangement.

Coker was surprised when Bunter stood up to him. Peter Todd got a real shock when Bunter knocked him out. But the biggest and most amazing thing of all was Bunter's success as a bowler.

He got Wharton first ball. He brought off the hat-trick by getting Frank Nugent and Inky with the next two. In the event the Remove were all out for 56. Wally had taken eight wickets, and had caught the other two men from other bowlers! And in the end he won the match for his side by his batting at a critical time.

And all the time the only fellow who had smelt a rat at all was Sammy Bunter. That guileful youth had been bribed to silence. It was through him that the truth came out; but that was not until Wally had gone back to the hated office stool, and Billy had returned, sunburned and self-satisfied as ever, from the Margate Parade.

The second appearance of Wally at Greyfriars was connected with an elaborate spoof on the part of the scheming Owl. Wally came over to see his cousin, and ran against Percy Bolsover, who was amazed when the fellow he took for Billy Bunter, instead of accepting a bumping, handed out one. He understood when he knew that it was the other Bunter. The Famous Five and their chums were very glad to see Wally again. They would have liked his help in their coming match against St. Jude's, but for that it was necessary that someone should take his place in the office at Canterbury, and Billy flatly refused to do that, asking haughtily whether he looked like an office chap, and adding that it would be derogatory to his personal dignity as a gentleman.

But after Wally had gone Billy thought out a plot. He allowed himself to be bribed to go and be an "office chap" for an afternoon, and let Wally come and play. But he did not go. It was W. G. B. who played in the first innings of the match, and did—well, much what might have been expected of him. He had pretended to go to Canterbury, and had, of course, collected his fare—first-class—in advance. He had insisted upon a luncheon-basket. But he dodged back. It was the unexpected turning-up of Wally, who had managed to get part of the afternoon off, that exposed the fraud. And Wally came into the team instead of Billy, and after all the Remove won, though I fear the laws of cricket were badly cracked, if not actually broken, by that substitution!

Anyway, Billy Bunter was bumped, and Wally was the hero of the hour. He will always be sure of a welcome from Wharton & Co.—as soon as they are sure that he is Wally and not Billy, that is.

A LITTLE KNOWN BUNTER — WALTER GETS A PROFILE IN MAGNET 533 (1918).

BESSIE BUNTER AS A BUFFOONING FATTY IN SCHOOL FRIEND OF THE EARLY '20'S.

IN 'MAGNET' DURING THE 30'S BESSIE WAS ARROGANT, CONCEITED AND INCLINED TO SMACK BOY'S HEADS WITH VERY LITTLE PROVOCATION.

THEY SAY ABSENCE MAKES THE HEART GROW FONDER, BUT TRY TELLING THAT TO MY BEASTLY BROTHER, BILLY!

LEFT: BESSIE BUNTER IN THE 30'S GIRLS WEEKLY, 'THE SCHOOLGIRL' BECAME 'A PLUMP & LOVABLE DUFFER'. RIGHT: IN THE 80'S COMIC STRIP VERSION FROM 'TAMMY' THE WHEEL HAS TURNED FULL CIRCLE AND SHE ENDS AS SHE BEGAN — AN INFLATED CLOWNING CARICATURE!

requesting fixtures with the school's junior eleven, or dates with the gorgeous Marjorie. One compassionate elderly lady used to post packets of meat for the Greyfriars cat, and several readers were inspired to send parcels of tuck for the ever hungry Fat Owl. Despite his unappetising aspects, Bunter's popularity never seems to have become dimmed. His success prompted Frank to produce other fat boys—at St. Jim's, Rookwood and so on—and influenced other authors of school stories so that for some time an overweight fourth-former became virtually statutory in the genre. Billy Bunter developed a younger brother, Sammy, who was a member of the Greyfriars Second Form. Apart from a small difference in height, Bunter minor and Bunter major looked almost identical in the illustrations by Chapman and Leonard Shields. Their personalities were also very much alike; Sammy was as gluttonous and self-centered as Billy, and equally averse to soap and water, or any kind of physical exercise. However, he lacked his major's edge of arrogance, unbridled conceit and low cunning. Sammy came to the fore rather more in Chapman's pre-war Bunter-brothers picture-strips in the Popular than in the text stories.

Bessie Bunter was dreamed up in 1919, and given a trial run in *Magnet 582* in a story called 'The Artful Dodger'. The first ever picture of her was by C.H. Chapman. She is depicted sitting in a bun-shop, smiling smugly, and looking every inch a Bunter. She was to crop up in many subsequent *Magnet* stories, and her definitive likeness in this paper was the one eventually established by Leonard Shields's pictures. In the *School Friend* and its successor paper, the *Schoolgirl*, Bessie's illustrators were G.M. Dodshon and T.E. Laidler respectively. When Chapman drew her, he used his gift for caricature with some relish, giving her corkscrew curls and funny, fussy clothes. Shields, Dodshon and Laidler, however, stuck more strongly to the velour-hatted, lisle-stockinged, gymslip-garbed between-the-wars schoolgirl image. Frank's purpose in creating Bessie was to provide a humorous character for the cast of Cliff House School who were to star in a new girl's paper, the *School Friend*. This began on 17th May 1919, and could truly claim to be the first ever schoolgirl's weekly. R.T. Eves, its original editor, started it after realizing from correspondence how many girls were enjoying the *Magnet;* he knew too that hardback schoolgirl novels were greatly in vogue, so it seemed likely that a story-paper exploiting dormitory larks, sporting endeavour ('They stung me fearfully for this new hockey stick but it's a real ripper') and bosom chumships would be a winner. It was! Frank created Bessie in the traditional Bunter mould; like Billy, she rolled rather than walked, had 'fat paws' instead of hands, wore owl-like spectacles over wily little gooseberry eyes, listened at key-holes, told lies and had an insatiable appetite for all kinds of grub. Bessie is even more domineering than her brother. She usually gets the better of Billy by frightful nagging, or swiping him one if he tries to sneak off with more than his share of the Bunter family's tuck. Using the pen-name of 'Hilda Richards,' Frank foisted onto Bessie conceit and vanity which sat oddly on her inflated circumference, and triggered off many slapstick incidents: "Even a crusty old stick might stretch a point for a pretty girl," she declares, referring to her brother's august form-master, Mr. Quelch. Another of her favourite sayings is that 'Every boy admires a girl with a good (i.e.: Bessie-like) figure'.

The girls of Cliff House School included engaging characters such as the already mentioned Marjorie Hazeldene, Barbara Redfern – the Captain of the Fourth Form who seemed a female representation of the Harry Wharton/born leader type – and Clara Trevlyn, a tomboy, splendid at games and inclined towards feminism: ('That's a boy all over – no gumption!). Rather surprisingly, Frank Richards, the doyen of the boys' school story, was allowed to write only the first four or five of the Cliff House exploits in the *School Friend.* Early responses from readers apparently indicated to the editor that Frank did not perhaps have quite the right touch for girls. There is an element of truth in this for, although his *School Friend* writing is extremely enjoyable, it is spiced with send-up, which, though satisfying to the adult reader might have lacked appeal to the pubescent girls of 1919. Bessie, for example, is a parody of the unreasonable and disagreeable female who expects special treatment on account of her sex. She is a disaster area not only for her brother, but for every Greyfriars boy whom she encounters, accosts and abuses: ' "You've crushed my hat," said Bessie crossly. "Can't you see? Blind as well as clumsy!...All boys are clumsy." ' Well brought up boys of the period, of course, were bound to act in accordance with the rules of chivalry, however, charmless and ungrateful the girl who solicits their attention might be, while Bessie cheerfully disregards all the rules of schoolgirl honour and reasonable behaviour. It was in order for Frank to exercise his parodist talent to amuse by introducing girls into the *Magnet* as squealing sillies or man-hating schoolmistress martinets, but what gave boys a good laugh was not quite so endearing in the girls' paper.

It was suggested editorially that Frank's female characters would have to been smoothed out by other authors. Bessie was not so much smoothed as reduced, becoming plump rather than fat, and a loyal and loveable duffer instead of a conniving bossyboots. There were other reasons behind the decision to take Frank off the *School Friend.* At that time he was already producing for the Amalgamated Press between 50,000 and 60,000 words every week (on Greyfriars, St. Jim's and Rookwood) as well as regularly writing other stories for the same publishers. Herbert A. Hinton, the then editor of the *Magnet,* was alarmed at the potential of the new girls' paper; he felt that its editor, Eves, was in the process of stealing his star writer – and possibly a lot of the *Magnet's* readers. And he was convinced that even the prolific Frank would be unable to maintain a high enough output to keep four weekly papers *(Magnet, Gem, Boys' Friend* and *School Friend)* flourishing. It was galling for Frank to lose this assignment, particularly when he had set up the school (Cliff House), a host of characters for it, and also its environs. The only heart-warming aspect of this incident is that the girls who read the *School Friend* showed a certain delicacy of feeling. Whereas Billy, the somewhat retarded clowning fatty of Greyfriars, was acceptable, even attractive, to boy readers, similar buffooning and obesity in a girl was upsetting to the *School Friend's* audience, who saw Bessie as an object of sympathy rather than merriment.

In spite of the difficulties attendant on her creation, Bessie Bunter in picture-strip form was eventually to outlive Billy. His cavorting in *Valiant* ended in 1976 but she, after a period in the post-war *June* and *School Friend,* continued in *Tammy* well into the 1980's. She may not be a particularly loveable sister, and she is certainly nobody's sweetheart but she *is* a survivor, representing, like Billy, the triumph of the underdog. Cecil Orr was the artist who started her off in comic strip, and Arthur Martin took over when Orr died.

18

Placenta Amissa

'HEU, me miserum! Quanta ac qualia patior!' Porcius, cui erant oculi rotundi, facies rotundior, venter vel rotundissimus, in ludo stabat et mensas omnes circumspiciebat. Porcius valde esuriebat (quando autem eius stomachus non latrabat?), nihil non edere paratus erat, sed iam nihil cibi, ne escam quidem videre poterat. 'Eheu' iterum gemebat cum subito pedum sonitum audivit. Iamque et esuriebat et timebat, nam omnes ludum ante vesperum intrare vetiti erant. Celeriter igitur ad angulum tenebrosum cucurrit, ubi sellae quaedam fractae congestae erant, et pone eas se celavit. Statim fere intraverunt, non magister, sed duo alii discipuli, Verrucius Nugensque, amici quos Porcius eo tempore videre nolebat. 'Non hic est,' inquit Verrucius, post quam circumspexit. 'Haud dubie, mi Verruci,' respondit Nugens, nam vix illud corpus obesum non videre potuimus! Sed quid nunc facies?' 'Hic relinquam—non ante vesperum huc redibit—tum ei hoc dabo'. Parumper silentium erat, tum Porcius eos exeuntes audivit. Primum immotus manebat, dein aegerrime surrexit, et circumspiciens animadvertit in mensa fascem quendam, mappa obvolutum. Primum constitit, ~~tum celeriter ad~~ ~~res cucurrit, quas silentio~~ ... cum ~~nemo ad~~ ... ad

bella! Etiam magis iam esuriebat Porcius—sed cuius placenta? Nonne relinquere debuit? Tandem autem exclamavit, 'Quod inveneris, tenes! Per Cererem et Persephonem, nunc vero famem meam hac bella placenta depellam!', et statim partem magnam secuit atque manifesta delectatione esse coepit. Ubi iam hanc comedit, paulum cunctatus tandem placentam reliquam auferre constituit: et iam erat exiturus cum fores patefactae sunt, et intravit Macer, pue~~r~~ haud semper Po~~rcio amic~~... ~~mi Porci~~ ... hab ...

BUNTER IN LATIN.

Bessie's resilience defies changes in social attitudes and literary fashions. For her the wheel came full circle and in *Tammy,* some sixty-five years after her creation, she was as gargantuan and greedy and comically awful as she was in in the 1919 *School Friend.*

In some ways it is strange that, amongst the host of sympathetic boy and girl characters which tripped off Frank Richards's typewriter, it is the Bunters who are most talked about and resilient. Billy in particular seems likeley to be raising chuckles not only now but for future generations. Librarians have protested that making his exploits available is unfair to boys who, through no fault of their own, are overweight; educationalists have objected to the Greyfriars saga and Bunter's part in it for other reasons. But nothing seems to stem the tide of his popularity. Frank Richards wrote richly allusive narratives, which were demanding and difficult for young people, but boys and girls were so entranced with the stories that they happily coped with whatever their author gave them as part of the package. They even relished his Latin jokes, his preoccupation with the schoolmasterly aspects of Quelch and his laspses from realism to caricature and back again.

Bunter, like several of Frank's characters, *is* overdrawn, yet for generations of children he is a friend or mate—always on their side, and never supporting the big guns of authority.

Frank Richards gave us hundreds of splendid vignettes of Billy in a variety of circumstances. One which stands out shows Mr. Quelch's capacity to inflict 'condign punishment' on the ever-unreformed Bunter whenever occasion demands: 'Bend over that boat, Bunter!' Another is of Bunter scuttling to some secret spot or other to consume the jam tarts which he has just snaffled from one of his form-mates: 'As he blinked to and fro through his big spectacles, Bunter could see no pursuers. Like Moses of old, he looked this way and that way, and there was no man'. Bunter's illustrators as well as his author have also provided us with indelible images. Chapman's luridly larger than life schoolboy, Shields's similar but subtlely better-looking portrayal and Frank Minnitt's rumbustiously attractive strips are all part of the Bunter who has enriched the childhood of so many, and who has thrown light on a wide range of human foibles and pretentiousness. Long Live the Fat Owl of the Remove!

BILLY BUNTER IN DREAMLAND!

SIR JIMMY'S PAL!

A Grand Long Complete School Tale of Harry Wharton & Co.

The Magnet 1ᵈ Library

No. 491. Vol. 11.

THE BOWLED BUNTER!

AGAINST HIS OWN SIDE!

The **Magnet** 1ª Library

No. 493.. Vol. 11.

BUNTER IN WARLIKE MOOD!

BILLY BUNTER'S BIRTHRIGHT!

The **Magnet** Library

WAR TIME PRICE. 1 1½ d.

No. 538. Vol. XII.

THE HEROIC BUNTER!

1-6-18

The Magnet Library

1½d.
WAR TIME PRICE.

No. 544. Vol. XIII.

WILLIAM THE WARLIKE!

WILL HE GET WET?

13-7-18

The **Magnet** Library

WAR TIME PRICE.

1 1/2 d.

No. 548. Vol. XIII.

SIR JIMMY'S ENEMY!

BUNTER IN A NEW RÔLE!

10-8-13

The Magnet

WAR TIME PRICE.

Library

1½d.

No. 550. Vol. XIII.

PUT TO THE TEST!

BUNTER BUNKS!

Copyright in the United States of America.

24-9-16

The **Magnet** Library

WAR TIME PRICE.

1 1/2 d.

No. 559. Vol. XIII.

A CASE OF CONSCIENCE!

THE BRAVE, BAD BUNTER!

26-10-18

The Magnet Library

No. 677.   Vol. XVIII.   Jan. 29th, 1921.

BILLY BUNTER TO THE RESCUE!   (A dramatic moment in the long complete School Story inside.)

No. 683. Vol. XVIII.   March 12th, 1921.

RUCTIONS IN COKER'S STUDY!
(A Surprise for the Great Horace.)

The Magnet Library

With which is incorporated The Greyfriars Herald.

1½d.

No. 684.   Vol. XVIII.   March 19th, 1921.

WHO SAID THE AGE OF MIRACLES WAS PAST?

A surprise for Mr Quelch. in the long complete school story, "Bunter the Swot!" (inside.)

The Magnet Library

With which is incorporated The Greyfriars Herald.

1½d.

No. 685. Vol. XVIII.   March 26th, 1921.

BILLY BUNTER UPSETS THE CREW OF THE RIVAL BOAT!

(A Screamingly Funny Incident in the Long Complete Story inside.)

The Magnet Library

With which is incorporated The Greyfriars Herald.

1½d

No. 693. Vol. XVIII.   May 21st, 1921.

THE LIE THAT LED TO TROUBLE FOR BILLY BUNTER!

(An episode from the long complete tale inside.)

The Magnet Library 1½d

No. 697. Vol. XVIII.

June 18th, 1921.

BILLY BUNTER FALLS ASLEEP AT AN UNUSUAL TIME!
(An Amazing Incident from the long complete tale inside.)

No. 701. Vol. XVIII.   "BILLY BUNTER'S LUCK!"   July 16th, 1921.

BILLY BUNTER ENTERTAINS HIS FRIENDS AT THE ELYSIAN CAFE!

(One of the many surprises in the long complete tale in this issue.)

HARRY WHARTON & CO. IN FRANCE!

See the Long Complete Story, "Caravanners Afloat!" in this issue!

The Magnet Library

1½d

No. 708. Vol. XX.   FOUR-PAGE SUPPLEMENT INSIDE.   September 3rd, 1921.

BILLY BUNTER DIDN'T WANT COAL—BUT HE ASKED FOR IT!

(An amusing incident which occurs when Bunter speaks French!)

THE BEST ALL-SCHOOL STORY PAPER
FOR BOYS AND GIRLS!

The Magnet Library

1¹/₂^d

No. 710. Vol. XX.   FOUR-PAGE SUPPLEMENT INSIDE.   September 17th, 1921.

WHY BILLY BUNTER DID NOT WIN THE CYCLE RACE!

(A humorous incident in the grand story of school and sport in this issue.)

The Magnet Library 1d ½

No. 673. Vol. XVIII. Jan. 1st, 1921.

Sinseerly Yore Edditer

PORTRAIT OF THE EDITOR OF OUR SUPPLEMENT!

("BILLY BUNTER'S WEEKLY" is the funniest thing you've ever read!)

BILLY BUNTER'S WEEKLY.

This jernal has no conneckshun what-evver with "Wharton's Weakly Weekly."

EDDITED BY
William George Bunter.

No. 1.   Week Ending January 1st, 1921.

IN THE EDDITER'S SANKTUM ; or, YOUR EDD T. R SPEEKS !
By W. G. Bunter.

My deer Readers,—At larst the grate day has dorned! At larst a long-felt want has been supplide (as I always say after a good feed at the tuckshopp), and " Billy Bunter's Weekly "—MY week.y—has appeered, to delite the harts of thowsands!

It was my intenshun to make a moddest charge for each issew—a bobb, or sumthing like that—but the edditer of the kompanion papers wouldn't here of it. "My deer Bunter," he said, "this is not to be a munny-making stunt. Yore paper will be priceless. It will be givven away with the 'Magnet Lybrary, for nicks!"

With grate relucktanse I had to bough my head to this dessizion, and, to cut a long story short, here we are!

Of corse, this is not my 1st littery vencher. I wunce ran a jernal called the "Weakly Grub," but, for sum reeson or other, noboddy would dijest it! It had a serkulashun of two — my miner Sammy and myself—and yet they say that jernalism is a paying game!

For sum time I have been attached to the "Greyfriars Herrald " as sub-deputy-sub-edditer. But Wharton had nevver aloud me to air my views. He has kept me in the background, and now he will pay the pennalty, for I have no dout that this brite and clevver little jernal of mine will sweep the "Herrald " off the markitt! It serves Wharton rite for not knowing a good man when he saw one!

You will doutless wish to no, deer reeders, the names of the brillyunt and tallented jernalists on my staff. They are as folloes:

Edditer ... ... William George Bunter.
Sub-Edditer ... W. G. Bunter.
Sports Edditer ... Billy Bunter.
Fiting Edditer ... Bill Bunter.
Speshul Reporter Bunter Major.
Offis Boy ... ... The Owl of the Remove.
Jeneral Factotum The Prize Porpuss.

It will be notissed that I have ritten pracktikally the hole of the 1st number, in order to give the paper a reely good start off. On going to press, I diskovered a kupple of blank kollums, so I aloud Coker of the 5th to fill them with his drivvel. Coker isn't a bad sort of fello in his way, but he can't spell for toffy!

In fewcher issews other peeple will be givven a look in. But I want to give the nessesary toan to the 1st number by doing it myself.

Do not fale to rite and let me no, deer reeders, what you think of my Weekly. And now I must finnish, as I have konsidderable pressure on my space. (That beest Bolsover major is sitting on me!)

Yore Edditer and Chum,
BILLY BUNTER.

BUNTERISMS!

I have it on good orthority that Harry Wharton is in the sanny suffering from shock. The appeeranse of "Billy Bunter's Weekly " has farely boled him over! Verrily, the "Greyfriars Herald " will have to look to its lorrels!

Our edditorial offis is No. 7 Study. Peter Todd, Alonzo, and Tom Dutton have maid objeckshuns. They say that the edditer takes up to much room, which is ridikulus. As if a slim fello like me could ever get in the way!

When the proofs of this number arived from the printers, I showed them to Quelchy, our respeckted Form-master, and arsked him what he thort of my new vencher. "Their is wun grate drorback, Bunter," said he. "What's that, sir?" I inkwired. And then Quelchy had the check to say that the speling was all rong! Why, if I were to ask my reeders to see how many speling errors they could find in this issue, they'd be farely done!

Kuriously enuff, the printers all komplaned that their were a lot of speling mistaiks. "Shall I korreckt them, Master Bunter?" arsked the foreman printer, wringing me up on the tellyfone. "If you do," I replide, "I shall korreckt you—with a kricket-stump! You jolly well leeve my speling alone!" "Oh, all rite!" groaled the foreman. And I could here him nashing his teeth over the wires!

Now that I am a reel live edditer, I meen to throw my wate about, and to interjuice sum much-needed reforms at Greyfriars. In the 1st plaice, I shall adverkate that the tuckshopp be kept open day and nite, and that a sistem of creddit be aloud!

I shall allso insist that the felloes should be fed akkording to there dimenshuns. That is to say, a skinny skarecrow like Toddy should be kontent with one helping only, but a plump fello like me should have at leest ½-a-duzzen ●

Yet another improvement I have in mind is the widdening of all the keyholes. At present it is often very diffikult to here what is being said in the varyus studdies.

It's wunderful what a lot of infewense you can weeld when you're the edditer of a flurrishing organ like this! "Billy Bunter's Weekly " may shape the destinny of the new wurld. Who nose?

EXTRAX FROM MY POST-BAGG.
By Billy Bunter.

WHARTON'S WILY WAYS.

"To the Editor,
"'Billy Bunter's Weekly.'

"Dear Porpoise,—I have heard all about your new venture, and wish you luck with it. I've no doubt that your rag will be amusing—though not in the sense you intend it to be!

"You seem to imagine that the ' Greyfriars Herald ' will now have to shut up shop. But let me assure you that you are right off the wicket! We do not regard your weekly as a serious rival, and we shall have no sleepless nights on account of it.

"By the way, would you mind sending us a presentation copy of your first number? We'd like to frame it as a curiosity, and have it hung in our study. (Bob Cherry says it would be a good wheeze to have its editor hung as well)!—Yours,
"HARRY WHARTON."

(Just like Wharton to be beestly sarkastic! The reel reeson why he wants a copy of our 1st number is so that he can cribb things from it for the "Greyfriars Herald." Nuthing doing—Ed.)

BESSIE'S BRITE SUGGESTION!

"To the Edditer,
"'My Bruther's Weakly.'

"My deer Billy—I've herd all abowt yore Weakly,' and think it's a grate stunt!

"I hope yore serkulation will reech what you are yoreself—a substanshul figger! If I can find time I'll kontribute a ' Cliff House Kollum.' But I must insist upon having a share in the prophets!
"Yore luvving sister,
"BESSIE."

(Many thanks, Bessie! I shall be glad to konsidder a "Cliff House Kollum," which shall be pade for at the rate of two doc-nuts. But I'm afrade you can't have a share in the prophets, as you suggest. You see, they will be dished out amongst the members of the staff. Hope you won't think we're cannibuls.—Ed.)

QUELCHY ON THE WAR-PATH.

"To the Editor,
"' Bunter's Weekly.'

"Dear Bunter,—I regret I cannot see my way to allow you to publish my ' History of Greyfriars ' in serial form in your paper, as you suggest. You would probably pervert the spelling, and make me an object of ridicule. You might also be tempted to insert comments of your own, which would make the ' History ' appear more like a comic feature than anything else.

"You also suggest that I should contribute a love romance to your columns. Any more of this impertinence, and I shall be compelled to correct you.—Yours grimly,
"HORACE H. QUELCH."

(Nuff sed!—Ed.)

THE MAGNET LIBRARY.—No 675.

HOW TO WRITE A SHORT STORY.
An Artikle of Grate Interrest to Budding Orthers.
By the Edditer.

It's easy enuff to write a short story—when you know how.

I think I may say without being thort boastful or konseated, that noboddy is better kwallified to give instruckshun on this subjick than W. G. B.—my 'onnered self. You see, all my life I've been a champyun story-teller!

If it is yore ambishun, gentle reeder, to become a Wells or a Kipperling, I should advise you to studdy this artikle carefully.

Nuthing is more trajjick, to my mind, than the specktacle of a yung orther struggling for fame and forchune and getting nuthing for his pancs, unless it's a slipp of paper bearing the folloing words:

"The edditer regrets that he cannot make use of this kontribushun, and he advises the writer to go and berry it!"

When I 1st started to write stories, I got kwite a number of these slips of paper—rejeckshun forms, I think they are called. I papered the walls of my studdy with them, and made pipe-spills for Skinner. (Skinner loves a pipe, and it's nuthing unusual to see him rolling along the Remove passage with a kwid of baccy in his cheek.)

Well, after a bit, I said to myself, "Sumthing is rong. No edditer will look at my stuff. Why is it?"

Over and over agane I arsked myself this queschun. And then I set to work to find out where I was at fawlt.

At last I came to the konklusion that their was nuthing the matter with my stories, eksept that they were week in plot, and that the dialogg, grammer, speling, and karrackter-droring were all rong.

I made up my mind to konker these fawits, and to-day I am in the very front rank of orthers, and have no diffikulty in finding a markitt for my stuff.

When I used to write for the "Weekly Grubb," they pade me at the rate of tuppence a kollum, which, you will admitt, is pretty good foing.

But, to come to the point, as Quelchy said when he sat on a tin-tack.

I will assume that the fello who reads these lines is ankshus to make good as a short story writer. Very well. He must 1st of all think of a smart, novvel title for his yarn.

A stale title, such as "John Jones," or "Timmerthy Tubbs," is no good at all. It konveys nuthing.

This is the sort of thing you want:

"Who Killed Cock Robbin?"

or,

"Who Pinched Percy's Pie?"

This gripps the reeder's interrest at wunce. He says to himself: "Ah, who done it? How did he do it? Why did he do it?" and so fourth.

Having thort out a good title, you go ahead with the plot. It must be a stiong, griping plot. And you must keep the reeder on the tender-hooks, as Inky would say, untill the last chapter. Don't go and give the whole show away in Chapter 1 by saying:

"Jeremy Jaggers stole into the skool tuck-shop at dead of nite. When he emerjed, their was a newly-made rabbit-pie tucked under his arm."

That sort of thing won't do at all As I say, you must keep the reeder on tender-hooks. Keep him in a state of brethless suspense untill the end of the story, when it will come out that Jeremy Jaggers didn't pinch the pie at all, but that the tuckshopp dame had eaten it herself in a moment of forgettfulness.

Now, it is very important that you should start off yore story with plenty of brite, snappy dialogg. Don't begin in this fashun:

"It was midnite, and the sun was high in the hevvens. The wind was sobbing in the trees, the skies were weeping, and the gale was skwalling. Silense rained as Jeremy Jaggers krept towards the tuckshopp——"

Of corse, this descripshun reeches a high littery standerd, but it won't satisfy a reeder who likes thrills.

This is how yore narratiff should begin:

"He shall die!"

"Die?"

"Ay!"

"Why?"

"He pinched my pie!"

A spirrited opening of this sort will thrill the reeder to his hart's core.

Now we come to karrackter-droring. You must tell yore reeders eggsactly what sort of a fello Jeremy Jaggers is. "A thin, weedy spessimen, with a sallo komplecshun and a face like a boot." Or, "A plump, hansom-looking chap, with fare hare, a cupple of black eyes and brimming over with good-yewmer."

Unless you size up yore karrackters in this way, yore reeders will have no interest in the story.

So much for that.

We now come to two very important things—grammer and speling.

It's serprizing how few budding orthers no the ruddyments of there own langwidge. They frekwently fall into the trap of making there hero say, "I did it," instead of "I done it," or "You were," insted of "You was." Of corse, that sort of thing won't be tollerated by any self-respecting edditer!

Speling is no less important.

Only one fello in a duzzen knows how to spell propperly. I arsked Wharton the other day how many k's their were in "ekspeckt," and he ansered "Nun, of corse!" I told him their were two, and he larfed as if it was a huge joke. Pore fello! I can't help feeling sorry for him.

Fancy the edditer of the "Greyfriars Herald" not being able to spell a simple word like that!

Even Dick Penfold, who is supposed to be streets above everybobby else in class, can't spell to save his life. He sent me a poem for this issew. In the 1st verse he spelt "kwallities" with a "q." Did you ever here of such a thing in all yore natcheral? It's enuff to make Jack Johnson, the kompiler of the English Dickshunary, tern in his grave!

I think I have now put my reeders wise on the subjick of short story writing.

But just wun more tip.

When yore story is written, mind you send it to the propper ¼. For instance, it's not a bit of use sending a pirate story to the "Sunday Pulpit." On the other hand, it is ekwally foolish to send an artikle on "How to Cook a Stake" to the "Vegetarian's Guide." You will land yoreself in the soop if you do.

If yore story deels with footbawl, send it to a footbawl paper. If it's about the war, send it to the "War Cry." If it's about boxing, send it to "Punch." If it's about nuthing in particular, send it to the "Greyfriars Herald," bekawse they don't mind what sort of tommy-rot they publlish!

I have now said enuff to put all budding and perspiring orthers on the road to suck-sess. If they follo the direckshuns I have lade down in this artikle, they will soon be earning pots of munney. And I should like them to remember that my postle-order hasn't yet terned up, and if they'd care to send me a few bobb in the meentime—well, they no my address!

A KRUSHING KALLAMITY!

A Short but Novvel Novvel from the Tallented Pen of

HORACE COKER.

LARST weak, finding time hang 'sumwhat hevvily on my hands, I hit upon a brillyunt brane-wave. (As you no, my brane is the most powerfull organ at Greyfriars.)

I desided to give peeple lessons in the diffikult and danjerous art of motor-sykling.

"This," I refleckted, "will be a ripping way of filling my time—and my pockitts!"

Akkordingly, I displayed the folloing announsement on the skool notiss-bord:

"NOTISS!
HORACE COKER,
The Renowned Trick-Cyklist,
is willing to reseeve pupills, and to instruckt them in the perrilus but plezzant art of motor-cykling.

Fee—a bobb a lesson!

Don't brake yore neck by trying to lern on yore own akkount. Come and konsult Coker, the eggspert, who has ridden over twenty thowsand miles without loss of life or limm!"

I antissipated roping in kwite a crowd of pupills, but I was dissappointed.

For a cupple of days I had no pupills. And I was just beginning to despare when Skinner of the Remove came along.

"With reference to yore announsement, Coker," he said, "I should like to be tort how to ride a motor-bike. That's a topping bike you've got, and what's more, you're a topping rider! I no a clevver fello when I see one."

"Enuff of flattery!" I said sharply. "A bobb, please!"

Grately to my sorprize, Skinner handed over the coin. (I didn't diskovver till afterwards that it was a bad one.)

Well, to cut a long story short, I gave Skinner a lesson—a lesson he'll remember to his dying day!

We went miles and miles that afternoon. We ran down two chickens and a prize pig—I don't mean Billy Bunter!—we had over a duzzen kollisions with cars, carts, prams, etc., and we explored at leest three duck-ponds. It's a wunder we didn't finnish up at the Cottage Hospittal!

I fownd Skinner a very apt pupill. He pade close attenshun to evverything I told him, and at the end of the afternoon he was able to ride for kwite six yards without' shooting off at a tanjent.

"You have made eggsellent progress," I said, when we got back to Greyfriars. "When will you take the neckst lesson?"

"I don't think I shall need any more lessons," he replide. "I'm kwite at home on your motor-bike now, old man. Can I borro it to-morro afternoon?"

"No, you can't!" I grouled.

"Why not?"

"You're only a novvis yet, and I'm not going to lend my eighty-ginny bike to a duffer who duzzent no how to get out of the way of a steem-roller when he sees one coming!"

"Look hear——"

"If you care to take a ferther corse of instruckshun," I said, "I mite konsidder the matter."

"Ratts! I tell you I'm an eggspert rider!" said Skinner. "Yore mashine will be as safe as the Bank of England in my hands."

But I wasn't having any. I didn't want my valuable motor-bike to be smashed to peaces by a klumsy klown like Skinner.

The cad of the Remove walked away in high dudgeon.

I was sorry to lose my only pupill, but it couldn't be helped.

The folloing afternoon a party of 5th-Formers, inkluding myself, were standing in the skool gateway chatting to Prout, our respeckted Form-master. Prout is the only other person at Greyfriars who posesses a motor-bike. Of corse, his bike isn't a patch on mine. I beleeve he picked it up cheep at a cleerance sale of old iron.

"Skinner, you yung raskil!" I showted, with klenched fists. "I-I'll pulverise you!"

While we were talking, Bob Cherry came dashing up. He was neerly sufferkated with merriment.

"Bless my sole!" mutterd Prout. "What is the matter with you, boy?"

"Ha, ha, ha!"

"What has happened?"

"Ho, ho, ho!"

"I kwite fale to understand the kawse of this unseemly larfter!" said Prout.

Bob Cherry kontrolled himself with a grate effort.

"It—it's Skinner, sir!" he gurgled. "He's come an awful kropper, and he looks like a 5th of November guy! You nevver saw such a pickcher in all yore life!"

Prout frouned.

"I am serprized that you should snigger at a skoolfello's missforchune, Cherry!" he said. "Where is Skinner now?"

"When I larst saw him, sir," said Bob Cherry, "he was in the hoarse-pond!"

"What!"

"It seems that he borroed Coker's motor-bike without leeve——"

"Grate Scott!" I ecksclaimed.

"And the bike ran away with him

down the hill, and he took a hedder into the pond! He's not badly damidged, sir, but I'm afrade I can't say the same for the bike!"

Krimson with rage, I strode up to Bob Cherry.

"You—you mean to say that that cheeky yung fagg has busted my bike?" I rored.

"Yes. He's smashed it beyond rekkernition!"

"Then I'll jolly well do the same to him!" I cride savvidgely. "That bike cost eighty ginnies! Just think of it! My self-starting, twin-sillinder, umpteen hoarse-power ' Whirlwind'—smashed to attoms!"

"Kalm yoreself, Coker, in this krisis," said Prout. And I notissed that he was grinning, although he tride hard to keep his face strate.

"Why are you larfing, sir?" I arsked irritably.

"Ahem! I—I reelly cannot help it, Coker! In the first place, Cherry's narratiff is highly diverting; and, sekkondly, I cannot help feeling releeved to no that your motor-cykle is out of the way. It was a konstant sauce of danger to peddestrians, and to farmers' fouls! Ha ha, ha! Pray ekscuse me! Ha, ha, ha!"

Prout seemed to think it jolly funny; but I didn't!

A few minnits later a muddy and bedraggled figger came staggering in at the skool gates. Beside him he dragged what appeered to be a shapeless mass of old iron.

"Skinner, you yung raskil!" I showted, with klenched fists, "I-I'll simply pulverise you for this!"

Prout was still chuckling.

"It was very thortless of you, Skinner," he said, "to destroy Coker's propperty in this way—very thortless indeed! Ha, ha, ha!"

Skinner blinked at Prout with wartery eyes.

"This isn't Coker's propperty, sir!" he stammerd, indikating the batterd bike. "It's yours!"

"What!"

"I—I meant to borro Coker's motor-bike, sir, and I borroed yours by mistaik!"

Prout stopped larfing very suddenly. He looked as if he was going to have an applepleetick fit.

"You—you depraved yung raskil!" he splutterd. "You—you have wantonly destroyed the deerest trezzure of my life! Follo me at wunce to my studdy!"

And Prout strode away with a brow like thunder, while Skinner folloed with the reckage.

As for me, I was simply konvulsed with merriment. And I called to mind the old proverb: "He who larfs last larfs longest!"

THE END.

MY DIARY FOR THE WEEK.

By Lord Mauleverer.

MONDAY.—Woke up. (Rather an unusual proceeding, begad!) Fearfully cold weather; frost on the window-panes. Decided to stay in bed until the brekker-gong went. For one morning only, you know. Mustn't make a practice of this sort of thing! Crawled downstairs at length, and found the bacon cold, and Quelchy very heated! He gave me a hundred lines. I must try and make a start on them to-morrow. "Never do to-day what you can put off till to-morrow," as the proverb says.

TUESDAY.—Dreamed I was at the North Pole. Awoke suddenly to find Bob Cherry squeezing an icy sponge over my classic features. Oooooch! Bitterly cold morning; decided to have another forty winks. Bob Cherry ordained otherwise! Meant to make a start with my impot to-day, but fell asleep while I was thinking about it. Must make a point of tackling it to-morrow, or Quelchy will be furious!

WEDNESDAY.—"Oh, it's nice to get up in the morning; but it's nicer to stay in bed. And it's awful when, without warning, a bolster descends on your head!" Bob Cherry again! I feel strongly roused. Suffered a good deal from insomnia to-day. Couldn't sleep, except at odd intervals. Fully intended to make a start with my impot, but decided it was too much fag.

THURSDAY.—Overslept, and crawled downstairs just as morning lessons were beginning. Quelchy went for me baldheaded. Gave me a fearful jawing, and wound up by asking me for my impot. Told him I hadn't made a start yet, but hoped to do so as soon as weather, wind, and tide permitted.

FRIDAY.—Overslept again, but managed to scramble down to brekker in the nick of time. "Where is your imposition, Mauleverer?" barked Quelchy. "I—I really haven't had time to get down to it yet, sir," I replied. "If it is not in my hands by nine o'clock to-morrow morning," said Quelchy, "there will be trouble." Resolved to tackle impot without delay. Went to my study after brekker, and wrote four lines, then dropped into a doze. Wrote four more lines in the afternoon, and yet another four in the evening, and went to bed in a state of physical exhaustion!

SATURDAY.—I had fully intended overnight to be up with the lark, so that I could finish my impot. But my strenuous exertions of the previous day had worn me out, and instead of getting up with the lark, I got up with the sparrow! At nine o'clock Quelchy sent for me. "I want to see your imposition, Mauleverer!" he said. "Where is it?" "It's still in the stocks, sir," I answered. "That is where you deserve to be!" retorted Quelchy. "Do you mean to say you have not completed the imposition I gave you nearly a week ago?" "Nunno, sir. I—I've been too tired." "Then I will endeavour to restore you to an animated condition!" said the sarcastic beast. Then the sword of Damocles—in other words, Quelchy's pointer—fell; and I am compelled to write these lines in a standing-up attitude. Such is life!

THE MAGNET LIBRARY.—No. 673.

OUR HART-TO-HART TALKS.

Konducted by "UNCLE BILL."

(All reeders who are in trubble of any sort, either threw there own falt or threw the falt of serkumstances, are rekwested to send fool detales to the offis of this paper. Onverlopes should be marked "Uncle Bill," and a remittanse of sixpense should be enklosed.)

"SORROWFUL SMITHY" (Studdy No. 4).—I deeply simperthize with you, my chum, in the loss of yore current cake. You say it was on yore studdy table at four o'klock on Wensday afternoon, and that at two minnits past four it was gone. It's a mistery to me how it vannished, but I can only konklood that it did the cake-walk! Yore suggestion that it was taken by "sum theeving rotter" is absurd, as I was in Friardale at the time! I have thort of a little verse which may konsole you, in sum mezzure, for the loss of your cake. Hear it is (the verse, not the cake!):

"Old Muther Hubbard, she went to the cubbard
  To get her pore dog a bone;
But when she got their the cubbard was bear,
  And so the pore dog had nun!"

"HARTBROKEN HORACE" (Fifth Form) rites in the folloing strane: "Deer Uncle Bill.—Can you tell me, threw the medyum of yore paper, how I can become farely good-looking, so as to attrakt the memlers of the fare secks? At present I am panefully aware that my face resembles a hatchet, and the other day sum-one referred to it as a landslide! What I want to no is, how can I devvelop manly bewty, and become sort after by the yung ladies at Cliff Howse?"

Alass, my pore Horace! I feer it will be impossibul for you to improve yore natcheral appeeranse. Can the thingummybobb change his skin, or the leppard his spotts? You mite try a brisk massage nite and morning with sand-paper, and see if that has any effeckt. It may possibly remove the sharp corners. But you can never hope to be anything like as good-looking as your Uncle Bill. Sum are born bewtiful, sum acheeve bewty, and others have bewty thrust upon them. But I feer, Horace, that you don't come in either of these kattygories. But remember, my chumm, that their is such a thing as bewty of sole, as well as bewty of face and figger; and if you have a bewtiful sole, why, nuthing else matters! You should kommit the folloing lines to memmery:

"I care not if this face of mine
Be neither fare nor splendid;
My sole is bewtiful and fine
  (For I've just had it mended!")

"R. DUPP" (Remove Form).—I am very greeved to here that you are on the rox—in other words, stoney. But I feer you will will get no help from this ½. You see, yore Uncle Bill is in the same bote himself! I would willingly lend you five bobb if I had it, but my titled rellations leeve me alone nowadays. Wish they'd leeve me "a loan" instedd! In my stoney periods (which are farely frekwent) I often find grate konsolashun in these touching lines:

"Mary had a little lam,
Its fleese was wite as snow;
And evverywhere that Mary went
That lam was sure to go!"

STOP PRESS.

HAVE A LOOK AT THE CHAT PAGE, AND LEARN WHAT HAPPENED AFTER "B. B.'s W." HAS GONE TO PRESS.

OUR AGGERNY KOLLUM.

FARE FILLIS.—What have I done that you should shun me so? Please meet me Wensday evening at six, by the style in Friardale Lane, and let me take you to the piekchers. If you don't turn up, I shall perrish of a broken hart.—HORACE C.

CLAUDE HOSKINS.—Come back to your heartbroken and grief-stricken studdy-mate. So sorry I kicked you out last night, but your sonata in E flat got on my nerves so much that I wasn't responsible for my actions. Come back—come back! I've had the piano stored away in one of the lumber-rooms—ditto your violin and cornet. Do not stay away any longer from your sorrowing HOBBY.

ADVERTISER, a young nobleman, would be glad to hear of a job (Government office preferred). Guaranteed to sleep peacefully all day, and not disturb anybody. Will accept a four-figure salary; won't look at anything less. Smartly dressed, charming manner and appearance, and delightfully drowsy. Insists upon getting work where there isn't any to do. Too much fag to state further particulars about pedigree and abilities.—Apply LORD MAULEVERER, "Slackersville," Remove Passage, Greyfriars.

MONEY LENT! ONE PENNY TO FIVE BOB! On note of hand only. No awkward inquiries as to applicant's private life and habits. No silly references required. Strictest secrecy guaranteed. Loans have already been made to the Editor of this paper, who promises to refund when his postal-order arrives. If you want to set yourself up in business, or purchase a house, or a Ford car, do not hesitate to leap at this generous offer. No dealings with minors.—THE FISHY FINANCE COMPANY, Study No. 14.

BOLSOVER MAJOR.—Will meet you in the gym on Saturday afternoon, as arranged. You are requested to provide your own ambulance.—BOB CHERRY.

FAG wanted immediately. Advertiser simply dying for a smoke!—Apply GERALD LODER, Sixth Form Passage.

MISSING! A pair of football boots (size ten) from my study. If the fellow who bagged them will report to me, he will hear of something to his disadvantage!—GEORGE WINGATE.

THOUSANDS ARE STARVING IN TIMBUCTOO! All contributions in the shape of grub (pastries preferred) will be gladly welcomed. They should be forwarded without delay to Box B.B., office of this paper.

HAIR permanently removed from face by safe and simple method. Come and be shaved by Fisher T. Fish, the barbarous barber! No blunt penknives used. No lifelong disfigurement caused.—THE GREYFRIARS TOILET SALOON, Study No. 14.

No. 107.
New Series.
Week Ending—
Feb. 5th,
1921.

The Popular

1½d

20 Pages.

SPLENDID MONEY PRIZE COMPETITION INSIDE.

FATTY WYNN

BAGGY TRIMBLE

PRIVATE EDITOR

BILLY BUNTER and HIS FOUR FAT SUBS

SAMMY BUNTER

TUBBY MUFFIN

PORTRAITS OF THE EDITOR OF OUR SUPPLEMENT & HIS FOUR FAT SUBS

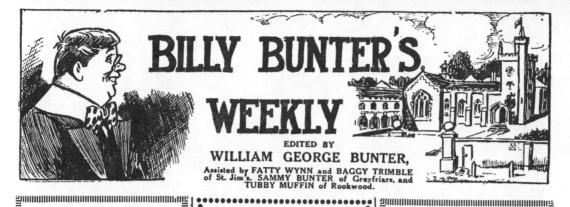

BILLY BUNTER'S WEEKLY

EDITED BY
WILLIAM GEORGE BUNTER,

Assisted by FATTY WYNN and BAGGY TRIMBLE
of St. Jim's, SAMMY BUNTER of Greyfriars, and
TUBBY MUFFIN of Rookwood.

IN YORE EDDITER'S DEN!

My Deer Reeders,—Most of you have herd of my famus "Weekly," and those who haven't are not worth trubbling about!

In the past my little jernal has appeered in spazzums, by the curtesy of the Edditer of the Companion Papers. But arranjements have now been maid to publbish it evvery week, and this, being the 1st number, is No. 1.

I feel sure that the publbicashun of my wunderful "Weekly" will make the popular POPULAR popular. It will give a toan to the paper—it will lend it a personallity. As John Ruskin, the famus inventor of rusks, said, "A paper without Billy Bunter in it is like a house without windoes."

In previous issews of my paper I have been ass enuff to do all the donky work, but now that my jernal is to appeer evvery week I reelize that I shall need help. Four subb-edditers have been engaged, and the fool staff is as follies:

EDDITER, Soopreme Kontroller, Soul Manniger, Chairman, President, Bored of Direcktors, and Head Cook and Bottle-washer - - - W. G. BUNTER.

SUBB-EDDITOR and Speshul Korrespondent for the Lower Skool at Greyfriars SAMMY BUNTER.

SUBB-EDDITER and Speshul Korrespondent for Skool House at St. Jim's BAGGY TRIMBLE.

SUBB-EDDITER and Speshul Korrespondent for New House at St. Jim's FATTY WYNN.

SUBB-EDDITER and Speshul Korrespondent for Rookwood TUBBY MUFFIN.

I think you will all agree that I've got a very relyable staff to lean upon. We shall stick together threw thick and thin, and cudgel our branes in order to provvide our reeders with a fine feest (of fickshun) each week.

Don't forget to tell all yore pals, unkles, cuzzens, nevvews, neeces, and ants about this new vencher of mine. Their is sertain to be a tremenduss demand for neckst week's issew, so you are strongly advised to order it at leest a fortnite in advanse!

Duly orthentikated kontribushuns are welcomed, and will bo pade for at the rate of a doe-nut per kollum. I supply hedings as per page 2. By the by, it mite bee just as wel to menshun that I shal not bee able to publish anything of a sort as that which Pon has writen about. Altho I consider myself a very gay dog, I am reely. Perhaps if Wingate or any of the masters got hold of the "Weekly," as they mite, 4 they reely can't resist the temptashun sometimes, they might give me a licking for leeding yung inoosut fellos, like my readers, in-to ways they considder ar bad form. Please take this as a warning if yu ar thinking of riting stuf like Racing News of Sure Tips.—Your stout pall,

Yore Edditer

WHARTON ON THE WAR PATH!

"To the Barrel-like Being who Presides over 'Billy Bunter's Weekly.'

"Dear Porpoise,—So the Editor of the Companion Papers is allowing you to run your ridiculous rag each week in the POPULAR? No wonder you have been swelling so visibly of late!

"I wish you joy of your new scheme. At the same time, I should like to trickle into your ear a word of warning. If you start cribbing any ideas, stunts, wheezes, brainwaves, or plots from the 'Greyfriars Herald,' your scalp will be removed and suspended over the school gateway, as a solemn warning to other would-be cribbers. Compray-voo?—as they say in France.—Yours in deadly earnest, "HARRY WHARTON."

(Bah! As if I should want to lift anything from a stale, stodgy, skurrilus rag like the "Greyfriars Herald"! I have a sole that rises above such petty meenness. Their is nuthing in the "Herald" worth cribbing, and I'm sure I don't no what Wharton is cribbing about! By the way, if he will advanse me sumthing on my postle-order, I shall be pleesed to allow him and his palls to kontribewt okkashunally to my "Weekly."—Ed.)

WHY DOES ALONZO CARRY ON SO?

"To the Editor, 'William Bunter's Weekly.'

"My Dear Bunter,—I learn on good authority that you are launching your periodical in the pages of the POPULAR.

"This being the case, I shall be pleased to contribute a number of articles—not more than two billion words in length—on topics of general interest. I enclose an essay on 'The Porpoise: Its Life and Habits,' also a story entitled, 'The Tale of a Tub.' Kindly publish these in your next issue, under the signature of Yours fraternally, "ALONZO TODD."

(Sorry, Lonzy, but I've no room for yore kontribushuns. You see, I've already eaten 15 doe-nuts, a duzzen sossidge-rolls, and a plum-cake! In any case, I don't want anything deeling with a porpuss. I'm quite capable of writing my own ortobiography!—Ed.)

A SUJESTION REJECKTED!

"To the Editor of 'Billy Bunter's Weekly.'

"Dear Billy,—I should like to congratulate you on your new venture—I mean, the 'Weekly' of yours. At the same time, I should like to suggest to you a feature which would be very popular with the majority of your readers, especially yourself, as you are such a gay dog. Why not run a column for Racing News, with free tips?

Yours horsely, "C. PONSONBY (Highcliffe School)."

("Oh, reely, Pon, how could I put such a thing in my grand jernal as yu sergest! Old Quelchy might get hold of it.—Ed.)

THINGS WE WANT TO NO!

WHEN is the "Greyfriars Herald" going to shutt up shopp?

AND when is it going to stopp talking shopp?

WHEN are the tuckshopps at Greyfriars. St. Jim's, and Rookwood going to remane open day and nite for the konvenience of the Edditer and his four fat subs?

WHY did Harry Wharton tern pail when he herd that my "Weekly" was going to appeer in the POPULAR? (Evvidently he terned pail bekawse he thort the "Greyfriars Herald" would kick the bucket!)

WHY duzzent Mr. C. H. Chapman make me a more hansom figger? From his sketch of me, anybody would think I was inklined to be a trifle plump!

WHAT did Fatty Wynn? (A plaice on the staff of "Billy Bunter's Weekly," of corse!)

WHY was Tom Merry? (Bekawse he was allowed to kontribewt!)

WHY wasn't Gordon Gay? (Bekawse he couldn't have a finger in the pie!)

AND, now we are on the subjick of konundrums, what did Doctor Locke? (His studdy desk, bekawse he new I was on the prowl!)

WHEN is Coker of the Fifth going to put that motor-bike of his in porn?

WHAT would happen to this "Weekly" of mine if my miner went on strike?

WHY don't I get invited to Cliff House more often?

WHEN is that jellus beest Wharton going to give me a plaice in the Remove footer teem?

WHEN is Greyfriars going to wake up to the fackt that their is only one sootable kandidate for the kaptaincy of the Remove? (Moddesty forbidds me to menshun names!)

AND when—oh, when is my postle-order going to arrive?

WHO will be the first to klaim the afoursed postle-order when it does arive?

AND whose going to be unlucky?.

IF the Edditer of the POPULAR will let me judge the compeetishun he's runnin'?

HOW long will it be befour Quelchy arsks me to publish his "Hisstory of Greyfriars" in cereal form?

WHO put the wire harebrush in Loder's bedd?

AND did Loder see the poynt?
THE POPULAR.—No. 107.

TUBBY MUFFIN'S MUMBLINGS!

(It seams to me that Tubby Muffin thinks to much about grub.—Ed.)

My Deer Reeders,—As the subb-edditer and speshul korrespondent for Rookwood I have the onner to address you.

This page is the only part of "Billy Bunter's Weekly" that's worth reeding, so I should advise you to reed, mark, lern, and inwardly dijest my kollum very slowly, so that you may enjoy it to the fool.

It was, of corse, only fitting that I should be givven a plaice on the staff. I know more of what goes on at Rookwood than anybody else. You see, I spend at leest five minnits a day at evvery keyhole in the skool, and kwite a lot of useful informashun filters threw to my ears.

I am writing this in my studdy. Only one of my studdy-mates—Higgs—is prezzent. The other—Teddy Grace—has cleered out, bekawse he says he can't stand having ink splashed over his grilled kipper. He's gone to have tea with that well-meening but idiottick clown, Jimmy Silver.

Well, deer reeders, hear we are! Or, to put it more planely, we are hear! (Pass the doe-nutts, Higgs!) I've got a page to myself evvery week, and okkashunally I shall let Jimmy Silver & Co. air there views. Not that there views are worth airing. You see, they're too dry!

I suppoze you have read all about me in the "Popular," jentle reeders? But I must say that Mr. Owen Conquest makes me out to be an awful pigg. In reallity, I'm nuthing of the sort. (Pass the jam-roll, Higgs!) I'm an eggsellent fello in evvery way, and it is kommon nollidge that I ought to be kaptin of the Classical Fourth at Rookwood. Howevver, we don't allways get our dessert in this world. (In fackt, I was refewsed a fifth helping at dinner-time!)

Mr. Conquest deskribes me as a fat and greedy gormandizer, but I can assure you (After you with that rabbitt-pie, Higgs!) that I'm a slim, hansom fello who nevver eats more than is good for him. (You mite shy over the current-cake as well, Higgs, their's a good chap!)

I think you will all agree that the Rookwood items in this issew beets all the rest of the feechers put together! I've perswaded Mornington—the chap with the eye-glass, you know—to write me an artikel, and he has oblijed with "Hints to Yung Foot-bawlers." The hints seem rather kweer to me, but I suppoze they're all rite. Anyway, Morny looked kwite serious when he handed me his artikel, so I hardly think he's pulling my legg.

And now, deer reeders, I am too fool of emoshun—and rabbitt-pie—to write any more this weak, but neckst weak I shall be going strong! (Now, Higgs, I've finnished my skribbling, so you can pass me the wipped creem wallnuts, the butterd skones, the jam-sandwidge, the toast, the marmerlaid, the minse-pies, and the patter-cake biskits!—Thanks!)

Bong swore, deer reeders!

Yore affeckshunate pal,
TUBBY MUFFIN.

FATTY WYNN'S WARBLINGS!

(Wynn is a member of Figgins & Co., New House, St. Jim's.—Ed.)

My Dear Readers,—I expect you'll rub your eyes on seeing my name as a member of the staff of "Billy Bunter's Weekly."

In the ordinary way, I don't have anything to do with Billy Bunter. I don't approve of his piggishness, and I don't care if he gives me the sack for saying so!

But when Billy came over to St. Jim's to see me the other day, and told me that he was launching his paper in the "Popular," I realised that something would have to be done to save the venture from being a compleate failure. Neither of the three sub-editors—Sammy Bunter, Baggy Trimble, and Tubby Muffin—has had any journalistic experience; so I thought I'd make a fourth "sub," and save "Billy Bunter's Weekly" from an untimely fate by getting a number of St. Jim's fellows to contribute. We've got brains at St. Jim's; but as for Greyfriars and Rookwood—why, one's an annexe of Colney Hatch, and the other's a home for incurables!

I hesitated at first about taking on this job. But Billy Bunter overcame my scruples by bribing me with a bag of doughnuts, and I promised to edit a special St. Jim's Page every week. I shall bag a column myself, of course; and I don't much care who fills the other two, so long as the spelling is an improvement on Billy Bunter's!

I can't help saying that I consider the editor of the companion papers has been guilty of favouritism in allowing Billy Bunter to publish his paper every week in the "Popular." It would have been much wiser to have handed over the job to a sensible fellow like me. Bunter's got no more idea of running a weekly journal than the man in the moon. And I'm jolly certain he won't get much help from his minor, or from that brainless idiot, Baggy Trimble. Neither will that equally brainless barrel, Tubby Muffin, be of much assistance.

Still, Bunter showed sound common-sense in making me one of his "subs," and so long as the St. Jim's items appear every week, there will be no fear of the paper going under. Billions of boys and girls will buy it for the St. Jim's features alone. They won't want to read Billy Bunter's balderdash!

Of course, Figgins and Kerr, my two studymates, were awfully ratty when they heard that I had promised Billy Bunter my support.

"You're a champion chump, Fatty!" growled Figgins. "You'll lose all your self-respect by going in co with Bunter!"

"Yes, rather!" said Kerr. "You're a perfectly priceless pumpkin, Fatty, to get mixed up with a scheme of this sort!"

"Let's bump the fat idiot!" roared Figgy. "I won't let you contribute to the St. Jim's Page if you do!" I chimed in.

And so Figgy and Kerr let me off. You see, they're both fond of seeing their stuff in print, and in their hearts they envy me my job of sub-editor and special correspondent for St. Jim's.

You will see that I've persuaded Monty Lowther to do a feature, and the other St. Jim's feature is what they call a symposium, I believe. I organised it myself.

I must ring off now, dear readers, as I've got an important appointment with Baggy Trimble at the tuckshop!

Look out for some topping St. Jim's features next week!

Your plump pal,
FATTY WYNN.

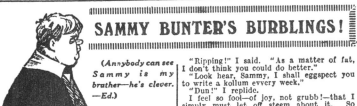

SAMMY BUNTER'S BURBLINGS!

(Annybody can see Sammy is my bruther—he's clever. —Ed.)

I awoke one morning to find myself famus. My major sent for me, and told me the glad news that his "Weekly" was going to be pubblished reggularly in the "Popular."

"Grate, Billy—grate!" I eggsclaimed. "The fame of the 'Popular' will eggspand—and so will yore napper!"

"Do you insinnuate that I shall suffer from swelled head?" demanded Billy.

"Nunno! Not at all! I say, Billy, I'm to be cheef subb-edditer, of corse?"

"Of corse!"

"That's the stile! Nuthing like keeping it in the fambly! You ought to make Ant Rebeccer yore Fashun Edditer."

"Bother Ant Rebeccer!"

"And Bessie can kontribewt a Needlework Kollum."

"Bessie shall do nuthing of the sort! I don't want any members of the other secks interfering with my 'Weekly.'"

"All rite. Keep yore hare on! Who are the other subb-edditers?"

"I'm going to get Fatty Wynn, Baggy Trimble. and Tubby Muffin."

THE POPULAR.—No. 107.

"Ripping!" I said. "As a matter of fat, I don't think you could do better."

"Look hear, Sammy, I shall eggspect you to write a kollum evvery week."

"Dun!" I replide.

I feel so fool—of joy, not grubb!—that I simply must let off steem about it. So hear goes! (Didn't no I was a poet, did you?)

AN ODE TO DICKY NUGENT.
By Sammy Bunter.

If you're waking, call me early, call me early, Dicky deer,
For to-morro will be the gladdest day of all the glad New Yeer!
Of all the glad New Yeer, Dicky, the gladdest day—not ½!
For I'm to be on the staff, Dicky—I'm to be on the staff!

My major Billy says to me; he says to me, says he,
"You're going to be my rite-hand man!" I cride in French, "We, we!"
The felloes hear can scoff and sneer, and cackle, chipp, and chaff;
But I'm to be on the staff, Dicky—I'm to be on the staff!

My bruther's 'Weekly's' going to be a reelly ripping jernal,
For Billy will be G.O.C., and I shall be his kernel.
They'll find us tuffish nuts to crack, I prommiss you (don't larf!)—
For I'm to be on the staff, Dicky—I'm to be on the staff!

We meen to make things hum, you no, in this old sleepy skool;
With toping tails and artikels the 'Weekly' will be fool.
Can't stop for more—I must be off to get my annual barf.
But isn't it stunning news, Dicky? I'm to be on the staff!

Well, what do you think of that, boys and girls? I don't believe there's a poet like me in the skool. I think I shall have that bewtiful poem set to musick, and publish it in my bruther's "Weekly."

Billy might do what Wharton never done. He might have a peece of musick in his "Weekly." Wharton never had sence enough to think of a feeture like that. Blessed if I don't see what Hoskins, the musickal chap, says about it.

Any old how, that's a stunt I'm going to bare in my mind, reeders. Of corse, though I'm cheef subb-edditer, I can't put anything in this bit of mine. Billy has the larst word, just like he allways takes the last bit of grubb. (That's a bit of soft sope, reeders, 'cos Billy might be in a better frame of mined when I tackle him about the musick.)

Well, I've reeched the end this week, so I remane,

Yours stuntfully,
SAMMY BUNTER.

DICK GRUNTER'S DARING!
By PETER TODD.

(Note : Peter assures me that the karrackters in this story are ficktishus. But I have my doubts !—ED.)

"I say, Horton——"

It was Dick Grunter, of the Remove Form at Grey Towers, who spoke.

Dick was a plump, athletic-looking fellow, strikingly handsome, in spite of the peculiar growth in the middle of his face. Some people said that this strange growth was Dick Grunter's nose. Others declared it was a deformity. On top of the growth was perched a pair of enormous spectacles.

Harry Horton, the captain of the Remove, was in his study, drawing up the list of players for the match with Wycliffe. His chums—Bob Berry, Frank Truegent, Johnny Bullock, and Hurree Warble—were with him.

"I say, Horton," repeated Dick Grunter, "I suppose I'm down to play against Wycliffe?"

"There's something wrong with your 'supposer,' then!" growled Horton.

Dick Grunter's eyes glittered behind his spectacles.

"You know jolly well that I'm entitled to a place in the team!" he said wrathfully.

Bob Berry chuckled.

"If we were to give you a place in the team, Grunter," he said, "there'd be such an outcry that soon we shouldn't have a team in the place!"

"Ha, ha, ha!"

"Oh, really, Berry! This is sheer personal jealousy on Horton's part. He knows what a player I am, and he's afraid of being shown up by me. That's why he always keeps me out of the side. But I'm fed up with taking a back seat. I'll raise an eleven, Horton, that'll lick yours into a cocked hat! And then you won't be able to overlook my claims any longer!"

A roar of laughter greeted Dick Grunter's threat.

"Ha, ha, ha!"

"You've some hopes of licking the Remove team, Porpoise!"

"The hopefulness is terrific!"

Dick Grunter shook a fat fist at the laughing juniors.

"I'll get up a team this very afternoon!" he said. "And I'll make your own rag-time eleven look a set of novices!"

"Rats!"

Having formed his daring resolve, Dick Grunter rolled out of the study, and at once started to raise recruits for his eleven.

There were plenty of fellows willing to enlist under Dick's banner. Sinner and Stoop and Swott promptly rallied round; and Bisher T. Bish guessed and calculated that he would show Harry Horton & Co. how to play football. A Chinese junior named Lun Wung also agreed to play.

Harry Horton's eleven laughingly accepted Dick Grunter's challenge, and at two o'clock the rival elevens lined up on the footer-field.

Joker of the Fifth consented to act as

referee, and there were loud cheers as he blew his whistle for the game to commence.

"Play up, Gunter!"

"On the ball!"

Dick Gunter made a handsome figure in his tight-fitting jersey, which was split from the nape of his neck to the small of his back.

Harry Horton & Co. were the first to attack, but they could make no impression on a resolute defence, in which a burly youth named Bolshevik major greatly distinguished himself.

All through the first half Harry Horton's men kept up a terrific bombardment. But, try as they would, they could not get through.

At the interval the score-sheet was blank—

and so were the faces of Harry Horton and his baffled followers.

Dick Grunter laughed gaily as he munched a rabbit-pie.

"We've got 'em groggy, you fellows!" he said. "They're played to a standstill already. We shall be all over 'em in the second-half!"

"Yep! I guess they'll look pretty sick by the time we've finished with 'em!" said Bisher T. Bish.

The game was resumed in a sensational fashion.

Dick Grunter rolled the whole length of the field, and all efforts to bowl him over proved unsuccessful. He wound up by firing in a terrific shot at point-blank range, and Cowstrode, the goalie, was beaten all ends up.

"Goal!"

"Good old Grunter!"

Dick Grunter fairly purred with delight.

"This is where we score!" he chortled.

Harry Horton & Co. played up desperately. But they were not in the same street as Dick Grunter's eleven, who fairly ran them off their feet.

Goal after goal came from the nimble and graceful feet of Dick Grunter. His shooting was deadly—almost as deadly as that of Mr. Snout, the master of the Fifth.

Five minutes from the end, no less than nine goals had been registered by Dick Grunter. And Harry Horton's eleven had not yet opened their account.

The crowd clamoured for Dick Grunter to put on another goal.

"Make it ten, Dick!"

"Get into double figures!"

In the very last minute Dick Grunter received a pass from Bisher T. Bish. He raced through on his own, bowling over Johnny Bullock and Bob Berry as he ran.

When within shooting distance he paused.

"Horton," he said, "I will now drive the last nail into your coffin!"

And then Dick Grunter shot, falling heavily into a puddle as he did so.

The muddy water splashed into his face; and then—he woke up to hear the rising-bell clanging, and to see Bob Berry standing over his bed, squeezing a wet sponge over his features!

THE END.

ARTHUR AUGUSTUS D'ARCY.—Most decidedly, dear boy! I consider that no fellow looks at his best in Etons. They are not striking enough. They lack a satisfactory colour-scheme. In my opinion, the wearing of fancy waistcoats should be made compulsory, and pink socks with green stripes should be universally worn. All neckties should be red, white, and blue, with a dash of yellow. All trousers should be striped in zebra fashion, and the lower part of these garments should be made of solid metal. They would then be dog-proof, and that beast Towser, who has no respect whatever for a fellow's trousers, would have to keep his distance. All jackets should be made to resemble the present style of footer jersey, viz., red and white stripes. I consider that these reforms are most urgently needed. Not for one moment, however, would I dream of banishing the "topper," which is the distinguishing mark of a gentleman. Any fellow found wearing a bowler hat should be gated for the rest of the term! And anybody misguided enough to wear a trilby or a Homburg, should receive a fearful thrashing!

TOM MERRY.—Abolish Etons? No jolly fear! Etons are jolly comfy, and any fellow who talks of abolishing them has got bats in his belfry!

MONTY LOWTHER.—By all means abolish Etons, and let's wear coats of mail. Public floggings would then be a luxury!

HERBERT SKIMPOLE.—Any revolutionary departures or innovations of a sartorial nature are to be unceremoniously deprecated, as being derogatory to the—— (Shurrup, dictionary!—F. W.)

JACK BLAKE.—Etons should be abolished in favour of khaki. I know that khaki is the correct wear, because I once heard a sergeant-major say, as he surveyed a squad of Tommies: "Right dress!"

PERCY MELLISH.—I certainly think Etons should be abolished. When a chap goes out after lights out and happens to be seen by some silly idiot of a prefect, he is immediately recognised as some St. Jim's chap. Ordinary clothes would not give the prefects such a chance of knowing who's out late at night.

GEORGE FIGGINS.—I think Etons should remain. At the same time, I do not think it fair that tailors should charge a chap who is a little bit long in the leg extra for his suit.

GEORGE HERRIES.—I think that some chaps at least should be made to wear Etons, even if they were abolished. My dog Towser has a great liking for the trousers which go with an Eton suit, as more than one tailor's dummy knows. Why deprive dogs of their legitimate pleasures?

WALLY D'ARCY.—Yes, certainly abolish Etons. The collars we have to wear with the suit are too big. One can't hide ink when it happens to get upon one's collar, and with a fatheaded major always howling about

cleanliness, it gets on one's nerves! (And Gussy will get on your neck when he sees this!—F. W.)

HENRY MANNERS.—I must say I like the look of Etons, but there is one great objection. The pockets won't hold a decent-sized plate when one happens to be out taking photographs.

RALPH RECKNESS CARDEW.—Abolish them if you like, dear boy, but don't bother me any more.

MISS MARIE RIVERS.—What a funny question to ask me, Wynn! I should not like to see Etons abolished, for I must say you all look pretty little boys in your best suits. (Ow! I sha'n't ask Miss Marie any more questions!—F. W.)

SPECIAL MESSAGE FROM BAGGY TRIMBLE

"My Deer Reeders,—That beest, Fatty Wynn, has crowded me out this weak, and in any case, I couldn't have ritten a kollum for this issew, as I'm in the sanny, suffering from severre infernal panes. You see, I herd that they eat frogs in France, so I tried toad-pie, and, oh, the aggerny and pane! I hope—ow!—to feel—yow!—better neckst weak—yow-ow-ow!

"Hopping you are all kwite well as it leeves me at present in grate angwish, I remain,

"Yores to a barf-bunn,

"BAGGY TRIMBLE."

Passing Opinions.

WHAT I THINK OF JIMMY SILVER.
By Tommy Dodd.

Jimmy Silver, the so-called leader of the Classical Fourth at Rookwood, is a champion fellow—in his own estimation !

I quite agree that Jimmy is a champion—a champion chump ! His footer would make the angels weep; and his cricket is a sight for gods and men and little fishes. He can't hold the most simple catch that comes his way, because, like our fat friend Tubby, he's always Muffin' !

What Jimmy Silver is doing here at all I can't imagine. It must have been a ghastly mistake that he drifted into Rookwood. His luggage was labelled "Colney Hatch," and the authorities of that well-known asylum, realising the danger of Jimmy Silver being at large, are scouring the country for him. It's an insult to Rookwood that a raving maniac like Silver should be allowed to remain here; and, to quote from a certain comic opera :

"Peace will come as soon as he
Is put in gaol for lunacy !"

As I have already stated, Jimmy Silver belongs to the Classical side, and I've more than once had occasion to disfigure his Classical features! He fondly imagines he's cock of the walk. Curious how lunatics always harbour these sort of delusions, isn't it ?

I hear that there's a big controversy at St. Jim's on the subject of "Should Etons be Abolished ?" I certainly think they should—in Jimmy Silver's case. What he wants is a strait-jacket !

———

WHAT I THINK OF TOMMY DODD.
By Jimmy Silver.

As everyone knows, there are two sides at Rookwood. And the most "sidey" side are the Moderns.

The Classical side is a very exclusive concern. Only sportsmen and gentlemen are admitted.

The riff-raff, consisting of hooligans, tame lunatics, and brainless louts, are pitchforked into the Modern side.

And the biggest hooligan, the tamest lunatic, and the most brainless lout, is one Thomas Dodd !

I am continually having to keep Tommy in his place. Only the other day I found it necessary to dribble him across the quad. My pal Newcome, who is by way of being a poet, made up a Limerick about it :

"There was a young bounder named Dodd,
Who met Silver one day in the quad.
Said he, "You're an ass!"
Then he rolled in the grass,
And confessed that the ass was well shod !"

I'm afraid the Modern side will never be able to hold a candle to the Classicals —at any rate, not so long as it contains such a Dodd-ering idiot as Tommy Dodd ! Them's my sentiments, gentlemen ! And Raby, Lovell, and Newcome, my valiant trenchermen, heartily endorse them !

THE POPULAR.—No. 107.

HINTS TO YOUNG FOOTBALLERS.
By VALÉNTINE MORNINGTON.

I suppose it is the ambition of every young footballer to play for Aston Villa or Tottenham Hotspur, or some other famous club; to figure in the English Cup-Final at Stamford Bridge, and to make a name that will live in the history of the great winter game.

I will proceed to tell you how this ambition can be realised. I speak with some authority, because I come of a great footballing family. My great-grandfather, Squire Mornington, was skipper of his village team in the days when the goals were five miles apart, and when the ball was such a size that if you happened to get in its way as it rolled downhill you were smashed to a pulp.

Well, my great-grandfather turned out every year for the village, and he kicked more goals—and opponents—than any other player in the land. The epitaph on his tombstone runs as follows:

"Here lyeth ye squire; he'd so lustie a kicke
That any opponent who failed to looke slicke,
And gette out of ye way, was borne home to hys wife,
And did keepe to hys bedde for ye reste of hys lyfe!"

My great-grandfather's footballing ability was inherited by my grandfather, who founded the famous Lickham Rovers' club.

My pater, too, was hot stuff in his youth. They made him a linesman at the Cup-Final

in the year that somebody sloped off with the gate-money. It was rumoured that my pater had a hand in the business, because he was afterwards seen touring about the country in a Ford car. But then, Rumour's a lying jade!

I myself am a fine footballer. I play at outside-left for the Rookwood junior team— unless I happen to be left outside!

But to come to the point, as Mr. Bootles said when he sat on an inverted tintack. Here are some useful hints for the guidance of any fellow who wishes to make a Bloomer:

(1) Before playing in a match, always lay a solid foundation by having a heavy meal of pastry. A dozen veal-and-ham pies afford the best preparation.

(2) Treat the referee to a lime-juice-and-soda before the match—not as a bribe, of course, but merely to put him in a good humour.

(3) If you are a half-back, make a point of feeding your forwards. Give 'em a lump of toffee every five minutes!

(4) If you can't rob your opponent of the ball, rob him of his gold ticker when he isn't looking!

(5) Don't be afraid of using your fists. The more opponents you can put out of action the better your team's chances!

(6) Shoot straight and often. A catapult is the best weapon to use!

(7) If your side fails to carry off the honours, make sure that they have to carry off the referee!

If you follow these golden rules, you are bound to have a great future before you in the world of football!

EXTRACTS FROM "THE TIMES" IN 1950.
By MONTY LOWTHER.

THE HONOURABLE ARTHUR AUGUSTUS D'ARCY has been asked to put up for Member of Parliament for Bunkumville. He has answered that he is bound to refuse, as he already has too many ties.

———

SIR THOMAS MERRY has been appointed Governor of St. James' School, Sussex. He was once a pupil there, and rumour has it that he was very much in the eye of the public at the time.

———

MR. BAGLEY TRIMBLE has accepted the appointment of head chef at the Carlton.

———

MR. BERNARD GLYN has invented an aeroplane which will fly to Mars and back on a pennyworth of petrol.

———

MR. JOHN BLAKE, who was admitted to Colney Hatch Asylum ten years ago, shows no sign of coming back to his right senses.

———

MR. DAVID WYNN is opening a new restaurant in the Strand on the first day of next month. This makes the fifty-fourth that he has built this year.

———

SIR GEORGE KERR, the world-famous detective, has not yet solved the Mystery of the Poisoned Sandwich, which he first tackled in 1930. He is still hopeful of running the criminal to his lair, however.

———

LORD MACNOODLE, better known as Montague Lowther, is still drawing thousands of people to his play, "I Saw You !" at His Majesty's. He is now recognised as being the greatest humorist of the century.

———

MR. TAGGLES is retiring from the post of porter to St. James' School, after having slept at the gates for nearly eighty years.

———

MR. PERCY MELLISH, editor of "The Swindler's Gazette," has gone into the country for a rest. There are nasty rumours flying round the City.

———

THE GREEN MAN at Rylcombe, Sussex, was raided by the police yesterday evening. Racke and Crooke, the notorious crooks, were found gambling on the premises. It is to be hoped that they got a life-sentence this time as incorrigible rogues.

———

MR. GEORGE HERRIES, the well-known dog-fancier, is organising his twenty-third show this month.

BUNTER STRIP BY C.H. CHAPMAN FROM 'THE COMET,' 1956.

LEONARD SHEILDS

BILLY BUNTER *of Greyfriars*

It was a half-holiday, and Harry Wharton, the captain of the Remove Form at Greyfriars School, had received a food hamper that morning. With his chums, Bob Cherry, Frank Nugent, Johnny Bull and the Indian boy Hurree Singh, he set out for Friardale Woods.

IT'S A PERFECT DAY FOR A PICNIC AND THERE'S ENOUGH TUCK IN THIS HAMPER FOR ALL OF US!

THREE CHEERS FOR YOUR UNCLE, HARRY.

MMM! I CAN HARDLY WAIT!

A MINUTE OR TWO LATER, A FAT FIGURE EMERGED FROM THE SCHOOL GATES AND FOLLOWED IN THE WAKE OF THE FAMOUS FIVE. IT WAS THE EVER-HUNGRY BILLY BUNTER.

THOSE GREEDY BEASTS REFUSED TO INVITE ME TO THEIR PICNIC. MAYBE IF I FOLLOW THEM THEY'LL CHANGE THEIR MINDS.

BUT UNFORTUNATELY FOR THE FAT BOY, HE LOST TRACE OF THE REMOVE CHUMS IN FRIARDALE WOODS.

WHERE HAVE THE BEASTS GONE? OW! I FEEL WEAK WITH HUNGER. IF I DON'T GET SOMETHING TO EAT SOON I'M SURE I SHALL FAINT!

THEN, SUDDENLY, A MOST APPETISING AROMA WAS WAFTED TO BUNTER'S NOSTRILS. THE SUCCULENT SMELL DREW HIM LIKE A MAGNET, TOWARDS A SMALL CLEARING . . .

THERE'S NOBODY ABOUT . . . BUT THERE'S SOMETHING COOKING IN THAT POT. AND WHATEVER IT IS IT CERTAINLY SMELLS GOOD!

HIS MOUTH WATERING IN ANTICIPATION, BUNTER ADVANCED UPON THE COOKING POT AND RAISED THE LID.

RABBIT STEW! JUST WHAT I NEED TO KEEP ME GOING. WHAT A STROKE OF LUCK!

WHERE FOOD WAS CONCERNED, BUNTER HAD NO CONSCIENCE. SOON HE WAS SO ENGROSSED IN A HEARTY MEAL THAT HE FAILED TO NOTICE A SLIM GYPSY LAD COME OUT FROM THE TREES.

BUT THE GYPSY CERTAINLY DID NOT FAIL TO SEE THE FAT OWL OF THE REMOVE!

THE NEXT MOMENT BILLY BUNTER BECAME SHARPLY AWARE OF THE NEWCOMER'S PRESENCE . . .

HOI! THAT'S MY DINNER!

OW! HELP!

. . . AND THE GYPSY PUNCHED BUNTER ON HIS FAT NOSE!

BUNTER DID NOT STAY TO ARGUE THE POINT. HE PICKED HIMSELF UP AND WITH SURPRISING SPEED RACED AWAY.

YEOOOW! HELP! MURDER!

BY CHANCE, BUNTER'S FLEEING FEET LED HIM TO THE FAMOUS FIVE, WHO HAD JUST COMMENCED THEIR PICNIC...

HELP! I'VE BEEN ATTACKED! A HULKING GREAT GYPSY SET ABOUT ME FOR NO REASON AT ALL. HE MIGHT HAVE KILLED ME IF I HADN'T GOT AWAY FROM HIM!

BUNTER'S DISTRESS WAS QUITE OBVIOUSLY GENUINE AND THE REMOVITES FELT SYMPATHETIC.

POOR OLD BUNTER. HE'S CERTAINLY BEEN IN THE WARS. LOOK AT THE STATE HE'S IN!

HIS NOSE LOOKS A BIT THE WORSE FOR WEAR.

WE'LL GO AND FIND THIS GYPSY. HE WON'T BE IN A HURRY TO PICK ON ANY MORE GREYFRIARS FELLOWS AFTER WE'VE FINISHED WITH HIM! COME ON, CHAPS!

THE CHUMS HURRIED OFF, BUT A SEARCH OF THE WOODS FAILED TO REVEAL THE GYPSY...

PERHAPS HE'S GONE ACROSS THE STREAM AND INTO SIR HILTON POPPER'S GROUNDS.

WE DAREN'T FOLLOW HIM THERE. YOU KNOW HOW FURIOUS OLD POPPER GETS IF ANY OF US TRESPASS ON HIS LAND.

THE FURIOUSNESS IS TERRIFIC

HURREE SINGH, THE INDIAN BOY, HAD HIS OWN QUAINT IDEAS ON HOW TO SPEAK ENGLISH!

BUT HARRY WHARTON WAS CONVINCED THAT IT WAS THEIR DUTY TO TRACK DOWN BUNTER'S ASSAILANT.

THIS IS AN EMERGENCY. WE'LL HAVE TO GO ON SIR HILTON'S LAND. FOLLOW ME.

IF WE FIND THE SKULKING BRUTE WHO ATTACKED BUNTER, SIR HILTON WILL UNDERSTAND.

A WELL-DRESSED MAN WHO WAS RETURNING FROM A WALK THROUGH THE WOODS SAW THE CHUMS HURRY ACROSS THE NARROW PLANK BRIDGE AND HIS EYES BLAZED WITH ANGER...

WHY... THE YOUNG SCOUNDRELS! DELIBERATELY TRESPASSING! THEY'LL BE SORRY FOR THIS!

THE MAN WAS NONE OTHER THAN SIR HILTON POPPER, OWNER OF THE LAND IN QUESTION... AND A GOVERNOR OF GREYFRIARS SCHOOL!

BILLY BUNTER of Greyfriars

When Billy Bunter is punched by a young gypsy lad in Friardale Woods, he manages to convince Harry Wharton, Bob Cherry, Frank Nugent, Johnny Bull and Hurree Singh that he has been the victim of a savage assault.

The Famous Five leave their picnic and try to find Bunter's attacker, but enter Sir Hilton Popper's land and are seen doing so by Sir Hilton himself.

HIS FACE FLUSHED WITH ANGER, SIR HILTON POPPER HURRIED ACROSS THE PLANK IN PURSUIT OF THE FIVE CHUMS...

THE IMPUDENT YOUNG RASCALS! I'LL TEACH THEM TO TRESPASS ON MY LAND!

BUT IN HIS HASTE SIR HILTON WAS LESS CAREFUL THAN HE SHOULD HAVE BEEN. HIS FOOT SLIPPED ON THE WET PLANK AND HE LURCHED SIDEWAYS, HELPLESSLY...

AAH..!

SIR HILTON COULD NOT SWIM AND IN A MOMENT HE WAS BEING SWEPT ALONG BY THE FAST-FLOWING WATER. HE TRIED TO SHOUT FOR HELP, BUT HIS MOUTH FILLED WITH WATER AND A FAINT GURGLING SPLUTTER WAS THE ONLY SOUND HE COULD UTTER.

UUUUUURGH!

SIR HILTON'S STRUGGLES GREW WEAKER, BUT BY GOOD FORTUNE HIS PLIGHT WAS SEEN BY THE GYPSY BOY WHO HAD EARLIER MADE THE ACQUAINTANCE OF BILLY BUNTER.

WITHOUT A MOMENT'S HESITATION, THE LAD FLUNG OFF HIS RAGGED JACKET AND DIVED INTO THE WATER JUST AS THE MAN LAPSED INTO UNCONSCIOUSNESS.

WITH POWERFUL STROKES, THE GYPSY BOY SWAM TO SIR HILTON'S SIDE AND SEIZED HIM AS HE WAS ABOUT TO GO UNDER.

SIR HILTON WAS A HEAVY MAN AND THE GYPSY WAS ONLY SLIGHTLY BUILT... BUT THE LAD GALLANTLY FOUGHT HIS WAY BACK TO THE BANK WITH HIS BURDEN...

MEANWHILE, BILLY BUNTER, LEFT WITH THE PICNIC BELONGING TO THE FAMOUS FIVE, WAS FACING GREAT TEMPTATION...

THERE'S MORE TUCK HERE THAN HARRY WHARTON AND THE OTHERS CAN POSSIBLY EAT. AND BESIDES, THEY DON'T ENJOY JAM TARTS AND CREAM PUFFS AS MUCH AS I DO. I'LL TAKE A FEW... THEY'LL NEVER MISS THEM.

BILLY BUNTER WRAPPED NEARLY ALL THE CAKES IN PAPER AND WAS CRAMMING THEM INTO THE POCKETS OF HIS JACKET WHEN HE HEARD THE FAMOUS FIVE RETURNING FROM THEIR FRUITLESS SEARCH.

OOH, CRUMBS! THOSE BEASTS ARE BACK ALREADY! SUPPOSE THEY FIND OUT I'VE TAKEN THEIR CAKES?

BILLY BUNTER DID NOT WAIT TO DISCOVER WHAT THE FAMOUS FIVE WOULD DO AFTER FINDING A LARGE PART OF THEIR PICNIC MISSING. IN A PANIC, HE RUSHED AWAY THROUGH THE TREES AS FAST AS HIS SHORT LEGS WOULD CARRY HIM...

HEY! BUNTER... COME BACK!

OOER! THEY'VE SPOTTED ME!

THOROUGHLY SCARED, BUNTER TORE OFF HIS CAKE-LADEN JACKET AND FLUNG IT AWAY AS HE RAN...

IF THEY CATCH ME AND I HAVEN'T GOT ANY CAKES ON ME THEY WON'T BE ABLE TO PROVE ANYTHING!

BUNTER'S BACKWARD GLANCE WAS HIS UNDOING. THE NEXT INSTANT HE TRIPPED OVER A TREE-ROOT AND LANDED FULL LENGTH IN A SHALLOW DITCH OF WATER.

GROOOOGH!

MEANWHILE, THE GYPSY BOY HAD DRAGGED SIR HILTON POPPER TO SAFETY, AND, HAVING SATISFIED HIMSELF THAT THE UNCONSCIOUS MAN WAS NOT SERIOUSLY HURT, HE HURRIED AWAY.

PRESENTLY SIR HILTON'S EYES FLICKERED OPEN ... AT THE VERY MOMENT THAT BILLY BUNTER BLUNDERED ALONG. SEEING BUNTER WITHOUT A JACKET AND SOAKING WET THE BARONET MADE A VERY NATURAL ERROR ...

EH..?

AH...MY BRAVE RESCUER! WHAT CAN I SAY THAT WILL SHOW YOU HOW GRATEFUL I AM TO YOU?

YOUR SCHOOL SHOULD BE PROUD OF YOU, MY BOY. AND I SHALL SEE THAT YOU ARE REWARDED. WHAT DO YOU SAY TO THAT?

REWARD? WHY... THAT'S JOLLY DECENT OF YOU, SIR!

BILLY BUNTER HAD NEVER BEEN ONE TO QUESTION FATE'S FAVOURS AND AT THE MENTION OF A "REWARD" HIS EYES GLEAMED EXCITEDLY BEHIND HIS THICK SPECTACLES!

Billy Bunter flees after helping himself to food from a picnic belonging to Harry Wharton, Bob Cherry, Frank Nugent, Johnny Bull and Hurree Singh ... and in his panic he falls into a ditch.

Sir Hilton Popper, a local landowner has been saved from drowning by a gypsy lad, who hurries away. Sir Hilton regains consciousness just as the dripping wet Bunter appears and, under the impression that the fat boy is his rescuer, he promises to reward him ...

UNAWARE THAT BILLY BUNTER HAD STUFFED ALL THE CAKES FROM THEIR PICNIC INTO HIS JACKET POCKETS, HARRY WHARTON AND HIS CHUMS GAZED WONDERINGLY AFTER THE FLEEING FAT BOY.

WHAT COULD HAVE MADE BUNTER STAMPEDE LIKE THAT?

MAYBE THE GYPSY, WHOM HE SAID ATTACKED HIM, TURNED UP AGAIN.

YES ... AND BUNTER MAY NEED HELP. WE'D BETTER TRY AND FIND HIM.

WHILE THE FAMOUS FIVE WERE SEARCHING THE WOODS FOR BILLY BUNTER, SIR HILTON POPPER HAD TAKEN THE FAT BOY TO POPPER COURT, THE LARGE COUNTRY MANSION WHICH WAS HIS HOME.

NOW WE MUST DECIDE WHAT FORM YOUR REWARD IS TO TAKE, MY BOY.

I'VE ALREADY MADE UP MY MIND ABOUT THAT, SIR. I'D LIKE A NICE BIG FEED.

SIR HILTON INSTRUCTED A MAID TO SUPPLY BUNTER WITH ALL THE FOOD HE REQUIRED. AFTER CHANGING HIS CLOTHES, THE BARONET FOUND BUNTER STILL ENGAGED UPON HIS FAVOURITE PASTIME ... EATING!

UPON MY WORD! WHAT AN AMAZING APPETITE THE BOY HAS!

DELICIOUS! I'LL HAVE ANOTHER HELPING. OH ... AND LEAVE THOSE CREAM CAKES THERE, TOO!

IN GROWING AMAZEMENT SIR HILTON POPPER WATCHED FASCINATED AS BILLY BUNTER SPEEDILY DEVOURED PLATEFUL AFTER PLATEFUL OF CHOICE FOOD ... AND SLOWLY A DOUBT BEGAN TO FORM IN THE BARONET'S MIND ...

THE PLUCKY LAD WHO RESCUED ME FROM THE WATER APPEARED CONSIDERABLY SLIMMER THAN THIS YOUTH. H'M, I WISH I COULD REMEMBER MORE CLEARLY JUST WHAT HAPPENED.

THERE'S NOTHING LIKE A LITTLE SNACK TO KEEP A FELLOW'S SPIRITS UP.

MEANWHILE, THE MODEST GYPSY LAD WHO HAD SAVED SIR HILTON'S LIFE HAD COME ACROSS BUNTER'S JACKET IN THE WOODS ... THE JACKET WHICH BUNTER HAD DISCARDED DURING HIS HASTY FLIGHT BECAUSE OF THE EVIDENCE CONTAINED IN THE POCKETS ...

IT'S A BOY'S BLAZER ... BUT WHAT IS IT DOING HERE?

A MOMENT LATER, HARRY WHARTON, JOHNNY BULL AND BOB CHERRY, COMBING THROUGH THE WOODS FOR BUNTER, CHANCED UPON THE SCENE ...

LOOK.. A GYPSY! AND HE'S GOT BUNTER'S JACKET!

GRAB HIM! HE MUST BE THE FELLOW BUNTER TOLD US ABOUT!

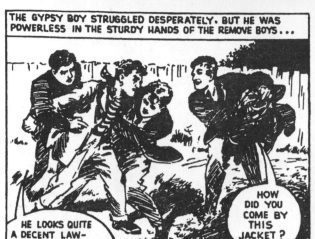

THE GYPSY BOY STRUGGLED DESPERATELY, BUT HE WAS POWERLESS IN THE STURDY HANDS OF THE REMOVE BOYS...

HOW DID YOU COME BY THIS JACKET?

HE LOOKS QUITE A DECENT LAW-ABIDING SORT OF FELLOW... BUT THERE'S NO DENYING HE HAD BUNTER'S COAT.

BUT THE GYPSY STUBBORNLY REFUSED TO ANSWER HARRY'S QUESTION.

AS HARRY HESITATED UNCERTAINLY, FRANK NUGENT AND HURREE SINGH, WHO HAD SPLIT UP FROM THE OTHERS, CAME HURRYING EXCITEDLY THROUGH THE TREES.

WE HAVE SEEN BUNTER... AND THE SURPRISEFULNESS WAS TERRIFIC!

YES, WE SPOTTED BUNTER GOING INTO POPPER COURT WITH SIR HILTON POPPER... AND SIR HILTON SEEMED QUITE PALLY WITH BUNTER!

HARRY WHARTON THOUGHT OVER THIS SURPRISING NEWS FOR A MOMENT AND THEN CAME TO A DECISION.

THIS GYPSY WON'T SAY A WORD, BUT THERE'S ONE WAY TO FIND OUT FOR CERTAIN JUST WHAT HE HAS BEEN UP TO. WE'LL TAKE HIM TO POPPER COURT AND SEE IF BUNTER RECOGNISES HIM.

AND SO, FIFTEEN MINUTES LATER, THE FAMOUS FIVE PRESENTED THEMSELVES AT POPPER COURT AND EXPLAINED THEIR MISSION TO THE MANSERVANT WHO OPENED THE DOOR.

PLEASE COME THIS WAY. I WILL TAKE YOU TO SIR HILTON.

SIR HILTON TURNED IN SURPRISE AS THE BOYS ENTERED THE DINING-ROOM... BUT AS HIS GAZE FELL UPON THE GYPSY BOY A LIGHT OF RECOGNITION DAWNED IN HIS EYES AND HE STEPPED FORWARD WELCOMINGLY.

AH... IT ALL COMES BACK TO ME AT LAST! YOU ARE THE BRAVE LAD WHO RISKED HIS LIFE TO SAVE MINE!

AS THE FAMOUS FIVE RELEASED THE GYPSY BOY, A SUDDEN THOUGHT CAME TO SIR HILTON AND HE WHIRLED UPON THE SHRINKING BUNTER.

SO..! THIS MEANS THAT YOU, AS I HAD BEGUN TO SUSPECT, ARE AN IMPOSTER... TAKING THE CREDIT FOR ANOTHER BOY'S BRAVE ACTION. HOW DARE YOU ATTEMPT TO TRICK ME IN THIS DISGRACEFUL FASHION!

BILLY BUNTER *of Greyfriars*

After wealthy Sir Hilton Popper has been saved from drowning he is under the impression that Billy Bunter is his rescuer, and takes the fat boy to his home to reward him. But when Harry Wharton and his chums arrive at Popper Court with a young gypsy lad, Sir Hilton recognises the gypsy as the boy who saved his life . . .

FUMING WITH RAGE, SIR HILTON WHIRLED UPON BILLY BUNTER.

YOU HAVE DEVOURED ALMOST EVERY SCRAP OF FOOD IN MY HOUSE AND ALLOWED ME TO BELIEVE YOU WERE MY RESCUER! HOW DARE YOU TRICK ME IN THIS FASHION!

HERE'S THE JELLY YOU ASKED FOR, MASTER BUNTER. OOPS!

BUNTER BACKED AWAY . . . AND CANNONED INTO THE MAID WHO HAD JUST ENTERED.

THE LARGE BOWL OF JELLY SHOT INTO THE AIR . . . AND LANDED UPSIDE-DOWN ON THE FAT BOY'S HEAD!

GROOOGH!

HA, HA, OLD BUNTER'S GOT HIS JELLY . . . BUT HE DOESN'T SEEM TO BE ENJOYING IT VERY MUCH!

THE ANGRY BARONET APPEALED TO THE REMOVE CHUMS . . .

BAH! GET THAT FAT FRAUD OUT OF MY SIGHT . . . THIS INSTANT!

CERTAINLY, SIR HILTON. COME ALONG, BUNTER.

I— I WAS JUST LEAVING ANYWAY.

LEFT ALONE WITH THE GYPSY BOY, SIR HILTON REGAINED HIS GOOD HUMOUR AND BEAMED HAPPILY AT HIS RAGGEDLY-DRESSED GUEST.

PLEASE, SIR. CAN I GO AS WELL NOW?

INDEED NOT! YOU SHALL NOT LEAVE THIS HOUSE UNTIL YOU HAVE TOLD ME YOUR NAME AND WHAT I CAN DO FOR YOU IN RETURN FOR SAVING MY LIFE

THE GYPSY LAD SHUFFLED HIS FEET AWKWARDLY.

MY NAME'S MICK, SIR. YOU'RE VERY KIND, BUT THERE'S NOTHING I'D LIKE YOU TO DO FOR ME . . . ER . . . EXCEPT MAYBE ONE THING . . .

YES, MICK? NAME WHATEVER DESIRE YOU HAVE IN YOUR MIND AND IF IT IS IN MY POWER TO FULFIL IT I PROMISE I SHALL DO SO.

THE GYPSY BLURTED OUT HIS WISH . . . AND A LOOK OF UTTER DISMAY CAME OVER SIR HILTON'S FACE.

PLEASE, SIR . . . IF YOU DON'T MIND I'D LIKE TO GO TO GREYFRIARS SCHOOL, THE SAME AS THOSE BOYS WHO WERE HERE JUST NOW.

YOU! A-A PUPIL AT GREYFRIARS . . . ?

MICK FLUSHED AT THE NOTE OF HORRIFIED AMAZEMENT IN SIR HILTON'S VOICE...

YOU TOLD ME YOU WOULD GRANT ANY WISH OF MINE IF IT LAY WITHIN YOUR POWER TO DO SO.

ER-TRUE, MY BOY... BUT WHEN I MADE THAT PROMISE I HAD NO IDEA THAT YOUR REQUEST WOULD TAKE THIS FORM.

WHAT YOU HAVE ASKED ME TO DO PRESENTS CERTAIN DIFFICULTIES. IN FACT, MANY DIFFICULTIES. PLEASE WAIT HERE WHILE I SEE WHAT CAN BE DONE.

AFTER SIR HILTON HAD LEFT THE ROOM A SCORNFUL SMILE TOUCHED THE GYPSY BOY'S LIPS AND HE STEPPED TO THE TALL WINDOW WHICH LED TO THE GARDEN...

HUH! I KNOW HIS SORT. FULL OF EMPTY PROMISES. I BET HE'S THINKING OUT A GOOD STORY TO TELL ME WHY I CAN'T GO TO THE SCHOOL. BUT WHEN HE HAS ALL HIS EXCUSES READY HE WON'T FIND ME TO TELL 'EM TO!

BUT MICK COMPLETELY MISJUDGED SIR HILTON POPPER. SIR HILTON HAD HIS FAULTS, BUT HE HAD NEVER BEEN A MAN TO GO BACK ON HIS WORD. AT THAT VERY MOMENT HE WAS CONCLUDING A TELEPHONE CONVERSATION WITH THE HEADMASTER OF GREYFRIARS SCHOOL.

THANK YOU FOR BEING SO REASONABLE ABOUT THIS UNUSUAL REQUEST, DR. LOCKE. I WILL ARRANGE FOR THE BOY TO CALL AT GREYFRIARS SCHOOL TODAY.

MEANWHILE, HARRY WHARTON AND HIS CHUMS WERE ACCOMPANYING BILLY BUNTER THROUGH THE WOODS...

YOU ARE AN ASS, BUNTER. FANCY TELLING US YOU WERE SET UPON BY A MASSIVE GYPSY, WHEN ALL THE TIME IT WAS A FELLOW NO OLDER THAN YOURSELF.

AND A JOLLY DECENT FELLOW, TOO!

BILLY BUNTER GLARED HAUGHTILY AT THE FAMOUS FIVE.

REALLY! IF YOU FELLOWS DON'T ACCEPT MY WORD FOR WHAT HAPPENED I DON'T WANT ANYTHING MORE TO DO WITH YOU. I'LL GO BACK TO SCHOOL ALONE.

HA! HA!

MIND YOU DON'T MEET ANOTHER GIANT GYPSY IN THE WOODS, BUNTER!

HIS FAT CHEEKS FLUSHED WITH INDIGNATION, BUNTER WADDLED AWAY THROUGH THE TREES. HE DID NOT NOTICE A SLIGHT MOVEMENT BEHIND SOME BUSHES, AND THE NEXT MOMENT...

GOT YOU!

OOOOOOW!

BILLY BUNTER *of Greyfriars*

When Mick, a gypsy boy, saves the life of Sir Hilton Popper, Billy Bunter claims to be the baronet's rescuer, but his trick is quickly discovered. Wrathfully the fat boy leaves Harry Wharton and his chums in Friardale Woods . . . but before he has gone very far he is pounced upon by a huge gypsy . . .

BUNTER'S FAT CHEEKS QUIVERED WITH FRIGHT AS HE GLIMPSED THE HARSH, BRUTAL FEATURES OF HIS CAPTOR...

OOOW!

AN INSTANT LATER THE POWERFULLY-BUILT GYPSY GAVE A GROWL OF DISAPPOINTMENT AND ROUGHLY PUSHED BUNTER ASIDE.

AAARGH! YOU'RE NOT THE BOY I'M LOOKING FOR!

SPEECHLESS WITH FEAR, BILLY BUNTER RACED BACK THE WAY HE HAD COME...

AFTER BUNTER'S HASTY DEPARTURE, THE BIG GYPSY HEARD THE SOUND OF SOMEONE APPROACHING. AS HE RECOGNISED THE NEWCOMER HIS LIPS TWISTED IN AN EVIL GRIN.

AH..! I'M NOT MISTAKEN THIS TIME! IT'S MICK SURE ENOUGH.

SO I'VE FOUND YOU AT LAST! I'LL TEACH YOU TO RUN AWAY FROM ME!

BARENGO!

LET ME GO! LET ME GO!

NOT LIKELY... YOU'RE COMING BACK TO THE CAMP!

BUNTER DID NOT PAUSE IN HIS HURRIED FLIGHT UNTIL HE HAD OVERTAKEN THE FAMOUS FIVE. THEY LISTENED WITH ASTONISHMENT TO THE STORY THAT POURED FROM HIS LIPS.

I'VE JUST BEEN ATTACKED BY A HUGE RUFFIAN... A GYPSY! HE'S A DANGEROUS BRUTE WHO OUGHT TO BE SENT PACKING. IF YOU CHAPS HURRY YOU'LL FIND THE BRUTE BACK THERE!

THE FIVE CHUMS REMEMBERED THAT BUNTER HAD ALREADY CLAIMED TO HAVE BEEN ATTACKED BY A GYPSY WHEN HE HAD RECEIVED A WELL-DESERVED PUNCH ON THE NOSE FROM MICK. BOB CHERRY GAVE A BROAD GRIN.

HA! HA! SURELY YOU DON'T THINK WE'RE GOING TO FALL FOR THE SAME STORY TWICE IN ONE DAY?

HUH...! HUGE GYPSY! HOPPIT, BUNTER! YOU'RE NOT WASTING OUR TIME AGAIN!

HARRY WHARTON GAZED THOUGHTFULLY AT BILLY BUNTER AS THE FAT BOY TRAILED AFTER BOB CHERRY, FRANK NUGENT, JOHNNY BULL AND HURREE SINGH.

WAIT FOR ME! D-DON'T LEAVE ME ALONE!

OLD BUNTER SEEMS REALLY SCARED. MAYBE I HAD BETTER TAKE A QUICK LOOK TO SEE IF THERE IS ANY TRUTH IN HIS STORY AFTER ALL.

HARRY HASTENED THROUGH THE TREES ... THEN HE BROKE INTO A RUN WHEN HE SAW THE MASSIVE BARENGO CARRYING A LIMP BURDEN THROUGH THE WOODS.

THAT UGLY BRUTE HAS GOT MICK... THE BOY WHO SAVED SIR HILTON POPPER'S LIFE.

WITHOUT A THOUGHT FOR HIS OWN DANGER, HARRY SPRANG TO THE RESCUE OF THE UNCONSCIOUS LAD...

HEY! PUT THAT BOY DOWN!

WITH AN ANGRY BELLOW, BARENGO DROPPED MICK TO THE SPRINGY TURF AND CLOSED WITH HARRY.

YOU YOUNG 'OUND! YOU'LL BE SORRY YOU TRIED TO MEDDLE IN BARENGO'S AFFAIRS!

AND HARRY FELT HIS SENSES REELING AS THE MAN'S STEEL-LIKE FINGERS TIGHTENED AROUND HIS THROAT!

BILLY BUNTER *of Greyfriars*

Mick, a young gypsy lad, has recently saved the life of wealthy Sir Hilton Popper, a governor of Greyfriars school. But in Friardale Woods Harry Wharton, the captain of the Remove Form at Greyfriars, sees the boy helpless in the hands of a brutal-looking ruffian.

Harry makes a gallant attempt to rescue Mick but is savagely attacked by the powerful man ...

HARRY FELT HIS SENSES REELING AS THE BIG GYPSY'S FINGERS TIGHTENED AROUND HIS THROAT ... THEN, SUDDENLY, THE MAN'S GRIP RELAXED ...

AAGH! THERE'S SOMEONE COMING!

THE MASSIVE RUFFIAN TURNED AND FLED ... AND HARRY SAW THE FAMILIAR FIGURE OF SIR HILTON POPPER APPEAR THROUGH THE TREES ...

UPON MY WORD! I CAME HERE TO SEARCH FOR MICK, THE YOUNG LAD WHO SAVED MY LIFE. BUT WHAT IS HAPPENING?

MICK IS OVER THERE, SIR. HE WAS ATTACKED BY THAT HULKING BRUTE ... AND SO WAS I.

HARRY AND THE BARONET HASTENED TO MICK'S SIDE, JUST AS THE LAD'S EYES FLICKERED OPEN ...

WHO WAS THAT RUFFIAN, MICK?

HIS ... HIS NAME IS BARENGO. EVER SINCE I CAN REMEMBER I HAVE LIVED WITH HIM AND HIS FOLLOWERS. BUT YESTERDAY I RAN AWAY BECAUSE I COULD STAND IT NO LONGER.

HE USED TO BEAT ME TO TRY AND MAKE ME STEAL FOR HIM. I'D RATHER DIE THAN GO BACK WITH HIM ... BUT I'VE NOWHERE ELSE TO GO.

YOU ARE WRONG THERE, MY BOY. I HAVE ALREADY MADE CERTAIN ARRANGEMENTS FOR YOUR FUTURE.

I HAVE BEEN IN TOUCH WITH DR. LOCKE, THE HEADMASTER OF GREYFRIARS SCHOOL, AND I AM SURE HE WILL AGREE TO YOUR BECOMING A GREYFRIARS BOY. I WILL TAKE YOU TO THE SCHOOL AT ONCE.

A GREYFRIARS BOY? OH, THANK YOU, SIR!

BUT AS SIR HILTON AND THE TWO BOYS MADE THEIR WAY THROUGH THE WOODS A PAIR OF SAVAGE EYES WATCHED THEM.

YOUNG MICK WON'T ESCAPE ME SO EASILY. I'LL FOLLOW HIM AND WAIT FOR A CHANCE TO GRAB HIM.

LATER THAT AFTERNOON SEVERAL GREYFRIARS BOYS STARED CURIOUSLY AT SIR HILTON POPPER AS HE ENTERED THE SCHOOL WITH HIS RAGGED COMPANION... BUT THE MOST CONCERNED ONLOOKER WAS BILLY BUNTER

C-CRUMBS! THERE'S SIR HILTON POPPER WITH THAT GYPSY WHO SAVED HIM FROM DROWNING!

THERE WAS A VERY GOOD REASON FOR BUNTER'S CONCERN. EARLIER THAT DAY THE FAT BOY HAD PRETENDED TO BE SIR HILTON'S RESCUER AND HAD ACCEPTED A REWARD FROM SIR HILTON BEFORE THE BARONET HAD BECOME AWARE OF THE DECEPTION.

THE BEAST MUST HAVE COME HERE TO REPORT ME TO THE HEAD. AND... AND THAT MEANS I SH-SHALL BE C-CANED! OH D-DEAR!

COURAGE WAS NOT ONE OF BUNTER'S STRONG POINTS. TREMBLING AT THE THOUGHT OF DR. LOCKE'S WRATH, HE FLED TO A QUIET PART OF THE SCHOOL GROUNDS, WHICH WAS OUT OF BOUNDS TO THE BOYS, AND APPROACHED A SMALL, LITTLE-USED DOOR.

I'M NOT GOING TO STAY HERE TO BE CANED. I'LL RUN AWAY WITHOUT ANYONE SEEING ME... THEN MAYBE DR. LOCKE AND OLD POPPER WILL BE SORRY FOR WHAT THEY'VE DONE!

BARENGO HAD SEEN MICK AND SIR HILTON ENTER GREYFRIARS AND HE HAD CIRCLED THE SCHOOL WALL IN AN EFFORT TO FIND A WAY OF QUIETLY ENTERING THE SCHOOL GROUNDS. HIS DARK EYES LIT UP WHEN HE SAW A SMALL DOOR OPEN AND A BULKY FIGURE COME SCAMPERING OUT.

AH! HERE'S A BIT OF LUCK. THE FAT KID'S IN SUCH A HURRY HE'S LEFT THE DOOR OPEN!

A MOMENT LATER, THE MASSIVE GYPSY HAD SLIPPED INSIDE...

I'M IN... AND NO-ONE'S SEEN ME. ALL I'VE GOT TO DO NOW IS FIND MICK... AND WHEN I GET ME HANDS ON HIM HE'LL BE SORRY HE WAS EVER BORN!

MEANWHILE, SIR HILTON POPPER HAD LEFT MICK WITH DR. LOCKE. IT DID NOT TAKE THE HEADMASTER LONG TO REALISE THAT THE BOY'S SCHOLASTIC KNOWLEDGE WAS ALMOST NIL.

I AM SORRY, MY BOY... BUT I FEAR THAT THE SUBJECTS TAUGHT IN EVEN THE LOWEST FORM AT GREYFRIARS WOULD BE FAR BEYOND YOUR GRASP.

FILLED WITH DISAPPOINTMENT, MICK TURNED TO THE DOOR OF THE STUDY...

I DON'T BLAME YOU FOR NOT WANTING ME AT YOUR SCHOOL, SIR. BUT DON'T BOTHER SIR HILTON AGAIN... I'LL JUST LEAVE QUIETLY.

BILLY BUNTER of Greyfriars

Wealthy Sir Hilton Popper is prepared to pay for Mick, a young gypsy lad, to become a pupil at Greyfriars School. But when Mick goes to the school to be interviewed by Dr. Locke, he is followed by Barengo, a rascally gypsy.

Meanwhile, Billy Bunter, under the impression that he is to be punished, decides to run away and leaves by a little-used door in the school wall. Barengo seizes his chance and enters the school grounds through the door which Bunter has left open . . .

BEFORE HE HAD GONE VERY FAR, A SUDDEN THOUGHT OCCURRED TO BUNTER. A MOST IMPORTANT THOUGHT AS FAR AS BUNTER WAS CONCERNED . . .

OO-ER! I HAVEN'T EATEN ANYTHING FOR A WHOLE HOUR. IF I'M GOING TO RUN AWAY I SHALL NEED TO TAKE SOME FOOD WITH ME TO KEEP MY STRENGTH UP.

BUNTER RETRACED HIS STEPS AND RE-ENTERED THE SCHOOL GROUNDS THROUGH THE SMALL DOOR . . .

I'LL COLLECT SOME GRUB FROM THE KITCHEN AND THEN START OFF AGAIN.

FORTUNE FAVOURED THE FAT BOY AND NO-ONE SAW HIM CREEP INTO THE DESERTED KITCHEN . . .

I'LL TAKE A LOAF OF BREAD, THESE PORK PIES, A POT OF JAM, SOME APPLES AND A CAKE . . . THAT LITTLE LOT SHOULD KEEP ME GOING FOR A WHILE!

HEAVILY-LADEN WITH GOOD FOOD, BUNTER HEADED BACK TOWARDS THE FAR END OF THE SCHOOL GROUNDS . . . BUT A SUDDEN SHOUT STARTLED HIM.

HEY, BUNTER! WHERE ARE YOU GOING WITH ALL THAT FOOD?

OOER . . .! IT'S WINGATE AND GWYNNE. I'D BETTER MAKE A RUN FOR IT!

WITH THE TWO PREFECTS IN HOT PURSUIT, BUNTER RACED AWAY . . .

BUNTER . . .! COME BACK, YOU ASS!

PANIC-STRICKEN, BUNTER SCAMPERED AROUND A CORNER. IN HIS BLIND HASTE HE CANNONED INTO A TALL FIGURE . . .

OOOOW!

. . . AND FOUND HIMSELF LOOKING INTO THE SCOWLING FEATURES OF BARENGO THE GYPSY!

THE BIG GYPSY CLAPPED A GRUBBY HAND OVER BUNTER'S MOUTH TO PREVENT HIM FROM CALLING FOR HELP. BUT WINGATE AND GWYNNE HAD ALREADY SEEN THE FAT BOY'S PLIGHT...

MY HAT! WHO'S THAT RUFFIAN?

I DON'T KNOW... BUT WE'LL SOON FIND OUT. *GRAB HIM, GWYNNE!*

...AND THE TWO STURDY PREFECTS HURLED THEMSELVES FORWARD.

MEANWHILE, IN HIS STUDY, DR. LOCKE HAD REACHED A RELUCTANT DECISION CONCERNING MICK, THE GYPSY LAD.

I AM SORRY, MY BOY... BUT I AM CERTAIN THAT THE SUBJECTS TAUGHT AT GREYFRIARS SCHOOL WILL BE BEYOND YOUR ABILITY.

I UNDERSTAND, SIR. I WON'T TAKE UP ANY MORE OF YOUR TIME.

AND WITH A HEAVY HEART MICK TURNED AWAY.

BUT BEFORE MICK REACHED THE DOOR IT BURST OPEN... TO REVEAL BARENGO, IN THE GRIP OF WINGATE AND GWYNNE.

UPON MY WORD, WINGATE! WHAT IS THE MEANING OF THIS?

WE FOUND THIS FELLOW LURKING IN THE SCHOOL GROUNDS, SIR. HE PUT UP QUITE A FIGHT, BUT WE MANAGED TO OVERPOWER HIM.

WHAT WERE YOU DOING IN GREYFRIARS, MY MAN?

I CAME HERE TO FIND THAT BOY. HE RAN AWAY FROM ME... BUT HE'LL NEVER DO IT A SECOND TIME! *I'LL TEACH HIM A LESSON HE'LL NEVER FORGET!*

AND MICK SHRANK BACK BEFORE THE SAVAGE GLITTER IN THE MAN'S DARK EYES.

DR. LOCKE COULD WELL IMAGINE WHAT MICK'S LIFE HAD BEEN LIKE WITH THE BRUTAL BARENGO.

ARE YOU THE BOY'S FATHER?

NO... HE'S NO RELATIVE O' MINE. HE'S A BEGGAR'S BRAT, LEFT IN THE FIELDS WHEN HE WAS A BABY. I BROUGHT HIM UP AND NOW HE'S GOT TO WORK FOR ME TO SHOW HIS GRATITUDE.

THE HEADMASTER WAS A KINDLY MAN... AND HE COULD THINK OF ONLY ONE WAY OF SAVING MICK FROM FALLING INTO BARENGO'S HANDS ONCE AGAIN.

THIS LAD WILL NOT BE RETURNING TO LIVE WITH YOU... *I HAVE JUST ACCEPTED HIM AS A GREYFRIARS' PUPIL!*

BILLY BUNTER of Greyfriars

Mick, a young gypsy lad, runs away from Barengo, a brutal gypsy, and is befriended by wealthy Sir Hilton Popper. Sir Hilton is prepared to pay for Mick to become a pupil at Greyfriars School.

Dr. Locke has just decided not to accept Mick as a pupil when Barengo appears at the school and to save the boy from falling into the ruffian's hands, the headmaster announces that Mick is now a Greyfriars boy...

BARENGO'S DARK EYES GLITTERED SAVAGELY.

MICK BELONGS TO ME... YOU TRY AND KEEP HIM AWAY FROM ME AND I'LL HAVE THE LAW ON YOU!

NONSENSE! YOU HAVE NO LEGAL RIGHT TO THE BOY AND HE REMAINS HERE.

WITH A BELLOW OF RAGE, THE RUFFIAN SPRANG AT THE HEADMASTER. BUT WINGATE AND GWYNNE MOVED JUST AS SWIFTLY...

NO YOU DON'T... YOU BOUNDER!

THANK YOU, WINGATE... AND YOU, GWYNNE. PLEASE REMOVE THIS PERSON FROM THE SCHOOL.

STRUGGLING FURIOUSLY, BARENGO WAS ESCORTED AWAY BY THE TWO PREFECTS. DR. LOCKE THEN SENT FOR HARRY WHARTON, THE CAPTAIN OF THE REMOVE FORM.

WHARTON... THIS NEW BOY WILL BE JOINING THE REMOVE FORM. PLEASE TAKE HIM TO MATRON AND ASK HER TO ARRANGE FOR HIM TO BE SUPPLIED WITH WHATEVER CLOTHING HE NEEDS.

YES, SIR!

DRESSED IN A GREYFRIARS BLAZER AND FLANNELS, MICK LOOKED VERY DIFFERENT FROM THE RAGGED WAIF OF THE WOODS, HE HAD BEEN BEFORE. AND MANY OF THE SCHOOL JUNIORS NOTED A SURPRISING FEATURE ABOUT HIS APPEARANCE...

I SAY... THAT GYPSY KID LOOKS JUST LIKE CECIL SMYTHE!

MY HAT... SO HE DOES! IF I DIDN'T KNOW HIM BETTER, I'D SAY THEY WERE BROTHERS!

THERE WAS ONE PERSON, HOWEVER, WHO CERTAINLY DID NOT AGREE WITH THESE COMMENTS... AND THAT WAS CECIL SMYTHE, THE CONCEITED SNOB OF THE FOURTH FORM.

WHAT ROT TO SAY THAT GYPSY LOOKS LIKE ME. RAGAMUFFINS LIKE HIM HAVE NO RIGHT TO BE AT GREYFRIARS AND I'M GOING TO MAKE IT MY BUSINESS TO SEE THAT HE DOESN'T STAY HERE LONG!

BILLY BUNTER ALWAYS TOOK A GREAT INTEREST IN NEW BOYS, FOR HE KNEW THAT THEY VERY OFTEN ARRIVED AT THE SCHOOL WELL-SUPPLIED WITH TUCK...

I SAY, MICK, OLD MAN, I EXPECT SIR HILTON SUPPLIED YOU WITH SOME EATS TO START YOU OFF AT THE SCHOOL. IT'S THE CUSTOM FOR A NEW KID TO STAND HIS FRIENDS A FEED... AND I'M YOUR FRIEND, YOU KNOW.

YOU MEAN YOU WANT ME TO GIVE YOU SOME FOOD?

THAT'S RIGHT. I'M NOT FUSSY... ANYTHING WILL DO.

ALL RIGHT. I HAVEN'T ANYTHING TO GIVE YOU NOW... BUT I'LL HAVE SOMETHING FOR YOU EARLY IN THE MORNING.

MICK WALKED AWAY, LEAVING BUNTER TO PONDER HIS STRANGE REMARK ... AND THE MORE BUNTER THOUGHT ABOUT IT THE MORE INDIGNANT HE BECAME.

IF HE HASN'T ANY FOOD NOW HOW IS HE GOING TO GET SOME BY THE MORNING? THE CHEEKY BEAST MUST HAVE BEEN PULLING MY LEG. I'LL TEACH HIM HE CAN'T DO THAT TO ME AND GET AWAY WITH IT!

BUT THE GYPSY BOY FULLY INTENDED TO FULFILL HIS PROMISE TO BUNTER. LATE THAT NIGHT, WHEN ALL WAS STILL, MICK ROSE FROM HIS BED, DRESSED HIMSELF, THEN QUIETLY OPENED A WINDOW ...

THE ONLY WAY I CAN GET SOME FOOD FOR THE FAT BOY IS BY CATCHING A HARE IN THE WOODS...IT WON'T TAKE ME LONG ...

MICK'S STEALTHY DEPARTURE DID NOT PASS UNNOTICED. QUIET THOUGH THE GYPSY BOY'S MOVEMENTS HAD BEEN, THEY HAD NOT ESCAPED THE ATTENTION OF BILLY BUNTER ...

HA! THIS IS WHERE I GET MY OWN BACK ON THAT CHEEKY NEW KID.

BUNTER REMEMBERED THE BITTER THREAT WHICH CECIL SMYTHE HAD MADE AGAINST THE NEW BOY. HE HASTENED TO THE FOURTH FORM DORMITORY AND QUIETLY AWAKENED THE SNOB OF THE JUNIOR SCHOOL.

I SAY, SMYTHE! THE NEW KID HAS BROKEN BOUNDS ON HIS FIRST NIGHT AT SCHOOL. I SAW HIM CLIMBING OUT OF A WINDOW ONLY A MOMENT AGO.

WHAT..?

SMYTHE'S EYES GLEAMED TRIUMPHANTLY...

THANKS, BUNTER. I SAID I'D GET THAT GYPSY TRAMP THROWN OUT OF GREYFRIARS... AND THIS IS MY CHANCE TO DO IT!

BILLY BUNTER *of Greyfriars*

Mick, a gypsy boy, has been befriended by wealthy Sir Hilton Popper and is now a pupil at Greyfriars School. Cecil Smythe, the snob of the Fourth Form, angered because several boys have remarked that he resembles the gypsy boy, is determined to vent his spite upon Mick. Smythe's chance comes when he discovers that Mick has secretly broken bounds on his first night at Greyfriars...

SMYTHE DRESSED SWIFTLY THEN QUICKLY CLIMBED OUT THROUGH A DORMITORY WINDOW.

I'LL TRY AND FIND WHERE THAT NEW KID HAS GONE. IF I CAN PROVE HE IS CREEPING OUT AT NIGHT TO MEET HIS GYPSY PALS THEN THE HEAD WILL HAVE TO EXPEL HIM.

SOON SMYTHE WAS HURRYING THROUGH THE TREES BEYOND THE SCHOOL BOUNDARY... COMPLETELY UNAWARE OF A FIGURE CROUCHED BEHIND A NEARBY BUSH...

THE MAN WAS BARENGO, THE MASSIVE GYPSY WHO HAD SWORN TO GET MICK BACK INTO HIS CLUTCHES.

WITHOUT WARNING... *BARENGO SPRANG* !

HAH! YOU LOOK A LOT DIFFERENT IN THEM FANCY CLOTHES, BUT YOU CAN'T FOOL ME! I'VE GOT YOU, MICK... AND YOU WON'T GET AWAY FROM ME A SECOND TIME !

THEN THE SAVAGE GYPSY'S GRIP RELAXED...

WAIT A MINUTE.. YOU'RE NOT MICK AT ALL, ALTHOUGH YOU LOOK LIKE HIM. WHO ARE YOU?

MY NAME'S SMYTHE— CECIL SMYTHE.

A STARTLED LOOK CAME OVER BARENGO'S BRUTAL FEATURES ...

SMYTHE...? YOU HOPPIT BACK TO SCHOOL AND FORGET YOU EVER SAW ME... *UNDERSTAND?*

ER... YES... CERTAINLY.

ONLY TOO RELIEVED AT HIS RELEASE, SMYTHE FORGOT HIS ERRAND AND SCAMPERED BACK TOWARDS GREYFRIARS .

SMYTHE... THAT NAME AGAIN, AFTER ALL THESE YEARS ! I CAN HARDLY BELIEVE IT.

On Mick's first day at Greyfriars, he had been informed by Billy Bunter that it was the custom for all new boys to treat Bunter to a snack of some sort.

Mick, not knowing that this was one of the ever-hungry Bunter's regular tricks, had confessed that he had no food to share ... and then mystified the fat boy by promising him something to eat first thing on the following morning.

It was in order to fulfil his promise that Mick had broken bounds during the night ...

THE BOYS IN THE REMOVE DORMITORY HAD JUST FINISHED DRESSING THAT MORNING WHEN MICK WALKED ACROSS TO BUNTER.

I GOT THAT FOOD I PROMISED FOR YOU, BUNTER. YOU'LL FIND IT IN YOUR LOCKER. I PUT IT THERE DURING THE NIGHT.

EH?

HIS MOUTH WATERING IN ANTICIPATION, BUNTER BENT TO OPEN HIS LOCKER.

MM! IS IT SOMETHING TASTY?

OH, YES. I'VE EATEN LOTS OF THEM, AND ALWAYS ENJOYED THEM.

EAGERLY BUNTER THREW OPEN THE LOCKER DOOR ... THEN, WITH STARTLING SUDDENNESS, A BROWN SHAPE LEAPED OUT ...

YAROOOH! HELP!

IT'S A HARE. PERHAPS I SHOULD HAVE WARNED YOU IT'S STILL ALIVE ... I ONLY CAUGHT IT LAST NIGHT!

SO TAKEN BY SURPRISE WAS THE FAT BOY THAT HE FLED FROM THE DORMITORY IN A PANIC ... WITH THE HARE HOPPING AFTER HIM ...

HA! HA!

OW! CALL IT OFF! HELP!

AT THE END OF THE CORRIDOR BUNTER CANNONED INTO A PLASTER BUST OF SIR PHILIP SMYTHE. IT CRASHED TO THE GROUND AND SHATTERED INTO FRAGMENTS.

NOW LOOK WHAT THE FAT FOOL HAS DONE!

SIR PHILIP SMYTHE, THE FATHER OF CECIL SMYTHE, WAS ONE OF THE SCHOOL GOVERNORS.

AFTER THE HARE HAD MADE ITS ESCAPE, CECIL SMYTHE HEARD THE FULL STORY FROM THE REMOVE BOYS ...

SO IT WAS REALLY MICK'S FAULT THAT ALL THIS HAPPENED. FATHER WAS VERY PROUD OF THAT BUST ... HE'LL BE FURIOUS WHEN HE LEARNS IT IS BROKEN.

WITH A GRIN OF TRIUMPH, THE SNOB OF THE FOURTH FORM TURNED AWAY ...

FATHER HAS ALWAYS HATED GYPSIES. IF I WRITE AND TELL HIM WHAT THAT GYPSY RAGAMUFFIN HAS DONE I'VE A FEELING THAT HE'LL SOON FIND A WAY TO HAVE MICK REMOVED FROM GREYFRIARS.

BILLY BUNTER *of Greyfriars*

Mick, a gypsy boy, is now a pupil at Greyfriars school. Cecil Smythe, the snob of the Fourth Form, angered because several boys have remarked that he resembles the gypsy boy, is determined to vent his spite upon Mick.

When a plaster bust of his father, Sir Philip Smythe, is broken, Cecil writes to his father, blaming Mick for what has happened . . .

SIR PHILIP SMYTHE'S FACE GREW SERIOUS AS HE READ HIS SON'S LETTER. FOR MANY YEARS SIR PHILIP, WHO WAS ONE OF THE GOVERNORS OF GREYFRIARS, HAD NURSED A GREAT BITTERNESS TOWARDS ALL GYPSIES.

UPON MY WORD! ACCORDING TO CECIL THERE IS A GYPSY RAGAMUFFIN AT GREYFRIARS. A GYPSY! I'LL GO TO THE SCHOOL THIS VERY INSTANT AND SEE INTO THE MATTER.

MEANWHILE, THE BOYS AT GREYFRIARS WERE ENJOYING A HALF-HOLIDAY. BILLY BUNTER ENVIOUSLY FOLLOWED MICK AND HIS FRIENDS, WHO WERE MAKING THEIR WAY TOWARDS FRIARDALE WOODS WITH A PICNIC BASKET.

THE BEASTS! WHEN I ASKED IF I COULD JOIN THEIR PICNIC PARTY THEY LAUGHED. ANYONE WOULD THINK I EAT A LOT.

IN THE HEART OF THE WOODS HARRY WHARTON SPOKE TO MICK AND THE OTHER BOYS . . .

WE'LL ALL HUNT AROUND FOR SOME TWIGS TO BUILD A FIRE. THEN WE CAN BOIL THE TEA-KETTLE.

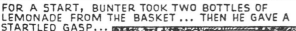

AND THE BOYS SET OFF IN VARIOUS DIRECTIONS.

A FAT FIGURE CAUTIOUSLY EMERGED FROM THE TREES AND ADVANCED UPON THE PICNIC BASKET.

TEE-HEE! THOSE BEASTS WOULDN'T INVITE ME TO THEIR PICNIC . . . SO WHILE THEY'RE GONE I'LL HELP MYSELF. IT'LL SERVE THE GREEDY BOUNDERS RIGHT.

FOR A START, BUNTER TOOK TWO BOTTLES OF LEMONADE FROM THE BASKET . . . THEN HE GAVE A STARTLED GASP . . .

OOER! THEY'RE COMING BACK! THEY MUSTN'T SEE ME!

AND BUNTER RACED AWAY.

I DIDN'T GET ANY FOOD . . . BUT I'LL ENJOY DRINKING THIS LEMONADE PRESENTLY.

AS HE REACHED THE EDGE OF THE ROAD THAT WOUND THROUGH THE WOODS, BUNTER GAVE A BACKWARD GLANCE ... AND THAT WAS HIS UNDOING. HIS FOOT CAUGHT ON A TUFT OF GRASS ... HE SPRAWLED FORWARD ... AND HIS PRECIOUS BOTTLES SHATTERED ON THE ROAD.

YAROOOP!

HARDLY HAD BUNTER WADDLED DISCONSOLATELY AWAY THAN A LARGE OPEN CAR APPEARED. IN IT WAS SIR PHILIP SMYTHE, ON HIS WAY TO GREYFRIARS SCHOOL ...

SUDDENLY, AS THE CAR ROLLED OVER THE SPOT WHERE BILLY BUNTER HAD TRIPPED, THERE CAME TWO MUFFLED EXPLOSIONS ... FOLLOWED BY THE SOUND OF ESCAPING AIR ...

HAWKINS! WHAT IS HAPPENING?

THE CHAUFFEUR HALTED THE CAR, AND AFTER A BRIEF INSPECTION, REPORTED TO HIS EMPLOYER ...

BOTH FRONT TYRES HAVE BEEN PUNCTURED BY BROKEN BOTTLES, SIR; WE ONLY HAVE ONE SPARE WHEEL, SO THIS MEANS I MUST WALK TO THE NEAREST GARAGE FOR HELP!

VERY WELL, HAWKINS. I SHALL REMAIN HERE UNTIL YOU RETURN.

A FEW MINUTES LATER AN UGLY UNSHAVEN FACE APPEARED ABOVE A BUSH AND A PAIR OF SAVAGE EYES GLARED GREEDILY AT SIR PHILIP.

I BET HE'S GOT A NICE FAT WALLET IN HIS POCKET. HEH! HE OUGHT TO KNOW BETTER THAN TO WAIT ABOUT IN A LONELY SPOT LIKE THIS!

THE MAN WAS BARENGO —THE BRUTAL GYPSY WHO HAD BEATEN AND STARVED MICK UNTIL THE BOY HAD RUN AWAY. BY GOOD FORTUNE MICK HAD BEEN BE-FRIENDED BY SIR HILTON POPPER, WHO HAD PAID FOR THE BOY TO BE-COME A PUPIL AT GREY-FRIARS.

BARENGO WAS DETER-MINED THAT MICK SHOULD RETURN TO HIM, AND FOR THAT REASON HE HAD REMAINED NEAR THE SCHOOL. BUT IN THE MEANTIME HE WAS NOT AVERSE TO FILLING HIS POCKETS BY ANY MEANS THAT PRESENTED ITSELF.

HIS CUDGEL RAISED TO STRIKE, THE BIG GYPSY MOVED STEALTHILY TOWARDS HIS UNSUSPECTING VICTIM!

BILLY BUNTER *of Greyfriars*

Cecil Smythe, the snob of the Fourth Form, annoyed because of the likeness between himself and Mick, the gypsy new boy, is determined that Mick shall not remain at Greyfriars.

Cecil writes to his father concerning Mick, and Sir Philip Smythe, who is one of the school governors, decides to pay a visit to Greyfriars. While stranded in his car in Friardale Woods, Sir Philip is unaware that Barengo, a brutal gypsy, is stealthily approaching ...

BEFORE BARENGO'S COWARDLY BLOW COULD DESCEND, A PORTLY FIGURE APPEARED ALONG THE ROAD. IT WAS BILLY BUNTER ... AND A SCREECH OF FRIGHT BURST FROM HIS LIPS ...

EEEEEH HELP!

THE FAT BOY'S CRY WARNED SIR PHILIP OF HIS DANGER ...

WHY... YOU RUFFIAN!

AAARGH!

PANIC-STRICKEN, BUNTER FLED THROUGH THE WOOD ... AND WAS SEEN BY MICK, THE GYPSY BOY ...

THERE'S BUNTER! SOMETHING HAS SCARED HIM. I WONDER WHAT?

MICK AND HIS FRIENDS FROM THE REMOVE FORM, HARRY WHARTON, BOB CHERRY, FRANK NUGENT, JOHNNY BULL AND HURREE SINGH, HAD BEEN COMBING THE WOODS IN SEARCH OF BUNTER ... FOR BUNTER HAD EARLIER HELPED HIMSELF TO FOOD FROM THEIR PICNIC BASKET.

BUT NOW MICK WAS ONLY CONCERNED WITH DISCOVERING WHAT HAD SCARED THE FAT BOY. HE HURRIED TO THE EDGE OF THE ROADWAY ... AND THE SCENE WHICH MET HIS GAZE CAUSED HIM TO CALL AS LOUDLY AS HE COULD FOR HIS CHUMS.

HARRY... BOB... JOHNNY! ALL OF YOU... COME QUICKLY!

FEARLESSLY THE BOY LEAPED FORWARD TO SIR PHILIP'S AID ...

... AND AS BARENGO TURNED TO DEFEND HIMSELF, SIR PHILIP WAS ABLE TO STEP DOWN FROM THE CAR.

BARENGO HAD HEARD MICK CALLING FOR HIS FRIENDS. HE TORE HIMSELF FREE AND FLED BEFORE FURTHER ASSISTANCE ARRIVED FOR SIR PHILIP.

THANK YOU, MY BOY. BUT FOR YOUR COURAGE I SHOULD HAVE BEEN OVERPOWERED.

BILLY BUNTER HAD FOUND SUFFICIENT COURAGE TO CREEP BACK AND WITNESS SIR PHILIP SPEAKING TO MICK. THE FAT BOY HURRIED TO GREYFRIARS AND SOUGHT OUT CECIL SMYTHE...

I SAY, SMYTHE. I RESCUED YOUR FATHER FROM A HULKING GREAT GYPSY THIS AFTERNOON. HOW ABOUT TREATING ME TO A TEA AT THE TUCKSHOP FOR MY BRAVERY?

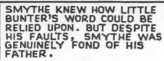

SMYTHE KNEW HOW LITTLE BUNTER'S WORD COULD BE RELIED UPON. BUT DESPITE HIS FAULTS, SMYTHE WAS GENUINELY FOND OF HIS FATHER.

MY FATHER SHOULD BE HERE SOON. IF WHAT YOU SAY IS TRUE, BUNTER, THEN I SHALL ASK HIM TO REWARD YOU.

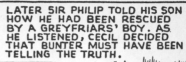

LATER SIR PHILIP TOLD HIS SON HOW HE HAD BEEN RESCUED BY A GREYFRIARS' BOY. AS HE LISTENED, CECIL DECIDED THAT BUNTER MUST HAVE BEEN TELLING THE TRUTH.

I THINK YOU SHOULD REWARD THIS FELLOW, FATHER.

INDEED YES. AND I KNOW WHAT FORM I SHOULD LIKE THE REWARD TO TAKE.

I WANT YOU TO EXTEND THE HAND OF COMRADESHIP TO THIS BRAVE LAD, CECIL. MAKE HIM FEEL THAT YOU ARE HIS FRIEND. HAVE I YOUR PROMISE THAT YOU WILL DO SO?

YES, FATHER.

GOOD. THE BOY IS WAITING OUTSIDE. I WILL CALL HIM IN.

CECIL SMYTHE EXPECTED TO SEE BILLY BUNTER APPEAR... BUT TO HIS UTTER AMAZEMENT IT WAS MICK WHO ENTERED THE STUDY...

YOU..!

THIS IS THE BOY WHOM YOU MENTIONED IN YOUR LETTER TO ME, CECIL. BUT I AM SURE YOU WERE QUITE MISTAKEN IN YOUR OPINION OF HIM. REMEMBER NOW... SHAKE HANDS.

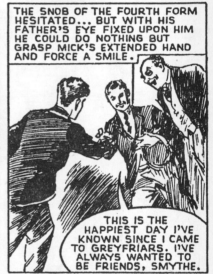

THE SNOB OF THE FOURTH FORM HESITATED... BUT WITH HIS FATHER'S EYE FIXED UPON HIM HE COULD DO NOTHING BUT GRASP MICK'S EXTENDED HAND AND FORCE A SMILE.

THIS IS THE HAPPIEST DAY I'VE KNOWN SINCE I CAME TO GREYFRIARS. I'VE ALWAYS WANTED TO BE FRIENDS, SMYTHE.

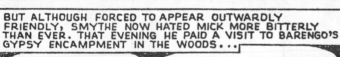

BUT ALTHOUGH FORCED TO APPEAR OUTWARDLY FRIENDLY, SMYTHE NOW HATED MICK MORE BITTERLY THAN EVER. THAT EVENING HE PAID A VISIT TO BARENGO'S GYPSY ENCAMPMENT IN THE WOODS...

OH... IT'S YOU, MASTER SMYTHE. WHAT BRINGS YOU HERE?

YOU STILL WANT TO GET YOUR HANDS ON MICK, DON'T YOU? WELL, I THINK I CAN HELP YOU DO IT.

MICK THINKS I'M HIS FRIEND NOW... *I'LL BE ABLE TO LEAD HIM INTO ANY TRAP YOU LIKE TO SET FOR HIM!*

BILLY BUNTER *of Greyfriars*

After running away from a brutal gypsy leader named Barengo, Mick, a gypsy boy, is befriended by Sir Hilton Popper and is now a pupil at Greyfriars School.

Annoyed because several of his form-fellows have remarked that he resembles the new boy, Cecil Smythe, the snob of the Fourth, is determined that Mick's stay at Greyfriars shall be a short one.

Cecil prepares a trap for Mick with Barengo . . .

WITH A WARM SMILE, CECIL SMYTHE APPROACHED MICK AFTER TEA WAS OVER.

IT'S A FINE AFTERNOON, MICK. HOW ABOUT A STROLL IN THE WOODS?

WHY, YES. THAT WOULD BE VERY NICE.

THE GYPSY BOY LIKED SMYTHE, AND READILY AGREED.

WITH A PUZZLED FROWN, BILLY BUNTER WATCHED THE TWO DEPART.

THAT'S STRANGE! I THOUGHT SMYTHE COULDN'T STAND THE SIGHT OF THAT NEW KID. NOW I WONDER WHERE THEY ARE GOING . . . ?

. . . FOR THE FAT BOY NEVER COULD RESIST POKING HIS NOSE INTO THE AFFAIRS OF OTHER PEOPLE.

SMYTHE LED THE UNSUSPECTING MICK ALONG A NARROW PATH. THEN SUDDENLY . . .

GOT YOU AT LAST!

BARENGO!

WE'LL HAVE HIM INTO THE NEXT COUNTY WITHIN AN HOUR.

THANKS, MASTER SMYTHE. HEH! JUST AS WELL YOU DON'T KNOW WHO MICK REALLY IS.

MYSTIFIED BY BARENGO'S STRANGE REMARK, CECIL SMYTHE RETURNED TO GREYFRIARS . . . JUST AS HIS FATHER, SIR PHILIP SMYTHE, ARRIVED.

CECIL . . . I HAVE MADE AN AMAZING DISCOVERY CONCERNING THE BOY KNOWN AS MICK. WHEN I SAW HIM HERE YESTERDAY I COULD NOT HELP NOTICING THE LIKENESS BETWEEN THE TWO OF YOU. . AND I THINK I KNOW THE REASON FOR IT. LISTEN . . .

It was a strange story that Sir Philip told. Many years before, in the course of his duties as a magistrate, he had sentenced a thieving gypsy ruffian to prison. The gypsy had sworn to be revenged, and after his release from prison he had kidnapped Sir Philip's infant son, Maurice, who had been little more than a year younger than Cecil. Despite all his efforts, Sir Philip had never traced the gypsy or the child . . . but now the recent events at Greyfriars had re-awakened his hopes.

WHERE IS MICK NOW, CECIL? I FEEL CERTAIN THAT HE IS MAURICE . . . YOUR BROTHER!

M-MY BROTHER!

AND IN THAT FATEFUL MOMENT CECIL SMYTHE REALISED THE AWFUL THING HE HAD DONE THAT DAY.

BREATHLESSLY, CECIL TOLD HIS FATHER ALL THAT HAD TAKEN PLACE IN THE WOODS, FULLY ADMITTING HIS GUILT.

SO . . . POOR MAURICE IS ONCE AGAIN IN THE HANDS OF THIS SCOUNDREL BARENGO. WHERE HAS HE BEEN TAKEN?

I-I DON'T KNOW, FATHER.

AT THAT MOMENT A FAT FIGURE CAME HURRYING THROUGH THE SCHOOL GATEWAY...

I SAY! MICK'S BEEN MADE A PRISONER BY THAT BRUTE BARENGO. HE'S IN A CARAVAN ON THE OLD THURBRIDGE ROAD... HEADING TOWARDS MINTON. I SAW IT ALL HAPPEN!

WHAT...? WHARTON... CHERRY... ALL OF YOU, INTO MY CAR! QUICKLY!

MEANWHILE, AS HIS CARAVAN MOVED ALONG AT TOP SPEED, BARENGO GRINNED EVILLY AT HIS PRISONER...

WELL, MICK... SO YOU'RE ONE OF US AGAIN! AND TO THINK IT WAS YOUR OWN BROTHER THAT BROUGHT US TOGETHER. BUT THERE... YOU WOULDN'T KNOW ANYTHING ABOUT THAT. HEH!

WITHOUT WARNING THE CARAVAN JOGGED TO A HALT... AND AS BARENGO LOOKED UP FROWNINGLY, THE DOOR BURST OPEN.

THERE HE IS! THAT'S BARENGO!

WITH A CURSE, BARENGO REACHED FOR HIS CUDGEL. BUT BEFORE HE COULD USE IT, SMYTHE LEAPED FORWARD.

NO YOU DON'T, YOU ROGUE!

IN THE HANDS OF THE STALWART REMOVÉ BOYS, BARENGO WAS HELPLESS. AWKWARDLY, SMYTHE TURNED TO FACE MICK, WHO HAD BEEN RELEASED FROM HIS BONDS BY SIR PHILIP...

CAN YOU FORGIVE ME?

WELL... YOU COULDN'T HAVE MEANT ME ANY REAL HARM, OTHERWISE YOU WOULDN'T HAVE COME BACK TO HELP ME!

IT WAS SIR PHILIP WHO TOLD MICK WHO HE REALLY WAS AND LATER THAT DAY A HAPPY CROWD OF BOYS GATHERED TO WATCH MICK LEAVE WITH HIS FATHER...

SEE YOU SOON... BROTHER!

SO-LONG, CHAPS... BUT I'LL BE BACK!... AND WHEN I RETURN MY BROTHER CECIL AND I ARE GOING TO BE THE BEST OF PALS!

The Magnet Library

With which is incorporated The Greyfriars Herald.

1½d.

No. 682. Vol. XVIII.   March 5th, 1921.

"THIN BUNTER!"
A SCREAMINGLY FUNNY COMPLETE STORY IN THIS ISSUE!

Thin Bunter!

A Screamingly Funny Long Complete Story dealing with the Chums of Greyfriars, and Billy Bunter the Owl of the Remove Form.
—— BY ——
FRANK RICHARDS.

THE FIRST CHAPTER
A Matter of Life or Death!

"Gammon!" said Bob Cherry emphatically.

"Honest Injun!" said Billy Bunter, with great earnestness.

The Famous Five of the Greyfriars Remove chuckled in chorus.

Billy Bunter's "Honest Injun" was not, as a matter of fact, celebrated for his honesty.

"I say, you fellows——"

"Bosh!" said Harry Wharton decidedly.

Billy Bunter turned his big spectacles on the chums of the Remove with a look that was like that of Hamlet's father—more of sorrow than of anger.

"If you're going to be unfeeling beasts——" he began.

'We are!" said Johnny Bull. "Now roll away, porpoise, and give us a rest!"

"But——"

"The pleasures of your conversation, old chap, pall in the long run," remarked Frank Nugent. "They've palled now. Buzz off!"

But William George Bunter did not buzz off.

"The meeting's in Study No, 7, at five," he said. "I hope you'll come. Squiff and Vernon-Smith and Redwing are coming. I've asked them, and they said they'd come. Toddy will be there. I asked that new chap, Drake, but the beast told me to go and eat coke——"

"A very sensible remark of Drake's!" observed Bob Cherry. "Why don't you go and do it?"

"Oh, really, Cherry——"

Harry Wharton pointed to the doorway of Study No. 1. The Famous Five were discussing football when Bunter rolled in—and the discussion waited for Bunter's departure. Football was ever so much more interesting than W. G. Bunter.

"Wharton, old fellow, I'm sure you'll come," said Bunter, unheeding the gesture of the captain of the Remove. "It's to save a fellow's life——"

"Rats!"

"A life-saving committee, really!" said Bunter. "You ought to come. It's up to you. I assure you, I'm serious!"

The fat junior looked serious enough .

"What rot!" grunted Johnny Bull. "It's only some more of your spoof, Bunter. What fellow is it then?"

"A Remove chap?" asked Nugent.

"Yes; and it's to save his life."

"Gammon!"

"Don't be later than five," said Bunter. And he rolled away at last, leaving Harry Wharton & Co. rather perplexed.

"It's all rot, of course," said Bob Cherry. "The fat bounder's pulling our leg again!"

"The rotfulness is terrific!" remarked Hurree Singh. "But if the esteemed Smithy is going—and Squiff——"

"It's some spoof," said Wharton. "Still, we may as well drop in—it's just on five now. If Bunter's pulling our leg we'll bump him!"

"Yes; that's a good idea!" assented Bob.

And the Famous Five left the study, and proceeded along the Remove passage to No. 7. They were, in point of fact, a little interested as well as puzzled. Billy Bunter's announcement that he had called a meeting in his study, with a view to saving a fellow's life, was rather startling. Harry Wharton & Co. were quite willing to lend a hand in saving anybody's life, if anybody's life was in danger, certainly. But they knew their Bunter of old, and they were chiefly wondering what kind of spoof the Owl of the Remove was planning in the recesses of his fat intellect.

There was only one fellow in Study No. 7 when they arrived there; that being Tom Dutton, one of Bunter's study-mates. Tom Dutton was deaf, and he did not hear them come in; and having his back to the door, did not see them. So he remained in ignorance of the arrival of five visitors, until Bob Cherry playfully leaned over him, and tapped him on the nose from behind. Then Dutton gave a jump and a startled yell:

"Oh, you silly ass!"

"Only waking you up, old top!" said Bob Cherry affably.

"Eh?"

"Where's Peter Todd?" asked Wharton.

"I don't call if odd." answered Dutton. "I call it fat-headed, to make a fellow jump like that!"

"Oh, my hat! Where's Peter?" shouted Bob.

"Sweeter? What's sweeter?"

"Help!"

"Ha, ha, ha!"

"I dont see what you fellows are cackling at," said Tom Dutton, rather crossly. "I never saw such a cackling lot as the Greyfriars Remove!"

"We've come to the meeting!" howled Johnny Bull. "We want to knw what the meeting's about!"

"If you mean Bob Cherry——"

"What?"

"I shouldn't call him a lout, said Dutton, shaking his head. "That's rather rough. A silly ass, if you like!"

"Deafness," remarked Bob Cherry, "is said to be an infliction. It is—there's no mistake about that. But it isn't the deaf chap who gets the worst of it. Hallo, hallo, hallo! Here's Toddy!"

Peter Todd came into the study with Billy Bunter. The latter had evidently rounded him up for the meeting.

"Well, what's it all about, Toddy?" asked Wharton.

"Don't ask me," answered Peter. "Bunter says there's a meeting, and he's got some silly asses to come to it. Are you some of them?"

"Why, you cheeky chump——"

"Hallo, hallo, hallo! Here's the giddy crowd!" said Bob Cherry, as Vernon-Smith, Redwing and Squiff came in together. "Now were all here, Bunter, get up on you hind legs and expound!"

"Oh, really, Cherry——"

"Life's short!" said Bob. "We'll give you exactly a minute and a half! If you don't come to the point by that time——"

"I say, you fellows, lead me your ears, you know," said Bunter, taking up a commanding position on the hearthrug to address the meeting.

'We'll lend you our ears," agreed Bob. "But we jolly well won't lend you anything else. So don't begin telling us that you're expecting a postal-order!"

"If he says the word 'postal-order', we'll lend him a boot!" suggested Nugent.

"Hear, hear!"

"I say, you fellows, do stop jawing and give a chap a chance to speak! You're like a sheep's head, Cherry—nearly all jaw!"

"Why, I'll——"

"Is this a meeting to hear Bob Cherry gas, or to hear Bunter talk out of his neck?" inquired Peter Todd.

"Order!"

"Go it, Bunter, and get it over!"

"Gentlemen——"

"Buck up!"

"Gentlemen, this meeting has been called for a very important object," said Bunter, blinking round at the attentive juniors. "Nothing short of saving the life of a well-known member of the Remove. A distinguished inhabitant of these ancient walls, in fact!"

"Oh, crumbs!"

"Name!" hooted Toddy.

"W. G. Bunter!"

"What?"

"Which?"

"Why——"

"Bump him!"

"Yah! Keep off, you silly idiots!" yelled Bunter, abandoning his majestic attitude on the hearthrug suddenly and dodging round the study table. "Give a chap a chance to explain——"

"Give him a chance!" said Wharton, laughing. "If he doesn't hand out a jolly good explanation, he will need somebody to save his life. Go on, you fat spoofer!"

And William George Bunter, having recovered his breath, proceeded to explain, judiciously keeping the table between him and the meeting.

THE SECOND CHAPTER
Reversing the Programme!

"Look at me!" began Bunter.

The juniors looked.

"Cut it short!" said Bob. "It's rather a painful operation looking at you, Bunter! We've got our eyesight to consider."

"If you're going to be a funny idiot Bob Cherry——"

"Get on with the washing!" rapped out Vernon-Smith. The Bounder of Greyfriars seemed to be getting impatient. He had already picked up a cushion—apparently for use on Bunter.

"Well, look at me!" said Bunter. "I suppose you've noticed that I'm getting thin?"

"What!"

"Eh!"

"Thin!"

"You!"

"Ye gods!"

Amazed stares were fixed on Bunter. So far as the meeting could see, there was no sign of thinness about the Owl of the Remove.

His circumference, which was enormous, seemed as enormous as ever; his diameter, which was astonishing, did not appear to be less astonishing than usual.

"Thin!" said Bunter firmly. "Of course, I never was fat——"

"Never!" gasped Bob Cherry.

"Well, hardly ever!" grinned Squiff.

"I've always had a good figure," said Bunter. "I never was skinny, like you fellows—never looked like a knife-blade seen edge-wise, like Toddy, for example."

"Why——" began Peter Todd warmly.

"Just healthily plump," said Bunter. "But this term I've been suffering from a food shortage—it's really awful!" Bunter's voice trembled with emotion. "If you fellows knew how I've suffered——"

"If you have tears, prepare to shed them now!" murmured Bob.

"Ha, ha, ha!"

"I call this laughter heartless, in the presence of a fellow who's fading out of existence before your eyes," said Bunter. "The whole term I've been nearly starving. You've seen, yourselves, Mr. Quelch refuse me a fourth helping at dinner. He doesn't care how a fellow suffers. Bolsover major kicked me yesterday for borrowing a cake from his study, though he knew I was hungry. That new fellow, Drake, threw a dictionary at me when I was looking at his tarts—just looking at them. And Rodney——"

"Come to the point, if you've got one to come to," said Vernon-Smith. "I'm getting tired of holding this cushion ready."

"I'm coming to it. This food shortage is killing me," said Bunter impressively. "I could make up for it at the tuckshop, but I've been disappointed about a postal-order——"

"Only one?" chuckled Bob.

"I've had a whole series of disappointments about postal-orders that I was expecting," said Bunter sadly. "That leaves me short of tin."

"Quite a new experience for you!" said Johnny Bull, with sarcasm.

"And the long and short of it is," resumed Bunter, "That this meeting is called to see what's to be done. My suggestion is that you fellows pass the hat round——"

"What!"

"And raise a fund, to be called Bunter's Fund!" said the Owl of the Remove firmly. "That, I think, is the only way of saving my life. Otherwise, you must prepare for a heavy loss."

"What loss?"

"My early death," said Bunter sorrowfully.

"But that wouldn't be a loss."

"Ha, ha, ha!"

"Oh, really, you fellows! How you can laugh in the presence of death—nearly death—I really can't imagine. It's worse than heartless. If you think you couldn't raise a fund, my next suggestion is that you should have me to tea in turn, one every day in the week, and stand me a really substantial spread each time. That might stave it off."

"Is that all?" asked Harry Wharton.

"That's all. I expect you to consider the matter seriously, and decide what had better be done. Remember, there's a life at stake."

"And you've brought us here to listen to this rot?" asked Bob Cherry.

"Oh, really, Cherry——"

"Bump him!"

"Scrag him!"

Whiz, went the cushion. Bunter dodged just in time, and the cushion landed on the bookcase.

There was a glass door to the bookcase—at least, there had been before Smithy hurled the cushion. Afterwards there wasn't!

Crash! Clink! Tinkle!

"You silly ass!" roared Peter Todd.

"Bunter's fault—he shouldn't have dodged!"

"Ha, ha, ha!"

"I say, you fellows——" howled Bunter.

"Shut up, Bunter! It's my turn now," said Bob Cherry. "Gentlemen, lend me your ears—the same ears that you lent Bunter will do. We've come here to have our legs pulled, just as we suspected. Whether that fat idiot really thought he would screw anything out of us with a yarn like this, I don't know; but he's quite idiot enough. Gentlemen, Bunter has called us together to consider the subject of his health, and I vote that we consider it."

"Why, you ass——"

"I'm glad to hear you take this line, Cherry," said Bunter. "You're talking sense for once."

"Thanks! Gentlemen," said Bob Cherry, "Bunter thinks it is up to us to look after his health——"

"Certainly!" said Bunter. "How'd you feel if you lost me?"

"Jolly glad!" grunted Johnny Bull.

"Oh, really, Bull, you beast——"

"So I vote that we look after his health," said Bob. "Now, in the first place, the chief thing wrong with Bunter is that he's too jolly fat."

"Hear, hear!"

"Second, he eats too much."

"Right!"

"Third, he's always cadging bobs and tanners, and spending them with Mrs. Mimble for tuck."

"He is—he are!"

"Fourthly, he never takes exercise enough."

"True!"

"As a committee in charge of Bunter's health," continued Bob, "I suggest we take the following programme. Nobody is to stand Bunter a feed of any kind for a whole week."

"Good!"

"Nobody is to lend him any money."

"Bravo!"

"And everybody is to see that he takes plenty of exercise."

"Hear, hear!"

"And I suggest that we begin by taking him for a trot round the quadrangle at top speed, and keep behind him to touch him up if he slacks."

"Hurrah!"

"Come on, Bunter!"

"Ha, ha, ha!"

Billy Bunter blinked at the meeting in horrified dismay. This was not at all the programme he had marked out; in fact, it was quite the reverse of that programme.

Undoubtedly, it was a programme that was likely to be good for his health. But it was not attractive to W. G. Bunter.

"You—you—you silly asses," spluttered Bunter. "I won't come! You silly rotters, I'm expiring already from—from famishment——"

"Come and expire in the quad," said Bob Cherry. "Kick him over this way, somebody, and give me a hold on his ear!"

"Yarooh! Help! Fire! Murder!" yelled Bunter, as the juniors closed round him.

"Ha, ha, ha!"

"This way, my fat tulip!"

"Yow-ow-woop!"

In the midst of a chuckling crowd of juniors, William George Bunter was whirled out of Study No. 7.

He howled with alarm and anguish as he was whirled along the Remove passage to the stairs.

On the staircase he was incapable of further yelling; all the breath was gone from his fat body.

He only gasped stertorously as the chuckling Removites marched him downstairs and out into the quadrangle.

"Ow!" moaned Bunter feebly. "I—I—I say, you fellows——"

"Kim on!"

"Wow!"

"Start him, Bob! You've got the biggest feet!"

"Ha, ha, ha!"

"Yarooooooh!"

Billy Bunter started. Harry Wharton & Co. kept pace, which was not difficult, William George's sprinting performances being a great deal like those of an elephant.

Bob Cherry trotted behind him, and every now and then, when Bunter slacked, he let out a reminding boot.

Billy Bunter trotted on desperately.

In spite of the fact that he was fading away, expiring, and expecting a very early demise, he managed to keep up pretty well, and he went right round the quad with the yelling Removites.

As he came opposite the School House doorway again he bolted into the house like a rabbit into its burrow.

The Removites crowded in merrily. The question of Bunter's health had been satisfactorily settled – from their point of view, at least. When Peter Todd came into his study he found the Owl of the Remove extended in the armchair, gasping feebly. Billy Bunter turned on him a look that might have melted the heart of a Hun. But it did not melt Peter Todd. He only chortled.

"Beast!" moaned Bunter feebly.

"Still suffering?" asked Peter.

"Dying!" said Bunter, with a moan.

"My dear old porpoise, you're like merry old Charles the Second, who was an unconscionable time dying," said Peter. "But you beat Charlie the Second – you're more unconscionable than he was. Can't you buck up?"

Groan!

"Get a move on, you know!" urged Peter.

Groan!

"Still bad?"

"Ow! Awful!"

"All right, I'll call in the fellows, and we'll give you another run round the quad!" said Peter, stepping to the door.

Bunter sat up suddenly.

"Yow! Stop, you beast!"

"But if you're still suffering——"

"Yah! I'm better!"

Peter Todd chuckled.

"You'd better remain better, then; it will be better for you," he remarked. "There's only one cure to be found for you in the Remove – plenty of exercise. Every time you groan you're going to get some more."

Groan!

"Hallo! At it again? Come on!"

"Yarooh! Leggo! I – I wasn't groaning. I – I was coughing!" stuttered Bunter.

"It sounded like a groan."

"It – it was a cough, you beast!"

"Well, you can cough, you beast, as much as you like," said Peter considerately. "But the next time you groan you go on another little run."

And Bunter did not groan again. His sufferings, whatever they were, he bore in heroic silence.

THE THIRD CHAPTER
Still Dying!

The next day William George Bunter wore a sad and sorrowful look.

It was the look of a fellow who was painfully misunderstood, but who tried to forgive his misunderstanders, so to speak. He told Peter Todd that he had lost a stone. Peter told him in return that there was plenty of stones on the road, if he wanted any. And when Bunter tried to explain that he was alluding to his weight, the heartless and unfeeling Peter walked away, whistling, without waiting for him to finish.

Undoubtedly there was a plentiful lack of sympathy for William George Bunter in the Greyfriars Remove.

Indeed, he was rather doubtful now about appealing for sympathy. The methods adopted by the Removites to improve his health were most disconcerting.

Billy Bunter did not want to sprint round the quad again with a helpful boot behind him.

He decided on a sad and reproachful countenance, which he hoped would penetrate the hearts of the unfeeling Removites with remorse.

But it didn't. Remorse seemed to be at a discount in the Remove. Bunter's pining looks were hardly noticed for some time; but at last Johnny Bull inquired – not politely, not sympathetically at all – why he was looking like a dying duck in a thunderstorm. And Johnny Bull did not even wait for an answer to the question.

Bunter felt bitterly that he might fade away to a shadow, and these fellows would not care. Certainly, he did not look shadowy yet.

Peter Todd found him that day anxiously scanning his reflection in the looking-glass in Study No. 7.

"Don't break that glass!" commanded Peter.

"Who's breaking it, you ass?" hooted Bunter.

"You're looking into it! It's not safe! Look at something stronger!"

"Beast! Look at the hollows in my face!" said Bunter pathetically.

"There's only one hollow I can see, but that is a jolly big one," said Peter. "I saw you fill it at dinner-time, though."

"You're like Cleopatra fiddling when the Needle was burning!" said Bunter bitterly. Bunter's classical allusions were sometimes mixed.

"Like which?" stuttered Peter. "Do you mean Nero when Rome was burning, you fat duffer?"

"I don't care who it was, you're like him! You'll be sorry when you see me expire at your feet. When you see me stretched in pallid death in the study you'll——"

"There'll be a row if you start dying in this study, Bunter. It's bad enough to have you living in it. Can't you go and die in a box-room?"

Evidently there was no evoking emotion in Peter's hard heart. Bunter gave it up.

At tea-time he looked into Study No. 1, and found Wharton and Nugent there. There was a cake on the table and Bunter cast an affectionate blink at the cake.

"Hand me the poker, Nugent!" said Harry.

"Eh? What for?"

"For Bunter!"

"Oh, all right!"

"I—I haven't come to tea," said Bunter sorrowfully. "I thought you fellows might like to know that I've lost weight."

"How many hundredweight?" asked Wharton. "Dash it all, you wouldn't miss up to half a ton or so!"

"I've lost nearly a stone."

"Advertise for it!" suggested Nugent.

"Eh?"

"Those cheap small advertisements in the 'Daily Mail', you know——"

"Yah!"

Bunter rolled away. He paused in the Remove passage, considering whither to bend his expiring steps. There was no sympathy for him in his own study. He thought of the Bounder, but the Bounder was a beast; of Squiff, but Squiff was another beast; of Drake, but Drake was a beast too. Rodney Ogilvy, Russell Linley; no, unfortunately they were all beasts. He decided finally on Lord Mauleverer, who was, perhaps, a beast, but not quite so beastly as the other beasts. he rolled along the Remove passage and put a dolorous fat face into No. 12. Lord Mauleverer was extended on a sofa, waiting for his study-mates to come in to tea.

He looked startled as Billy Bunter rolled into the study and sank down in a chair, with a groan.

"Begad! What's up, Bunter?" exclaimed his lordship.

Groan!

"I—I say, don't make that fearful row in a fellows study!" urged Mauleverer. "Dash it all, this isn't kind, Bunter! If you've got somethin' wrong with the works you might go into your own study."

Groan.

"To much to eat is it?" asked Mauly.

"I—I'm sorry!" said Bunter faintly. "I—I've come here to die, Mauly."

'Eh!"

"I don't want you to lend me five bob, old chap, though it might save my life. You don't mind me dying in your study, do you?"

"Yaas, I jolly well do, though!" excalimed Lord Mauleverer. "I've got a very strong objection."

Jimmy Vivian came into the study. Sir Jimmy stared at Bunter.

"Hallo! What's Bunter here for?" demanded Vivian.

"Begad! He says he's come here to die you know. Beastly bad form, I call it, to die in another fellow's study!'

Groan!

"Dying, is he?" said Vivian, without any signs of grief. "Well, I'll help him peg out, and put him out of his misery!"

Thump!

"Yarooooh!"

Billy Bunter bounded out of the chair as if he were made of indiarubber.

"Hallo! You're jolly lively for a chap at the last gasp!" exclaimed Vivian. "I'll give you another, and——"

But Bunter did not wait for another. He dodged out of Study No. 12 with a speed that was really creditable in a fellow at death's door.

In the Remove dormitory that night, after Wingate had put out the light, and gone, a deep and hair-raising groan resounded through the darkness.

"Hallo, hallo, hallo! That's Bunter—dying again!" said Bob Cherry. "Bunter, will you oblige the Form by dying quietly?"

Groan!

"Otherwise I shall come over there with a bolster!"

Groan!

There was a sound of scrambling out of bed. Then—

Whack!

"Yoop! Help!"

There were no more groans in the Remove dormitory that night. Bunter, apparently, had made up his mind to oblige the Remove by dying quietly. But in the morning he was still alive!

THE FOURTH CHAPTER
Doctor's Orders!

"Bunter!" Mr. Quelch's voice was not loud, but it penetrated into every corner of the Form-room.

All eyes turned on Billy Bunter.

Bunter was a youth with a fertile imagination. He would tell the most astounding 'whoppers' with an air of believing them; and there was little doubt that he did partly believe them, at least, while he was telling them.

He was supposed to have a half-belief in the existence of Bunter Court, and the titled relations of the Bunter family—indeed, some of the Removites thought that he really believed he had a postal-order coming!

Now, there was little doubt that Bunter had started the invalid 'stunt' with the intention of evoking sympathy, and raising the wind thereby; or, at least, a 'feed'. But the usual result had accrued.

Having repeated his 'whopper' a number of times, Bunter began to believe it himself. Such cases are not really uncommon.

A House of Commons orator, after explaining several times how necessary it is to have a crowd of idle officials living at the public expense, really begins to believe it necessary, in the long run, and is quite pained when his sincerity is doubted. So it was with Bunter. Having been a sham invalid for two days, on the third day he was feeling really ill.

He was convinced that he was losing weight; undoubtedly he had a feeling of emptiness—he always had! Once alarm crept in, Bunter was really alarmed. He could not help thinking how sad it would be if he perished in the bloom of his youth, and the sadness of that thought brought tears to his eyes, and dimmed his big spectacles.

He was certain that his cheeks were becoming hollow—though to other eyes they looked like over-ripe apples. He was convinced that there was a quarter of an inch to spare under this waistcoat, and certainly that had never happened before. Being ill—at least, being convinced that he was—Bunter did not feel up to Form-work. He felt that it was utterly rotten for a fellow who was ill—perhaps, dying—to have to grind Latin in the Form-room.

What use was Latin, anyway, to a fellow who was going to peg out? Even if he had a Latin epitaph, he couldn't be expected to write it himself. So, instead of standing up to construe, when Mr. Quelch called upon him, Bunter only gave the Remove-master a look of anguish and groaned.

"Hallo, hallo, hallo!" breathed Bob Cherry. "If that silly ass isn't beginning it here! Quelchy will scalp him!"

"The scalpfulness will be——"

"Terrific!" grinned Bob.

"Silence in the class! Bunter!"

"Yes, sir!" came from Bunter, in a feeble squeak, like the last farewell of a frog under a motor-lorry.

"What is the matter with you this morning, Bunter?"

"I'm ill, sir!"

"Indeed! You look perfectly well, Bunter!"

"I—I think I'm dying, sir!"

"Kindly do not be absurd!" snapped Mr. Quelch. He seemed as heartless as his pupils. "Have you a pain anywhere?"

"Only a—a sort of seeking feeling, sir!" gasped Bunter. "General weakness and debility, and that tired feeling, sir, and——"

"If you recite a foolish patent medicine advertisement, from the newspaper, Bunter, I shall cane you!"

"Oh!"

"However, if you say you are ill, the school doctor shall see you," said Mr. Quelch. "I have had to reprove you, Bunter, for habits of gluttony, and it is possible that you are suffering from the effects of gluttonous habits."

There was a supressed chortle in the Remove. William George Bunter blinked at his Form-master in speechless indignation.

"I shall not waste Dr. Pillbury's time by asking him to come here," continued Mr. Quelch, "as I do not, in point of fact, believe that you are ill at all. You will go immediately to Dr. Pillbury's house at Friardale, and see him, and request him to send me a written note stating what is the matter with you!"

"Yes, sir!" moaned Bunter.

He brightened a little. Getting out of morning lessons was something, if not much!

"I shall allow you one hour," said Mr. Quelch. "If you are not back in an hour, you will be caned, Bunter! Now go at once!"

Bunter went.

For an athlete like Bunter, it was nearly an hour's walk to the village and back, so his prospect of a happy "loaf" was cut off. Still, though Bunter was not fond of walking, walking was better than working, so he felt fairly cheerfull as he started.

He was back in the hour. He knew that Mr. Quelch was a gentleman of his word. He came into the Form-room with a note in his hand.

Mr. Quelch glanced at him.

"From Dr. Pillbury, sir!" said Bunter. "I've told him all my symptoms, sir—at least, I was telling him when he told me to be quiet, sir!"

The Remove-master took the note, and opened it. His brows knitted in a frown as he read.

"Bunter!"

"Yes, sir?" said Bunter quaking. "I—I hope he orders me plenty of—of nourishing food, sir, and—and lots of rest, and—and freedom from worry, sir, such as lessons——"

"Silence! Dr. Pillbury states that there is nothing whatever the matter with you——"

"Oh, sir!"

"Excepting that you are in a rather low condition——"

Bunter brightened again.

"I knew I was, sir! I——"

"Owing," said Mr. Quelch, in a grinding voice—"owing to lack of sufficient exercise, and eating too much pastry."

"Ha, ha, ha!"

"Silence in the class! Bunter's greedy and lazy habits are not a matter for laughter!"

Bunter spluttered with indignation.

"Why, sir, he's potty—simply potty if——"

"What!" thundered Mr. Quelch.

"Doctors don't know anything, sir! He's simply potty! Too much pastry! Why, he asked me, sir, how much pastry I ate yesterday, and I told him—only a cake and some tarts and a few doughnuts and a meringue

81

or two and not more than half a pound of sweets, beside the pudding at dinner, and——"

"That will do, Bunter! Dr. Pillbury recommends a restricted diet——"

"Oh dear!"

"And a long walk every day——"

"Wow!"

"I fear, Bunter, that you are not to be trusted to take a long walk without supervision," said Mr. Quelch severely. "I shall request your Form-fellows to see to it. Cherry, may I ask you to see that Bunter walks three miles after lessons, to-day?"

"Certainly, sir!"

"Wharton, will you be kind enough to see to it to-morrow?"

"With pleasure, sir!"

"I will ask Drake and Rodney to see to it on Friday and Saturday."

"Certainly, sir!"

"That, Bunter, will do you great good, I hope! We shall see whether you have improved by Saturday. Now you may go to your place!"

Billy Bunter limped to his place.

He sat in stony despair till lessons were over. After lessons Bob Cherry hooked an arm in Bunter's.

"Ready, old top?"

"Yow-ow-ow!"

Bunter had his first three-mile walk that afternoon.

At tea-time, anyone passing Study No. 7 in the Remove might have heard deep and anguished groans proceeding from that apartment.

It was Bunter – recovering from his three-mile walk, and anticipating the three-mile walk of the morrow!

THE FIFTH CHAPTER
Awful for Bunter!

"Ready, Bunter?" Harry Wharton asked that question after lessons the next day.

The captain of the Remove kept an eye upon William George as the juniors came out of the Form-room. He was quite anticipating that the fat junior would make an attempt to dodge. But Mr. Quelch's orders had to be carried out. The fiat had gone forth that William George Bunter was to have a three-mile walk after lessons, and Harry Wharton had undertaken to see to it. So he was seeing to it!

Billy Bunter blinked round him in alarm and anguish, and Wharton's cheery call made him jump.

"N-n-not quite, Wharton," he stuttered.

"Hurry up, then!"

"The – the fact is, Wharton, I'd rather go after tea," said Bunter. "I – I shouldn't like to make you late for tea, old chap."

"We can do three miles before tea," said Harry. "But we shall have to get a move on. Where's your cap?"

"I – I've lost it."

"Come out without it, then. Get a move on——"

"I – I say, old chap——"

"Shall I start him?" asked Bob Cherry, swinging back a heavy boot in readiness.

Bunter backed away.

"Oh, really, Cherry——"

"I'll come along with you," said Bob. "The pleasure of my company will make you forget the miles, Bunter. Besides, I shall be able to land you with my boot when you lag."

Bunter did not look grateful.

"I – I say, you fellows, I've got a pain——"

"Come and walk it off, then."

"I'm afraid walking would only make it worse," said Bunter pathetically. "I – I don't mind comin' three miles with you fellows if – if you'll telephone for a taxi."

"Ha, ha, ha!"

"I'll stand the taxi," said Bunter generously. "I'm expecting a postal-order by the first post to-morrow. I'll square then. All you fellows will have to do is to pay the driver to-day."

"Is that all?" asked Bob sarcastically.

"That's all, old chap."

Mr. Quelch came out of the Form-room. His gimlet-eye fixed upon Billy Bunter, and the fat junior quaked.

"Bunter!"

"Ye-e-es, sir?"

"Did I not direct you to take a three-mile walk immediately after lessons?"

"Ye-e-es, sir."

"Why are you not gone, Bunter?"

"I—I—I was waiting for Wharton, sir," stammered Bunter. "I—I don't want to hurry Wharton, sir. I—I like to be considerate to any dear school-fellows, sir."

"I'm ready, Bunter," said Wharton. "Come on! You coming, Bob?"

"Yes."

The chums of the Remove walked away with Bunter between them. As they came out into the quadrangle Bunter turned an imploring blink first to one side and then to the other.

"I say, you fellows——"

'Don't say anything, my fat old bean!" advised Bob Cherry. "You'll need all your breath for the third mile!"

"I—I say! Suppose we go as far as the stile and sit down?" suggested Bunter. "Quelchy wont know we haven't walked three miles."

"You fat bounder, Quelchy trusts me to see that you get your walk!" growled the captain of the Remove,

"That makes it all the easier to take him in, old chap!" urged Bunter. "I only wish he'd trust me!"

"Give him your boot, Bob!"

"Certainly!"

"Yah! Keep off!" roared Bunter. "I'm walking, ain't I? Beasts!"

And Bunter walked. A chortle from the juniors in the quadrangle followed the three walkers as they turned out of the gates. "Doctor's orders" were being carried out, and William George Bunter was sincerely repentant by this time he had pleaded illness in the Form-room the previous day. He was still dying, but he wished that he had decided to expire in secret.

Wharton and Cherry started briskly down the lane, with Bily Bunter lagging between them.

The hapless Owl of the Remove lagged more and more, until Bob Cherry dropped behind and gave him a gentle lift with a rather heavy boot.

Then Bunter bucked up wonderfully.

But he paused when the stile was reached.

"I—I say, you fellows! Hadn't we better sit down for a bit?" he inquired.

"What for?"

"I—I'm afraid you chaps are tired."

"Not a bit!" chuckled the captain of the Remove. "Quite fresh, in fact!"

"Fresh as a merry daisy!" grinned Bob Cherry.

"Well, I'm tired, anyhow!" snorted Bunter. "Let's sit down for a little while—say half an hour or so——"

"Get over the stile, lazybones!"

"I—I can't! My strength isn't equal to it!" said Bunter. "I'm suffering from a serious illness. You wouldn't like to see me roll in agony at your feet, would you?"

"I'm sure I don't mind, old chap, if you feel that way."

"Beast!"

"Still, if you can't get over the stile, we'll lift you over." said Bob considerately. "Take hold of his other ear, Wharton!"

"Yaroooooh!"

'Don't you want to be lifted over?" asked Bob innocently.

"Yah! Beast! Leggo!"

Evidently William George Bunter did not desire to be lifted over the stile by his fat ears. He contrived to scramble over unaided, and dropped breathlessly into the field.

His progress along the footpath was punctuated with groans.

"I−I say, you fellows, slack down a bit!" he mumbled. "I−I really can't keep it up! I'm suffering from my fearful exertions yesterday, you know!"

"Take it easy across this field, then," said Bob Cherry. "Is that bull yonder coming this way, Wharton?"

"Yes."

"Well, we'll get on, and leave Bunter to follow. Must be considerate−let him take this field easy."

Wharton and Bob broke into a run. There was a yell from Billy Bunter.

"Stop for me, you beasts! Yow-ow-ow! I shall be gored! You want me to be gored by that beastly bull! Beasts! Oh, my hat! Oh dear! Ooo-ooooop!"

Bunter's fat little legs went like clock-work.

The chums of the Remove kept ahead, trotting on cheerily, and Billy Bunter laboured heavily in their wake. He was puffing and blowing stertorously when the end of the field was reached.

But he did not dare to slacken speed till he was over the next stile. Visions of a ferocious bull, with lowered head and bloodshot eyes, floated before his terrified mind. He rolled over the stile, and collapsed into the next field spluttering.

"Ow, ow, ow! Where's that bull now, you fellows?"

"What bull?" asked Bob.

"Eh? That bull in the field we've just crossed!" roared Bunter.

"My dear chap, there wasn't a bull in the field," said Bob, in surprise. "The bull was in the next field to the left!"

"Why, you−you, beast, you said he was coming towards us!" shrieked Bunter.

"So he was. I forget to mention that there was a fence between him and us, old nut!"

"Beast!"

"You're improving!" said Bob. "If you keep up that pace, Bunter, we shall soon see you doing terrific stunts on the cinder-path! Come on!"

"I−I can't move!"

"Oh, I'll move you, old chap!" said Bob, and he took hold of Bunter's fat ear.

The Owl of the Remove found that he could move then, and he moved very quickly.

"Mile and a half," said Bob, as they came into sight of the village of Pegg. "Now you've only got to walk home, Bunter, and you'll have done your three miles."

Groan!

"Come on, Wharton! We shall never get home for tea at this rate," said Bob. "Shall I drop in at Fairdale to order a coffin for you, Bunter?"

"Beast!"

Wharton and Bob Cherry started for home at a swinging pace. Billy Bunter could be trusted to do the other mile and a half, as he was precisely that distance from Greyfriars.

The chums of the Remove were back in good time for tea, but William George Bunter did not roll in till calling-over. he had evidently taken the return journey by very easy stages.

And that evening, as on the previous evening, anguished groans could be heard proceeding from Study No. 7.

After his second three-mile walk William George Bunter found life scarcely worth living.

And on the morrow there was to be a third!

THE SIXTH CHAPTER
Still Walking!

"Drake, old chap!"

Billy Bunter addressed the new junior at Greyfriars in friendly, indeed affectionate, tones as the Removites were going to their Form-room the following afternoon.

Drake grinned down at the fat junior.

After lessons it was up to Drake to take Bunter on his next long walk, and he had no objection to taking the trouble. It was William George Bunter who had the objection.

"Well, my fat tulip?" said Drake.

"You—you're coming out with me after lessons?"

"Yes."

"I—I say, you're a chap with as sense of humour, I know," said Billy Bunter, blinking anxiously at the new junior.

Jack Drake nodded.

"That's me!" he said. "Lots of it! Tons of it!"

"I—I'm thinking of a joke on old Quelchy!" said Bunter, with a feeble giggle. "You—you'll help me, won't you?"

"Depends on the joke," said Drake. "Expound!"

"I—I'm going to pull his leg, you know, if—if you'll help. He—he thinks were going for a three-mile walk after lessons."

"So we are!"

"Well, my idea is to walk as far as —as the boathouse, and—and sit down there," said Bunter. "We—we'll have a nice rest, you know, and then when we come in Quelchy will think we've done the three miles. No end of a joke on him, what? He, he, he!"

Jack Drakes face remained perfectly grave. Bunter's feeble chortle died away miserably. Evidently Drake did not see the joke!

"Is that the joke?" asked Drake.

"Ye—es. Awfully good, you know! He, he, he!"

"Well, I'll take your word for it, Bunter. I dare say it would be no end funny, but——"

"You'll help me——"

"I'll help you to cover three miles."

"I—I mean——"

"Never mind what you mean, my fat tulip. That's what I mean." And Jack Drake went into the Form-room, leaving Bunter shaking a fat fist after him.

"Beast!" groaned Bunter.

"Hallo! Who's a beast now, old porpoise?" asked Peter Todd, coming along the passage. "Who has dared to blow in between the wind and your nobility?"

"I—I say, Peter, old chap——"

"Stony!" said Peter Todd.

"You silly ass! Do you think I'm trying to borrow anything off you?" howled Bunter.

"What did you call me an old chap for then?" asked Peter, in surprise.

"I say, Peter, don't be a beast! I—I've often admired you, Peter, for the way you can put up your hands. I believe you could knock out Harry Wharton or Bob Cherry if you tried. You could make rings round that new chap Drake, couldn't you, old fellow?"

"Possibly!" said Peter Todd, eyeing his fat study-mate. "What are you driving at now!"

"I—I think you ought to lick him, Peter," said Bunter eagerly. "I'll hold your jacket. Tackle him immediately after lessons, you know, and give him an awful hiding, such a fearful hiding that he won't be able to walk——"

"Ha, ha, ha!" roared Peter Todd, He understood now.

"Blessed if I can see anything to cackle at!" said Bunter peevishly. "You ought to lick him, Peter, after the—the awful things he's said about you."

"Oh, he's said awful things about me, has he?" said Toddy grimly.

"Frightful!" said Bunter hopefully. "He says your face is like a hatchet, Peter, and that you look like a walking telegraph-pole, and that you've got the manners of a bear, and the voice of a hyena! You ought to lick a chap for saying things like that about your, Peter."

"So I will!" said Peter Todd heartily.

Thump, thump, thump!

"Yarooooh!" roared Billy Bunter. "Wharrer you at, you silly ass! I was asking you to lick Drake—yaroooh!—not me, you howling chump!"

Thump, thump!

"I'm licking the chap who made those complimentary remarks about me," explained Peter. "Have some more?"

"Yow-ow-woop!"

Billy Bunter fled into the Form-room.

It was a dismal afternoon for Bunter. As a matter of fact, if he could only have realised it his new walking exercises were doing him good. But Bunter did not want good done to him in that strenuous way. Instead of giving his whole attention to Mr. Quelch that afternoon, W. G. Bunter was desperately cudgelling his brains for some means of dodging the walk that was to follow lessons. Peter Todd had failed him. Bunter felt that he was betrayed by his own familiar friend! Lessons drew to a close, and Bunter had not yet discovered a dodge. And when the juniors were dismissed by Mr. Quelch, Jack Drake joined Bunter at once in the passage.

"Come on, Bunter!"

"Hold on a minute, Drake!" gasped Bunter. "I—I say, I believe you're rather attached to Rodney, ain't you, old fellow?"

"Rodney? Oh, yes!"

"I'm rather alarmed about him," said Bunter.

"Alarmed about Rodney?" ejaculated Drake.

"Yes. He's looking pale."

"Pale?"

"Awfully pale! I'm afraid he's going to be ill," said Bunter. "D-d-do you think you ought to go out and leave him? D-d-don't you think you ought to—to—to stay in and look after the poor chap a bit?"

Drake chuckled.

"Can't be done! I've got to walk out with you," he said. "I told Quelch I would."

"I'll let you off!" said Bunter generously. "Of—of course, I should enjoy your company. But I'll go alone, old chap. You just go and look after poor old Rodney——"

"Poor old Rodney can look after himself for a bit!" grinned Drake. "Come on, you fat spoofer!"

"I—I say, Drake, old fellow——"

"Kim on!"

"Look here, I won't!" roared Buntrer. "I'll—I'll——"

"Bunter!" It was Mr. Quelch's voice.

"Oh, dear! Yes, sir?"

"Did I hear you refusing to walk with Drake?" demanded Mr. Quelch, looking out of the Form-room doorway with a severe frown.

"Oh, nunno, sir! I—I was just urging Drake to come in sir! I—I—I was bucking him up, sir. He—he's rather lazy!" gasped Bunter. "Come on, Drake! D-d-don't keep me waiting any longer!"

And Bunter scuttled away from Mr. Quelch's gimlet eye, followed by the grinning Drake.

William George Bunter tramped wearily down the lane by the side of the active new junior. At the stile he sat down to rest, and refused positively to budge. Jake Drake drew a pin from his jacket, with a throughtful air.

Bunter eyed the pin uneasily.

"Wha-a-at are you going to do with that p-p-pin?" he stammered.

"Stick it into you, old chap," answered Drake genially.

"Oh, really, Drake——"

"Where will you have it?" asked Drake.

"Yah, Beast! Keep off!" howled Bunter.

He did not want the pin at all. He rolled off the stile, and took up his weary tramp again. Jack Drake grinned and followed him. Whenever the hapless Owl of the Remove halted Drake drew the pin from his jacket, and Billy Bunter started again. At a mile and a half from Greyfriars Jack Drake allowed him to stop.

"Crawl home when you like, old top!" he said. "Ta-ta! This is doing you a lot of good, Bunter."

"If I don't come in," moaned Bunter, "you'll know that I've died on the way home, Drake."

"Right-ho! I'll try to bear it!" said Drake. "There'll be no end of dry eyes in the Remove, old chap."

Bunter was not home for calling-over that evening. He limped in half an hour after the roll had been called, and had to report himself to Mr. Quelch's study.

The Remove-master reached for a cane as he came in.

"You are late, Bunter!"

The two Bunters advanced upon Rodney. That youth did not seem very much alarmed. The prospect of being "put through it" by Bunter major and minor did not terrify him. "Mind, I'm going to smash you—you will not feel like walking when I've finished with you!" roared Bunter, pushing back his cuffs. *(See Chapter 7.)*

"Yes, sir," said Bunter, "I fainted several times on the way home, sir."

"What?"

"I'm not strong enough for these fearful exercises, sir! They're telling on me!" said Bunter pathetically. "I fainted on the road, sir, and had a narrow escape of being run over by a motor-lorry, which came by while I was unconscious, sir!"

Mr. Quelch's eyes glittered.

"How do you know a motor-lorry came by, Bunter, if you were unconscious?" he inquired very quietly.

Bunter started.

"I—I mean, it came by while I was conscious, sir! That's what I really meant to say."

"Hold out your hand, Bunter!"

"I—I say, sir, I—I fainted a second time, and—and dropped right down in the mud!" said Bunter, with a pathos that ought to have touched a heart of stone. "I—I thought you'd be sympathetic, sir."

"Undoubtedly I should be sympathetic, Bunter, if you were stating the facts," said Mr Quelch, in a grinding voice.

"Oh, sir! I—I hope you can take my word!"

"You fell down in the mud, Bunter?"

"Yes, sir. An awful crash!"

"Then how comes it that there is no mud on your garments?"

"Eh? I—I mean, I—I fell into—into a——" babbled Bunter, unable to think for a moment, what it was most judicious to have fallen into. Mr. Quelch gave him no time to think it out.

"You are a most untruthful boy, Bunter! I shall cane you twice, instead of once, for telling me falsehoods."

"Oh, dear!"

Swish, swish!

"Wooooop!"

"You may go, Bunter! I am glad to see," added Mr. Quelch, "that your walking exercises appear to be doing you good. Shut the door!"

Billy Bunter shut the door, and limped away, with feelings in his fat breast that could not have been expressed in words. And there was still Saturday to come, with another three miles!

THE SEVENTH CHAPTER
Putting Rodney Through It!

Dick Rodney was ready for Bunter after dinner on Saturday. He was not specially keen on a walk with Bunter, whose fascinating company he was far from enjoying; but he was willing to oblige Mr. Quelch. After dinner that day he tapped Bunter on the arm, as the Remove came out of the dinning-room.

"Ready?" he asked.

Bunter gave him a deadly look through his big spectacles. If looks could have slain, Rodney's life would have been in peril. But looks couldn't, and Rodney didn't turn a hair.

"Let's go out, and sit down," said Bunter. "I don't want to walk three miles."

Rodney shook his head.

"Can't spoof Mr. Quelch," he answered. "He trusts me, you know. Get a move on, and get it over! It's doing you good, too."

"You won't mind your own business?" asked Bunter savagely.

"But this is my business," said Rodney, with a smile. "Shall I ask Bob Cherry to start you?"

"Hallo, hallo, hallo, who wants me?" asked Bob Cherry, coming along.

"Bunter wants——"

"No, I don't!" roared Bunter. "Keep off, you beast! I'm going!"

"IIa, ha, ha!"

Bunter rolled out into the quad with Rodney. His minor, Sammy of the Second, was loafing near the steps, apparently waiting for Billy. The Owl of the Remove beckoned to him.

Sammy Bunter followed the two Removites down to the gates.

"Sammy coming?" asked Rodney.

"You'll see!" answered Bunter morosely.

"Well, come on!"

They started along the lane, Sammy Bunter following in their track. As soon as they were out of sight of the school gates, Bunter stopped. He turned his spectacles upon Rodney with a ferocious glare.

"Now, I'm going to give you a chance!" he said.

"Eh?"

"I'm not coming for a three-mile walk," said Bunter. "I'm fed up with it! Will you hang around, and let Quelchy think——"

"Can't be done."

"Then you're going to have such a thundering hiding that you won't feel up to a walk, you rotter!" said Bunter.

Rodney stared at him, and then burst into a laugh.

"My dear, fat idiot——" he began.

"Come on, Sammy!" shouted Bunter.

Bunter minor came up with a run.

"Oh!" ejaculated Rodney. "Two to one – what?"

"That's it," said Bunter. "Of course, I could lick you easily enough – precious few fellows in the Greyfriars Remove that I couldn't lick – but I disdain to take the trouble. Sammy's going to help me, and we're going to put you through it!"

"He, he, he!" came from Sammy. "Don't forget the toffee, Billy!"

"I'll give you the toffee afterwards," said Bunter.

Sammy shook his head. He knew his major.

"You'll jolly well give me the toffee first!" he answered. "If you don't, it's all off!"

"Look here, Sammy——"

"Look here, Billy——"

Billy Bunter, with a grunt, drew a packet of toffee from his pocket, and passed it to his business-like minor. Then he pushed back his cuffs.

"Come on!" he said.

The two Bunters advanced upon Rodney. That youth did not seem very much alarmed. The prospect of being "put through it" by Bunter major and minor did not terrify him.

Bunter paused before he reached close quarters.

"Look hear, Rodney——"

"Come on, old top!"

"I—I'll let you off if you'll help me pull Quelchy's leg——"

"Bow-wow!"

"Mind, I'm going to smash you!" roared Bunter. "You won't feel up to much walking when I've done with you!"

"Go ahead!"

"I—I'll give you another chance," stuttered Bunter. Somehow, even with the odds on his side, he did not seem very anxious to begin.

"Don't worry," answered Rodney cheerily. "I'm waiting to be put through it. If you don't put me through it pretty soon, I shall begin on you, and put you through it."

"Go for him, Sammy!" gasped Bunter desperately.

And Bunter, screwing his courage to the sticking-point—aided by the horrid anticipation of another three-mile walk—rushed on Rodney. And Sammy rushed on with him.

What happened next neither Bunter quite knew.

But they found themselves sitting in the dusty road, gasping for breath, and blinking dazedly.

Rodney smiled down at them.

"Is that the first round?" he asked.

"Yow-ow-ow!"

"Grooogh!"

"Are you coming on again?" chuckled Rodney.

"Yow! I'm not going to touch you!" gasped Bunter. "I—I despise you too much! Oh dear!"

"Then I'll touch you, old top!"

Rodney bent over the two Bunters, and grasped each by the collar. There was a gentle crack as their heads came together, and a simultaneous yell.

"Yooooop!"

"Now, come on!" said Rodney cheerily. "I'll take you both for a walk—three miles! Move on!"

"I'm not coming!" yelled Sammy, in alarm.

"You are, old chap! Now, in two seconds I start with my boot."

One second was enough for Bunter major and minor to start in. And they started. Rodney walked behind, and with infuriated faces the two Bunters tramped on in advance of him, and the remarks Sammy made to his major were most decidedly not of the kind that a respectful fag ought to have addressed to his elder brother.

That evening two Bunters instead of one were groaning at Greyfriars. Two Bunters were feeling that life was far from worth living. And in the Second Form, as in the Remove, there was a complete lack of sympathy for the sufferer, and the groans of the Bunters—like the groans of the Britons of old—passed unheeded.

THE EIGHTH CHAPTER
Vanishing Bunter!

Billy Bunter was losing weight! There was no mistake about it.

For he had expended sixpence at an establishment in Frairdale where they had a weighing-machine, and they had weighed him. He was losing weight—and six pounds had already gone!

Fellows to whom he told this tale of woe, almost with tears in his eyes, asked him whether the weighing-machine had broken down under the strain, and were surprised to learn that it hadn't.

They also told him not to be alarmed at the loss of six pounds avoirdupois, and not to worry till he had lost a couple of tons. That, they opined, might make a difference extensive enough to be noticeable. This, evidently, was what came of the doctor's orders – fewer helpings at meals, and long walks! Every day that week Bunter had had a long walk till Saturday. Sunday was a day of rest in every sense of the word to Bunter, as Mr. Quelch's orders did not extend over the week-end. Bunter fairly luxuriated in slacking on Sunday, and felt a little better. But on Monday he had himself weighed. And after that a settled gloom appeared on Bunter's fat face. He was fading away – dying by inches – disappearing gradually from sight – very gradually, it was true – but if this process was continued long enough it was certain that he would fade into nothingness, like the Ceshire cat whom Alice found in Wonderland. Of that celebrated cat, only the grin was left; but of Billy Bunter there would not remand even a grin; he did not feel like grining now. To grin and bear it was beyond his powers; he had to bear it, but the grin was conspicuous by its absence. The pathos of the situation appealed very much to Bunter. His emotions were very easily touched – on his own account. The thought of a handsome, athletic, popular youth, a credit to his school – and indeed, to humanity at large – being cut off in the bloom of youth, brought tears to Bunter's eyes.

And still the Remove fellows declined to take the matter seriously. They refused to believe that Bunter was dying at all. They declared that there was no such luck. When he said in the Common-room that he was dying by inches, Skinner actually advised him to go out to the stable and die by the yard!

"You'll miss me when I'm gone, Toddy!" Bunter told his study-mate sorrowfully.

Peter picked up a cushion.

"Possibly!" he assented. "But I shu'nt miss you while you're here! Watch that!"

The cushion whizzed, and Peter did not miss Bunter!

This was simply heartless treatment towards a youth who was dying by inches. Bunter really wondered how fellows could be so awfuly unfeeling. They were not alarmed about his health at all, while the Owl was getting into a state of great alarm. Even Mr. Quelch added insult to injury, for on Tuesday morning he remarked to Bunter in class:

"I am glad to see that you are looking better, Bunter."

"Better!" gasped Bunter.

"Yes, your complexion looks more healthy," said the Remove master, surveying him. "You are undoubtedly benefitting by consuming smaller quantities of such things as pastry and sweets, Bunter. Your walking exercise is also doing you good. Keep it up."

Now, what was Bunter to say to that? Evidently he couldn't tell Mr. Quelch what he thought of him. Against that there was a powerful reason – in the shape of the Form-master's cane. So Bunter went to his place silently and bitterly, only hoping that Mr. Quelch would be stricken with deep remorse when the fatal hour came.

All the Remove, as well as the Remove-master, were laying themselves open to the pangs of remorse at a later date. Bunter felt that, and it was a small solace. But not much.

So deep was his alarm that he exerted himself to walk down to Friardale and interview Dr. Pillbury on his own accord. He hoped that even a medical man would have sense enough to see in what a serious state he was.

But the school doctor displayed a total lack of sense – from Bunter's point of view. To the fat junior's intense exasperation, the doctor told him he was much better. Bunter pointed out that he had lost six pounds in weight, and the medical gentleman advised him to try hard to lose another six. And after that, six more!

Bunter rolled away in a state of utter disgust.

"What do they pay doctors for?" he asked Peter Todd. "I say, Peter, I believe old Pillbury is hand-in-glove with the Friardale undertaker. I do really! He is going to get a commission on the order for the coffin," said Bunter, with intense bitterness.

Peter grinned.

"Ought to be a jolly good commission on your size coffin," he said heartlessly. "Better try to hang on till timber comes down, Bunter; you'll bankrupt your pater at present prices."

"Beast!"

On Wednesday, when the Famous Five were going down to football, Billy Bunter stopped them.

"I want sixpence," he said.

"Telephone to one of your titled relations," suggested Bob Cherry. "I should think the duke would stand you a tanner!"

"Or the marquis and the viscount might put threepence each!" suggested Johnny Bull.

"Ha, ha, ha!"

"Will you lend me sixpence, Wharton?" said Bunter, in a feeble voice. "It may be the last time I shall ask you."

"Eh? Is your postal-order coming then?"

"I mean, I do not expect to live long now——"

"Not long," said Bob Cherry. "You'll never live long, but you'll live wide. You take out your length in breadth, you know."

Bunter did not condescend to heed that frivolous remark.

"I want to be weighed again," he said, in an expiring voice. "On Monday I had lost six pounds. Since then I've——"

"Used no other?" asked Bob.

"Since then I've lost much more. I want to know exactly how much. I—I should like to make some little preparations before I die," said Bunter sadly. "I forgive all you fellows. I hope I sha'n't haunt you afterwards. I may—but I hope not!"

"You'll make a fairly substantial ghost," said Nugent. "I'll tell you what, Bunter. After the sad event, you might drop us a line through Mr. Vale Owen. He does the wireless telephone bizney with spooks, you know."

Bunter sighed.

"You'll be sorry for all this some day," he said. "I may live another week——"

"Quite probable!" said Wharton, laughing.

"Even a fortnight——"

"Do!" said Bob Cherry. "We'll stand it somehow!"

"Ha, ha, ha!"

"Well, here's a tanner," said the captain of the Remove, laughing. "Go and get weighed, old porpoise. Mind, you're responsible if anything happens to the machine—that's understood!"

"Yah!"

Bunter rolled away. He cast a longing glance at the tuckshop, but he did not enter it. The fact that he kept the sixpence in his fat paw, instead of expending it on tarts, showed how deep-seated was his alarm. He rolled off to Friardale, and was weighed again. The Famous Five, on the football-ground, actually forgot Bunter and the dark shadow that hung over him. They were reminded of his existence when they came in to tea. Bunter met them in the Remove passage.

"Four pounds!" he said.

"Ask somebody farther along the passage," said Nugent. "Nobody here is going to lend you four pounds, old chap!"

"I mean, I've lost four pounds!"

"Rats! You've never had four pounds!"

"Weight!" shrieked Bunter.

"Oh, weight!" said Nugent. "Good! Keep on, and you'll get quite fit in the long run!"

Bunter went into his study, leaving the Famous Five chortling. Even yet their hearts were not touched.

When Peter Todd came in to tea, Billy Bunter was seated at the study table, with a sheaf of impot paper before him, and a pen in his hand.

"Working!" ejaculated Peter, in astonishment.

"Don't interrupt me, Peter," said the Owl of the Remove, in a far-away voice.

"What are you up to ass?"

"You can look at it if you like."

Peter looked, and gave a howl of astonishment. Upon the paper was written in Bunter's sprawling hand:

"Last Will and Tessterment of W. G. Bunter.

"To my studdy-mate, Peter Todd, I leave my valluable gold wotch, which cost twenty-five ginnis.

"To Tom Dutton I leave my byke, in good condishon, eksept that it needs new tires and saddel, and new peddles and front wheal.

"To my form-master, Mr. Quelch, I leave my forgiveness for being a Beest.

"To Wharton, Cherry, Nugent, Bull, and Inky I leave the Pangs of Reamorce."

91

"My only hat!" said Peter. "Awfully good of you to leave me your twenty-five guinea gold watch, Bunter! I dare say Mr. Lazarus will give me eighteenpence for it! To whom are you going to leave the seven-and-six you owe me?"

"Oh, really, Toddy——"

"Let's have tea now," said Peter unfeelingly, sweeping W. G. Bunter's last will and testament off the table to the floor. "You can make your will after tea, and peg out before supper – lots of time. But I think you ought to square up that seven-and-six before you peg out. Be just before you are generous, you know."

"Beast!" howled Bunter. "I jolly well won't leave you the twenty-five guinea watch now!"

"Bang goes eighteenpence!" said Peter.

"Yah!"

Peter Todd produced a tin of sardines and a cake for tea. Billy Bunter's eyes glistened when he saw them. The last will and testament remained neglected on the floor, while W. G. Bunter attended to the sardines and the cake. And he did not die before supper!

THE NINTH CHAPTER
The Only Way!

"Flummox's Fattening Fluid!"

"What?"

"Flummox's Fattening Fluid!" said Bunter.

Billy Bunter was reading from the advertisements of a newspaper. He had seemed for some time intensely interested in that newspaper, and now he looked up and gave utterance to the deep thoughts that were within him.

"According to what it says here," said Bunter, addressing the juniors generally in the Common-room, "This wonderful fluid will make anybody grow fat, however thin he may be. You might try it, Toddy. It's rather horrid to have a walking herring-bone in the study!"

Bunter blinked round.

"Who'll lend me four shillings?" he asked.

There was an unanimous silence.

Nobody seemed keen on lending William George four shillings.

"Four shillings," said Bunter, "is the price of the medicine, post free. Listen to this testimonial."

"What the thump——" began Bob Cherry.

"Listen to this," said Bunter. "There's a photograph of the patient who used the fluid, and his name and address, so it seems all right." And Bunter read out:

"A year ago I was emancipated. My friends thought that I was fading away. Doctors could do nothing for me. I went to all the hopsitals, and they gave me up as hopeless. Then my attention was called, by chance, to Dr. Flummox's Fattening Fluid. I bought a bottle, without much hope that it would benefit me. I considered my case too far gone. I was amazed to find that in the first week of taking the fluid I put on six pounds' weight. In the second week I put on four pounds more. I am now healthy, plump, and I owe this to Dr. Flummox's Fattening Fluid.–(Signed) H. Walker.

Bunter blinked round again.

"What do you think of that?" he asked.

There was a general chuckle.

"Topping," said Bob Cherry. "Did it increase his memory to such an extent that the became manager of the bank?"

"Eh? It doesn't mention his memory," said Bunter. "You're mixing it up with the Thingummy System——"

"Dr. Coughdrop's Pink Potions for Muddling Memories," said Bob. "Send us a cheque, and your memory improves to such an extent that you use no other. Worth a guinea a billion. But it won't wash clothes. Still, its the richest in cream!"

"Ha, ha, ha!"

"When I started taking your Terracotta Tabloids," continued Bob, "I was doorkeeper at a pub. My memory improved to such an extent that I immediately became Prime Minister——"

"Look here, you silly ass!" bawled Bunter. "This is a serious matter! Flummox's Fattening Fluid is what I want. I it may save my life!"

"Oh!"

"I'm fading away," said Bunter. "I've lost altogether ten pounds——"

"Leaving only a ton and half"

"My cheeks are hollow," said Bunter. "My waist is shrinking. My clothes hang loose about me——"

"Appearances are deceptive if they do," said Bob. "They looked to me as tight as a drum!"

"This fluid may restore me the flesh I'm losing, and save my life," said Bunter. "You fellows mayn't think it's worth four bob to save a fellow's life——"

"Depends on the fellow," said Johnny Bull. "Four bob to save your life would be reckless extravagance!'

"If I live till my postal-order comes, I shall get a bottle!"

"You won't!" said Bob.

"Ah, you realise that I was fading away!" said Bunter, feeling that he had made an impression at last.

"Not at all! But you're not likely to live to be as old as Methuselah, anyhow!"

"Ha, ha, ha!"

"Will you lend me four bob, Wharton, and have it back out of my postal-order?" pleaded Bunter. "Then I will forgive you for all your ingratitude.'

"My what?" ejaculated Wharton.

"Ingratitude!"

"Why you cheeky chump——"

"Then I must wait till my allowance comes," said Bunter. "I only hope you fellows won't suffer too severely from remorse if I expire before it comes. Whatever happens, I'll try to forgive you. Did you say you would lend me four bob, Smithy?"

"No, I didn't!'

"Did you, Drake?"

"No!"

Billy Bunter relapsed into dignified silence. He found some comfort in reading down the testimonials to Flummox's Fattening Fluid, however. According to the statements in the advertisement, that wonderful fluid would put flesh on anything but a telegraph-pole; and Bunter felt that his life might be saved–indeed, would be saved–if only he could obtain the bottle he needed. Four shillings stood between him and an early grave; but his unfeeling schoolfellows did not think it worth that sum to save him. Billy Bunter nobly determined to survive, if he could, till his allowance came.

He did survive.

The successful way in which Bunter, at death's door, was battling with his fate was really deserving of admiration.

When the postal-order for four shillings was despatched, Bunter waited for the bottle to arrive in keen anxiety. He told Peter Todd that he only hoped it wouldnt come too late! Toddy replied that he didn't see how that would matter. Fortunately, it did not arrive too late. Billy Bunter was still alive when it came.

He took the first dose immediately; According to the statement on the bottle, doses might be taken every two hours; and every two hours, so far as the exigencies of lessons allowed, Bunter took his doses.

It was rather nasty to the taste, he confessed to Toddy; but he felt that it was doing him good.

The following day the medicine was all gone.

Bunter waited anxiously for the result to show. He scanned his fat face in the glass incessantly, and pinched his podgy cheeks to ascertain whether they were becoming plumper. He did not feel any plumper; in fact, he had a feeling of being lighter on his feet. He puffed and blew less in coming up and down stairs. Another day passed in suspense. Were those lost ten pounds of flesh coming back, after all?

"Toddy, old man," said Bunter, when Peter came into the study that evening, "Look at me, old chap! Don't be a beast, for once! Look at me, and tell me whether there's any change."

Peter Todd looked at him.

He looked again.

A rather curious expression came over Toddy's face.

He came closer to Bunter, and examined him with attention. Bunter watched him anxiously through his big glasses. At last his study-mate was taking an interest in his painful case.

"My only Aunt Sempronia!" said Toddy at last.

"You—you notice a change?"

"Yes."

"The medicines doing me good?"

"Looks like it!"

"You—you think I'm putting on flesh?"

Peter shook his head.

"What——" ejaculated Bunter. "But you said there was a change——"

"So there is!"

"Wha-a-at is it then?"

"You're growing thinner!"

THE TENTH CHAPTER
Thin Bunter!

Thinner! It was true!

Peter Todd was the first fellow who noticed it.

Bunter was growing thinner!

That was the amazing result of twelve doses of Dr. Flummox's Fattening Fluid!

It was inexplicable; but there is was!

The Removites debated the matter with interest—quite interested in the amazing case of W. G. Bunter.

Possibly it was because the stuff was intended to make thin people fat, Bob Cherry thought that might be the explanation. Perhaps it hadn't any effect on fat people—or a reverse effect! Bunter—in spite of the loss of ten pounds weight—was still about twice as heavy as he ought to have been! That was it, perhaps!

Skinner was of the opinion that the "muck" they put in patent medicines might have any effect—the most unlooked-for effect—on anybody. How did you know how those rotten chemicals were going to work on your inside, Skinner asked. Might be anything in it.

Whether there was an explanation of the phenomenon or not, undoubtedly Billy Bunter was growing thinner!

His fat cheeks, after a few days, no longer resembled over-ripe apples. No longer were his waistcoat-buttons in danger of coming off when he stooped. No longer did he have to unfasten a button here and there after a meal.

His Eton jacket no longer looked on the point of bursting. His trousers began to sag round his knees.

His minor, Sammy of the Second, stared at him when they met. Sammy seemed hardly able to believe his eyes.

"You're getting thin, Billy!" he gasped. "Actually thin! Why, you wouldn't break the bottom out of a cab now!"

Bunter groaned.

"It's that rotten stuff!" he said. "They call it a fattening fluid, and it's reduced me to a shadow!"

"Well, not quite a shadow yet," said Sammy. "You can lose another fifteen stone and not miss 'em. But you're thinner! How does it feel?"

"I—I don't feel exactly bad—but its awful!" groaned Bunter. "Suppose—suppose this goes on!"

"You'll simply disappear from sight!" said Sammy, with a chuckle. "Funny, ain't it? I say, we ought to get some of that stuff for Bessie. If I were fat I'd take some."

"Why, you fat little beast, you're fatter than ever I was!" howled Bunter.

"He, he, he!" chuckled Sammy Bunter. "I say Billy, if you disappear, you know, can I have your pocket-knife?"

Bunter's answer to that question was a brotherly drive of his boot, and Sammy fled.

Bunter extracted a sixpence as soon as he could from a charitable Removite, and was weighed again. He had lost a stone!

He crawled back to Greyfriars in despair. Strange to relate, he had never felt better in his life, so far as

Bunter tried on one of Peter Todd's waistcoats and found that it met easily. "Ow! I've become a horrid skeleton like you," he said almost tearfully. "Your waistcoat is too wide for me, and I hoped the buttons would burst off!" (See Chapter 11.)

mere feelings went. But in such a case you couldn't depend on your feelings, Bunter realised. He had been a healthily plump fellow—not what you'd call fat! At least, that was his own fixed opinion. If he was losing his healthy plumpness, there was cause for alarm. Whether there was cause or not, Bunter was certainly alarmed.

Still, his Form-fellows did not share his alarm—his Form-master wasn't in the least alarmed. After returning from his weighing expedition, Bunter determined to see Mr. Quelch about it—he wasn't going to die from sheer neglect. And he marched into his Form-master's study, to beard the lion in his den, as it were.

"Please, sir——" began the Owl.

"Well, Bunter!" said Mr. Quelch, fixing a pair of gimlet-like eyes upon the Owl of the Remove.

"Look at me, sir!"

"I am looking at you, Bunter. What do you mean?" snapped Mr. Quelch.

"I've lost over a stone in weight, sir."

Mr. Quelch looked interested.

"Indeed! Are you sure?"

"I've had myself weighed, sir."

"That is quite a good idea, Bunter!" said Mr. Quelch approvingly. "I congratulate you!"

"Wha-a-at?"

"Dr. Pillbury's treatment is evidently proving successful," said Mr. Quelch. "He will be delighted to hear that you are losing flesh!"

"I–I——"

"You must see him to-morrow and tell him," said the Remove master. "If this successful treatment is continued, Bunter, you may became as healthy and normal as any other boy in the Remove."

Bunter gasped.

"But—but I'm dying, sir——"

"Nonsense!"

"I'm losing flesh, sir–fading away–vanishing by inches–I mean, by pounds!" wailed Bunter. "Soon there'll be nothing left of me, sir! Perhaps a course of rich and nourishing food, sir, might——"

"Nonsense! You are improving greatly!" said Mr. Quelch brusquely. "It may be that you are losing flesh too rapidly, beneficial as it must be in the long run. You may consult the doctor. I shall certainly congratulate him on his success."

"It wasn't the doctor, sir–it–it was the medicine——" groaned Bunter.

"Eh? What medicine?"

"Dr. Flummox's Fattening Fluid!" said Bunter dismally. "It–it's worked the wrong way about, sir!"

"Have you been buying and consuming patent medicines, Bunter?" exclaimed Mr. Quelch angrily.

"One bottle, sir, of Dr. Flummox's Fat——"

"You utterly absurd boy! You may ruin your health by consuming the noxious compounds advertised in the newspapers! I shall cane you for this, Bunter, as a warning for the future."

"Oh, my hat!"

"Hold out your hand, Bunter!"

Swish!

"Go to the doctor to-morrow, Bunter! Now leave my study! And if you ever purchase any more patent medicines——" Mr. Quelch gave a terrific frown, and left the rest to Bunter's imagination.

The Owl of the Remove limped from the study. He groaned dismally as he went down the corridor! He had gone to his Form-master for help and sympathy; and he had been caned! And he had a foreboding that he would not get any sense of the doctor when he saw him. He was right! Dr. Pillbury called at the school the following day, and saw Bunter. And the fatuous medical gentleman actually rubbed his hands with satisfaction when he saw him!

"Splendid!" he exclaimed.

"I'm feeling awful——" moaned Bunter.

"Nonsense! You've never looked so well in your life!"

"I've lost a stone——"

"Famous!" said Dr. Pillbury. "Keep on! You may lose another! We must hope so. And another! Let us hope for the best! Why, you may have quite a normal figure ultimately, Bunter, if this goes on! I am very satisfied with this case–very! I have never treated a patient so successfully! Mind you keep off pastry. Never touch sweets! Long walks–what, what! And football–undoubtedly football will help on the good work! Why, Bunter, at this rate we shall not know you soon!"

"But–but——"

"What an exceedingly pleasant surprise for your father when you go home for the holidays!" said the

"Open this door, you fat fraud !" shouted Wharton. Bunter did not speak. In fact, he couldn't. His mouth was full of ham and beef, and his powerful jaws were going like clockwork. He had no time to waste on words. Bang ! Bang ! The juniors outside were furious. (*See Chapter 11.*)

doctor, rubbing his hands. "You will mention to Mr. Bunter that I treated you? Remember that! Bless my soul! I am very pleased indeed with this case!"

And the medical gentleman dismissed Bunter with that. The Owl of the Remove rolled away with feelings too deep for words.

And the next day he was thinner still!

THE ELEVENTH CHAPTER
Desperate Measures!

Billy Bunter was the object of great interest at Greyfriars in these days. Generally, he was not considered a personage of very much importance. But now there was no doubt that he excited general attention. Great men in the Sixth Form would look at him in the quad, and even speak to him. Coker of the Fifth even took the trouble to measure his circumference, and was astounded to find that a yard-measure would meet round him! The Remove fellows every morning asked him how many stone he had lost. There was great excitement when it was learned one day that Mrs. Kebble, the housekeeper, had "taken in" a waistcoat for Bunter!

A week had made a wonderful change; another week made it still more wonderful. Fags in the Second Form urged Sammy Bunter to try Dr. Flummox's Fattening Fluid, which, it was hoped, would work in reverse order with Sammy, as with his major. Skinner advised Bunter to write to the Flummox Company, and suggest to them the idea of selling their fattening fluid as an infallible anti-fat remedy, and offer a testimonial for a guinea, which, Skinner said, was the usual rate for testimonials.

But Bunters feeling towards Dr. Flummox were little short of Hunnish. He would willingly have dosed Dr. Flummox with his own mixture till he vanished into nothingness!

Bunter wished fervently that he had never seen that advertisement at all, or that he had spent the money on a memory system or on becoming a cinema actor through the post. Anything would have been better than the awful disaster that had befallen him.

That graceful figure of ample proportions which had often delighted his admiring eyes in the looking-glass – where was it now? Gone from his gaze like a beautiful dream! Lost to sight, though to memory dear!

Certainly, he did not feel unwell. He felt better, in fact. He was not so short-winded as of old. But from these considerations Bunter drew no comfort. he had always prided himself on being a fellow with a figure. Now where was the figure? Poets have told us eloquently of the feelings of a lioness robbed of her cubs. But they were nothing to the feelings of W. G. Bunter, robbed of his circumference!

There were some consolations, however. Bunter found that other fellows' clothes would fit him.

There was some satisfaction in borrowing Mauleverer's handsomest waistcoat, and never running out of shirts!

For it had come to that – any fellow's waistcoat would fit Bunter now! If it had stopped there! But it did not stop there! The strange and mysterious process was continuing! There came a time when even Peter Todd's waistcoat was too large for Bunter!

Bunter tried it, and found that it met easily – too easily! He told Peter the result in expiring tones:

"I'm as skinny as you now, Peter!"

"You mean you've got a healthy, slim figure like mine?" asked Toddy.

"I mean I've become a horrid skeleton like you!" said Bunter, almost tearfully. "Your waistcoat is too wide for me. I've tried on your best one. I hoped the buttons would burst off. But they didn't!"

"Rather lucky for you they didn't!" said Peter Todd grimly.

"What's going to be done, Peter?"

"Looks to me as if you're going to be done!" answered Toddy. "Perhaps you'll stop now you're the right width. After all, you didn't want to be double-width, did you?"

"I can count my ribs!" moaned Bunter.

"Have you got the right number?'

"Eh? Of course!"

"Then what does it matter? If there were any missing, of course——"

"I think you're an unfeeling beast, Peter! There's just one little bit of silver lining to the cloud,' said Bunter. "My appetite's still splendid!"

"Even Dr. Flummox couldn't reduce that!" grinned Peter Todd.

"If I had plenty of nourishing food, I think I might recover,' said Bunter. "I never get enough! Peter, old chap, weve always been pals——"

"First I've heard of it!"

"I–I always admired you, Peter——"

"Then you're not totally lacking in judgment,' said Toddy. "But you've never mentioned it before.'

"I've always – always loved you, old chap! Don't you think you ought to make an effort, and – and have a jolly good spread in the study every day, so that——"

"So that you can rival the earth's circumference once more?" chuckled Peter Todd. "I don't!"

"When you see my coffin brought in Toddy——"

"You'll save something on that coffin now!" said Peter Todd thoughtfully. "At the present price of timber——"

"Yah!"

Thin Bunter wandered disconsolately out of the study. He did not roll, as of old. He was quite light upon his feet. His new, airy feeling needed getting used to. What worried him chiefly was the development of his appetite. When he had been fat, his appetite had been remarkable. Now that he was thin, it was more than remarkable. It was alarming. Bunter could always have consumed the rations of two or three fellows. Now he felt as if he could consume the whole Remove's allowance of provisions, and then look round for more!

His fears of an early and sad decease were quite swallowed up, as it were, in this new consideration. In these days Billy Bunter wandered up and down and to and fro, like a lion seeking what he could devour. "Tuck" in the study cupboards had never been quite safe from Bunter. Now it was more unsafe than of old.

Bunter haunted the school shop till Mrs. Mimble was quite cross and ratty at the mere sight of him. Had Bunter possessed a large supply of cash, Mrs. Mimble would have done a roaring trade. One single customer would have been enough to keep her little business in a most flourishing state. But Bunter's postal-orders had not come; he was impecunious as well a hungry. He exerted all his eloquence on Mrs. Mimble. He tried to make her understand that big modern businesses were built up on a system of credit. Mrs. Mimble declined to understand. Perhaps she did not want to build up a big modern business. At all events, she firmly refused to give Bunter credit.

Meanwhile Mr. Quelch, faithfully acting on Dr. Pillbury's advice, was keeping an eye on Bunter at breakfast and dinner, and ruthlessly cutting down second and third helpings — not to mention fourth, fifth, and sixth, which the unhappy Owl could easily have negotiated.

Slim Bunter was concious of an aching void inside him, and the graceful, slim figure he was developing brought him no comfort whatever. His decrease of weight, fortunately, added to his sprinting powers, which was all to the good, for Bunter was becoming a desperate cupboard-raider, and he had a great deal of dodging to do.

Often and often he would be seen fleeing for his life down the Remove passage, or bolting downstairs three steps at a time — even sliding down the banisters at breakneck speed — with some infuriated junior raging on his track. One afternoon he even bolted into Mr. Quelch, with a pie under his arm, and Bolsover major charging after him. Which led to a painful scene in Mr. Quelch's study, featuring the cane!

Bunter had tea in Hall that afternoon, and then tea in Study No. 7, and then dropped into No. 12 to see Lord Mauleverer, and had tea with him. Then he wandered forth, looking for something to eat. He peered into Study No. 13 through his big spectacles, and his eyes glistened at the sight of a heap of parcels on the table. Little Wun Lung, the Chinee, was there, half-asleep in the armchair, and he blinked up suspiciously as Bunter stepped in.

"Fattee Buntee goey away!" said Wun Lung.

"Feed on — what?" asked Bunter.

"Bob Chelly askee some fellee to tea," said Wun Lung. "No askee Buntee. You loll off, fattee!"

Bunter took a cautious blink along the passage. Near Study No. 1, almost the whole length of the passage away, he spotted the Famous Five, coming towards him. Fat Bunter of old would have hesitated; but thin Bunter didn't hesitate. He whipped round on Wun Lung, grasped him, and whirled him to the door. The little Chinee yelled, and resisted. The Bunter of old would have been thrown off quite easily by the little active Chinee. But thin Bunter was active and nimble — and desperate. He sent Wun Lung spinning into the passage, slammed the door, and locked it.

Then he started on the parcels, newly arrived from the tuckshop, and packed with good things.

Bang!

Bunter did not even turn his head at that emphatic summons at the door.

Bang, bang! Thump!

"Hallo, hallo, hallo!" roared Bob Cherry. "Who's in here? Open this door at once! Do you hear?"

"Fattee Buntee in there!" gasped Wun Lung. "Eatee tuckee!"

Bang, bang!

"Bunter!"

"Open the door, you fat fraud!" shouted Harry Wharton.

Bunter did not speak. In fact, he couldn't. His mouth was full of ham and beef, and his powerful jaws were going like clockwork. He had no time to waste in words, either.

"Let us in, Bunter!"

Guzzle, guzzle! The juniors outside could hear the busy champing of a pair of hungry jaws. That was all they heard.

"The fat rotter!" ejaculated Bob Cherry.

"The thin rotter, you mean!" chuckled Nugent.

"Ha, ha, ha!"

"Look here, he's scoffing our spread!" roared Bob Cherry. "Why, I'll — I'll — I'll pulverise him! Bunter! You fat — I mean, you skinny rotter! Let us in at once, or we'll scalp you!"

Guzzle, guzzle!

Bang, bang, bang!

The ham and beef for five vanished. There were five eggs, and Bunter knew that raw eggs were nourishing. In two minutes they had helped to nourish Bunter. Then the cake went.

Thump, thump, thump!

A three-pound pot of jam was started on next, to an accompaniment of ferocious threats howled through

There was a crash, and a bottle splintered in the study grate. The Owl of the Remove had disposed of Dr. Flummox's Fattening Fluid. (*See Chapter 12.*)

the keyhole.

Bunter did not heed.

He had found a tablespoon, and he was ladling out the jam into his capacious mouth. The three-pound jar was emptied in record time. Luckily, there was more tuck—and Bunter was still hungry. A jar of marmalade followed the jam, then a tin of dry ginger—all was grist that came to Bunter's mill. Bob Cherry had expended an unexpected "tip" from his pater on that spread for the Co. It was intended to be a very handsome spread for five or six. It made a fairly handsome spread for one.

Guzzle, guzzle, guzzle!

"My hat! I'll slaughter him!" breathed Bob Cherry sulphurously. "I—I wish the beast hadn't thinned, if this is the result! Can you see what he's up to Inky?"

Hurree Jamset Ram Singh had put his eye to the keyhole.

"The esteemed villian is finishing the biscuits!" he said. "Everything else is gone, I think!"

"My word!" murmured Nugent. "If Bunter's negoitated that lot at one sitting, something will happen to him!"

Bob looked a little alarmed

"If he bursts——" he said.

"Ha, ha, ha!"

"The burstfulness will be terrific!"

"Bunter! You fat—skinny idiot, open the door!"

Guzzle, guzzle!

The last biscuit was gone, Billy Bunter leaned on the study table, breathing rather hard after his uncommon exertions.

He felt better—what he considered better. There was that delighful old feeling of fulness and strain under his waistcoat that he had not enjoyed for many a day. A feed like this twice or thrice a day would, he felt, restore him to his old proportions. Such good fortune was not to be hoped for; but at least he was going to make hay while the sun shone. Having cleared the table to the last crumb, and recovered a little, he turned to the cupboard, where he found a few more eatables. Standing at the open cupboard, he proceeded to demolish them.

In the Remove passage Bob Cherry was raging, and a crowd of Removites were roaring with laughter. There was a heavy sound in the study at last. Bunter had plumped down in the armchair to repose.

"Will you let us in, you villian!" Bob Cherry hissed through the keyhole.

Bunter answered at last, in a faint voice.

"It's no good, Cherry. There's nothing left."

"Have you scoffed the lot, you Hun?"

"The whole lot."

"I'll slaughter you! Let us in!"

"I—I c-c-an't!"

"Why can't you, you burglar?"

"I—I—I c-c-can't move!"

"You've made yourself ill, you awful beast!"

"Grooooogh!"

And then there was silence in Study No. 13, broken only by an occasional moan from a suffering youth inside.

THE TWELFTH CHAPTER
Same Old Bunter!

Harry Wharton & Co. retired from the scene at last. The feed had evidently gone the way of all feed; there was no hope of saving anything from the wreck. There was a frugal tea in Study No. 1, instead of the handsome spread that had been arranged in No. 13. Bob Cherry's face remained clouded with wrath. For once his good-humour failed him. While he contented himself with bread-and-"marger" and a sardine in Study No. 1, he was thinking of that stack of good things devoured by "Thin" Bunter, and thinking of vengeance. His determination was fixed—to slaughter William George Bunter at sight. This time the ruthless raider was not to escape the penalty of his iniquity. It was but seldom that Bob had a big remittance, and on this occasion he had expended nearly all of it on that feast for the Co.—and the feast had vanished into the interior regions of W. G. Bunter. It was an offence past forgiveness. Over tea Bob discussed what he would do to Bunter. Boiling him in oil was an adequate punishment, but there were certain objections to that. Skinning him alive would have been a well-deserved operation, but the same objections applied. Six dozen with a fives-bat did not meet the case, but was practicable. Bob Cherry decided on six dozen with a fives-bat.

After tea he returned to Study No. 13, with a fives-bat borrowed from Wharton. His chums went with him to lend a hand. Bob rapped on the door with the bat when he found it was still locked.

"Bunter!"

Groan!

"Open the door!"

Groan!

"I know you're shamming, you villian!" roared Bob Cherry. "I've got a fives-bat here for you!"

Groan!

"I'm going to smash you!"

Groan!

"Will you let me in?" shrieked Bob.

Groan!

"I—I—I'll make it twelve dozen!" gasped Bob. "Fancy shutting a fellow out of his own study after scoffing his spread! I—I'll make it twenty dozen! I'll break the bat on him! I'll——"

"Ha, ha, ha!"

"Oh, don't cackle! I'll squash him! I'll spiflicate him! I can't even get into the study to do my prep!" howled Bob.

"Better come to my study,' said Wharton, laughing. "Bunter may be really ill this time. He ought to be, unless he's got the inside of a boaconstrictor!"

"Well, he has!"

Groan! came from the study again.

"What's the matter with you Bunty?" called Harry Wharton, through the keyhole.

"Ow! I've got awful pains!'

"Open the door!"

"I can't move!"

"I'll move you presently!" growled Bob Cherry. "You can stay there till bed-time if you like—you'll have to come out for dorm. Then I'll pulverise you like a pancake!"

Groan!

There was a crowd in Study No. 1 at prep that evening—Bob Cherry, Hurree Singh, Mark Linley, and Wun Lung being there instead of in No. 13. No. 13 remained tenanted only by William George Bunter. Whether the Owl of the Remove was really ill after his tremendous "gorge" or whether he was spoofing, as usual, the juniors could not tell. Certainly he ought to have been ill. He had had tea three times before scoffing a spread that was rather ample for five or six fellows. His stowage capacity was amazing—but surely there was a limit, even with Bunter? The probability was that he was ill. Bob Cherry hoped that a vigorous application of the fives-bat would do him good. He intended to try.

It was nine o'clock when prep was over, and it wanted only half an hour to bed-time. The Famous Five repaired to Study No. 13. The door was still locked, and Harry Wharton tapped on it.

"Bunter!"

A feeble moan answered.

"Let us in, Bunter! If you're really ill we'll let you off!"

"We won't!" roared Bob Cherry.

"Yes, we will, old chap!"

"Well, if he's really seriously ill——" said Bob relenting.

"I—I can't move!" moaned Bunter. "I—I feel giddy, and—and I've got fearful pains, and—and—and I think I'm dying!"

"Bow-wow!"

"Yah!"

"Oh, leave him to rip!" growled Bob. "He'll have to come out for dorm."

At bed-time Bob Cherry thoughtfully, took the fives-bat to the Remove dormitory with him. His idea was to hand it to Bunter after lights out. Bunter was not in the dormitory when the Remove arrived there, and Wingate of the Sixth asked where he was. But Bunter came in while the captain of Greyfriars was asking for him.

He tottered in.

Bob Cherry fixed a grim look upon him but his expression changed. Billy Bunter did look really ill! He tottered to his bed and sat down. Wingate stared at him.,

"What's the matter with you, Bunter?"

Groan!

"Are you ill?"

"I'm dying, Wingate!"

"Oh, don't be a silly ass!" said Wingate crossly.

Groan!

"My hat! He does look pretty bad!" remarked Vernon-Smith. "But he's as thin as ever!"

"I—I think it was the ginger," said Bunter faintly. "It couldn't have been the jam. Three pounds of jam wouldn't hurt a chap! As for six pounds of ham and beef, that couldn't do a fellow any harm. It wasn't the sardines or the salmon or the cake! If it wasn't the ginger, perhaps it was the biscuits or the tinned fruits. The tinned fruits very likely. Couldn't have been the eggs, could it?"

"Ha, ha, ha!"

"Perhaps it was the lot together," said Squiff. "Blessed if I should like to have that little lot inside me!"

Groan!

"You horrid, greedy young rascal!" said Wingate. "You'd better go down to Mr. Quelch. You'll want looking after! Shouldn't wonder if you get colic or something!"

"Ow!"

Bunter detached himself from the bed, and departed moaning. The Removites turned in, and remained awake some time after lights out, waiting for Billy Bunter to return. But Billy Bunter did not return, His snore was not heard in the Remove dormitory that night at all.

The juniors came down in the morning very curious on the subject of Bunter. Harry Wharton asked Mr. Quelch where he was.

"In the sanatorium!" the Remove-master answered briefly. "Bunter is ill."

"Really ill , sir?"

"Yes, Wharton. The doctor is in attendance."

"Oh! Not in danger, sir?" exclaimed Harry.

"No, no. He appears to have over-eaten himself in an unsually reckless manner, and it appears, too, that he has been taking patent medicines, which may have lingered in his sytem and caused him harm. He will probably rejoin the class in a few days."

For a week Bunter's place in the Remove Form was vacant. For a week not a fellow in the Remove was requested to cash an expected postal-order for Bunter, or to lend him a "tanner." Skinner said that it was a rest-cure for the Remove, and expressed a charitable hope that Bunter would be laid up permanently.

"Might be ordered away for his health," said Skinner brightly. "Might be away a whole term! Think of that!"

But the juniors agreed that it was no use thinking of such Elysian possibilities, which were not likely to be realised.

At last it was announced that Billy Bunter would emerge from "sanny" and appear at dinner. The Removites were at the table when he came in, and every head was turned towards the doorway as a heavy tread was heard in the passsage without. That heavy tread seemed much too heavy for Thin Bunter. But——

He appeared at the doorway!

There was a gasp!

It was not Thin Bunter who appeared. It was Fat Bunter! That week in the sanatorium had done the trick; or, rather, worked the miracle! No doubt the last traces of Dr. Flummox's Fattening Fluid had worked out of Bunters' system, and allowed Bunter's economy to take its normal course. Tucks which had been taken in Bunter's garments had had to be taken out again. Once more he was, as Skinner put it, as broad as he was long!

Bunter rolled into the dinning-room, and grinned cheerfully at the Removites.

"I say, you fellows, I'm glad to be back," he said. "Have you missed me very much?"

"Not at all."

"Oh, really, Cherry!"

"You may sit down, Bunter!" said Mr. Quelch.

Bunter sat down.

His chair creaked under him as of old.

After dinner he rolled out with his fat, self-satisfied expression, which had been absent for so long.

Bunter, like Richard in the play, was himself again!

"Fat as ever!" grunted Peter Todd, in the study that day.

Bunter looked at himself in the glass with a satisfied smirk.

"A fellow with a good figure," he remarked, "is always envied by skinny bounders like you, Toddy! I'm accustomed to jealousy of my figure! I say, isn't it ripping to be well again, and for a chap of get his good looks back?"

"His what?" yelled Peter.

'His good looks. I'll tell you what, Peter', said Bunter impressively. "What I need now is feeding up! You wouldn't like to see me fade away again into a bony object like you, would you, old chap? One awful fright is enough for one study isn't it?"

"Why, you–you——"

"So I'll tell you what," said Bunter. "There ought to be a celebration over my recovery. You might have lost me. Think of that! My suggestion, Toddy, is that you should call a meeting of the principal fellows in the Remove, and consult with them with a view to standing a big celebration, to be followed, perhaps, by a series of extensive feeds like——"

"My dear chap, I think we ought to stand you something," said Peter, after some reflection. "Turn up here to tea, and you'll see."

"Oh, good!" said Bunter.

And he grinned gleefully.

He felt that he was being done justice at last.

Peter Todd consulted with the Famous Five. The consultation was punctuated by many chuckles. When it ended, the sum of four shillings had been raised among the juniors, and Peter Todd cycled down to Friardale to visit the local chemist. He came back with a bottle in his pocket.

At tea-time Peter and the Famous Five were gathered in Study No. 7, and Billy Bunter rolled in with a fat smirk.

"I say, you fellows, I'm ready!"

"Good!" said Bob Cherry. "So's the celebration."

Bunter blinked round the study. He could see no signs of a feed.

"Where's the spread?" he asked.

'Hand it out Toddy!" said Harry Wharton. "We've subscribed for this, Bunter, and the condition is that you scoff it all by yourself, without sharing out with anybody."

"Oh, I don't mind!" said Bunter. "In fact, that will suit me. Where is it?"

"Here you are!" said Toddy.

He laid a package on the table, and proceeded to untie it.

Bunter blinked at it.

It was quite a small package.

"I–I say, you fellows, what–what is——"

"Look!" said Peter Todd impressively.

The contents of the package were revealed–a bottle, and on the bottle was a well-known label!

"DR. FLUMMOX'S FATTENING FLUID!

Bunter blinked at it.

"All for you!" said Peter Todd, with owl-like gravity. "We've subscribed for this, Bunter, We only hope it will have the same effect as the last bottle. Pile in!"

"Go it, Bunter!" said the Famous Five encouragingly.

Bunter blinked at the bottle, and blinked at the Removites. He did not touch the valuable Fattening Fluid of Dr. Flummox.

"You–you–you——" he stuttered. "You beasts!"

"Go it, Bunter!"

"Ha, ha, ha!"

Harry Wharton & Co. walked out of the study, chuckling, leaving William George Bunter to enjoy himself. A howl followed them from the study.

"Yah! Beasts!"

Then there was a crash, and a bottle splintered in the study grate. The Owl of the Remove had disposed of Dr. Flummox's Fattening Fluid–not internally. The Greyfriars Remove had seen the last of Thin Bunter!

THE END

BILLY BUNTER
THE FATTEST SCHOOLBOY ON EARTH

H'M! NOW I WILL MARK BUNTER'S EXAMINATION PAPERS - WITH THE USUAL DISMAL RESULT, NO DOUBT!

NEXT MORNING

EXAMINATION RESULTS

HAVE I PASSED?

LET ME HAVE A PEEP!

OH! PLEASE - THIS IS EXCITING!

"EXAMINATION RESULTS
NAMES OF BOYS TO BE MOVED INTO ANOTHER FORM
CHERRY
JONES MINOR
TODD.
BOLSOVER
NUGENT.
AND
W.G BUNTER

- AND BUNTER! CAN IT BE TRUE -

OH JOY! MY FRIEND HAS PASSED AN EXAMINATION AT LAST! I WILL HASTEN TO TELL HIM THE GOOD NEWS!

DEAR BUNTER! YOU HAVE PASSED! CONGRATULATIONS! THIS IS INDEED A PROUD DAY!

EH? I'VE WHAT? COO! OO!

GOOD OLD FATTY! I'LL BET YOU SNOOPED -

BUNTER'S PASSED!

LET US GET BUSY, BUNTER! YOUR PARENTS - AND YOUR DEAR SISTER BESSIE MUST KNOW THE GOOD NEWS! TO COURTFIELD POST OFFICE!

TEE! HEE! A JOLLY GOOD IDEA, JONES MINOR. YOU CAN PAY FOR THE TELEGRAMS. 'COS I KNOW YOU'RE PROUD OF ME!

YES, INDEED!

EAT UP, DEAR BUNTER - I STILL HAVE A SHILLING LEFT!

YUM! I DESERVE ALL THIS FOR BEING SO CLEVER!

A TELEGRAM FROM OUR DEAR LITTLE BOY. LISTEN, MOTHER- WILLIAM HAS PASSED AN EXAMINATION AT LAST! HE LEAVES THE FORM HE'S REMAINED IN FOR SO LONG!

CRUMBS! NO! YES! I CAN'T BELIEVE IT - IS WILLIAM PULLING MY LEG? PASSED HIS EXAMINATION WITH FLYING COLOURS -

TO GREYFRIARS, MY DEAR. THIS IS INDEED A PROUD DAY FOR US!

MY WILLIAM!

I MUST RUSH OVER TO GREYFRIARS AND GIVE MY CLEVER BROTHER A BIG KISS!

DEAR WILLIAM WILL BE EAGER TO STAND ME A JOLLY GOOD FEED -

GREAT NEWS, MR. QUELCH! CAN WE SEE OUR DEAR LAD NOW?

DELIGHTED TO SEE - ER - OH - ER - YES -

MY WILLIAM WILL BE A GREAT MAN - SOME DAY!

PLEASE FOLLOW ME -

PRAY ENTER THE NEW CLASSROOM!

NOW, LITTLE BOYS - IF ONE AND ONE MAKE TWO, WHAT DO TWO AND TWO ADD UP TO?

GUR! THE SUMS AREN'T ANY EASIER THAN THEY WERE IN THE OTHER FORM!

BILLY BUNTER
THE FATTEST SCHOOLBOY ON EARTH!

1. Billy Bunter is the world's champion grub scoffer. But Bunter as a champion runner . . .! That's got you beat, but, believe it or not, the fat one had the whole school beaten when it came to a cross-country race.

2. Mr. Quelch, the master, was amazed. The only time he had known Bunter to run was when the dinner-bell rang. He was all at sixes and sevens wondering how Bunter had won six races in succession.

3. It was too good to be true! Billy was usually cross when he had to take exercise, but when it came to cross-country running, they couldn't keep him back. When Saturday came, he was there as usual.

4. Quelchy started with surprise when he saw Bunter again at the starting post. Then —bang!—off went his gun, and they were off. Billy Bunter bounded forward like a baby elephant and was soon well ahead.

5. But that sudden burst into the lead was just to lead the others up the garden. Billy's cross-country racing was a double-cross—it wasn't fair. Wheezing and panting, he dodged off and hid behind a tree.

6. The more he wheezed the more he chortled. He had a wheeze on! "Te-he!" he tittered from behind the tree. Those silly asses were barking up the wrong tree if they thought he'd be mutt enough to run for miles.

7. You see, the fat lad was in the running for a free feed. The first time he'd been forced into running, he'd dropped out soon after—and had landed into a bit of luck.

8. Waiting until the other lads had gone, Billy waddled along to a little cottage. Knock! Knock! He rattled on the knocker and grinned at the thought of a rattling good feed.

9. Billy was right, too Mrs. Goodheart gave him a hearty welcome. Billy wiped his feet clean, but meant to wipe a few plates clean, too—even though he had to knit socks.

10. Billy knitting socks did take the cake. But for a plate of Mrs. Goodheart's cakes Billy would have knitted woollen pullovers for billy-goats. Soon he was going strong.

11. Clickety-click! Clickety-click! Billy's needles were busy on the socks. But at the same time, he didn't half give that plate of cakes socks—he took them two at a time.

12. Munch! Munch The more cakes Mrs. Goodheart brought, the better Billy liked it. Then looking through the window, he thought he'd better go. He could see the other runners,

13. That was Billy's big idea. The course ran in a circle and Billy knew that he could join in with the others on their way back. So when the rest of the lads got near the cottage, he shot out and started running again.

14. Being so far in the lead at the beginning, the other lads thought that Bunter had left them standing. Of course, they didn't understand his trick, and when Billy finished the course first, nobody was surprised.

15. But there was a big surprise in store for Bunter. By this time, Quelchy believed that the fat lad could run, so he entered him for a championship cross-country race for all the schools.

16. Poor Billy was in a big mess. He had to go through with it, or Quelchy would find out his secret. Then came the big race—and it was the biggest mistake of Bunter's life.

17. He didn't stand an earthly against all these crack runners. After the first mile he began to crack up—and he didn't have Mrs. Goodheart's cottage to go to this time. He was in a state.

18. Billy was so slow that he couldn't even catch a cold, never mind catch up with the rest of the runners. But he got so hot that, at last, he had to drop out for rest. Panting, he parked his pants on a milestone.

19. But as the other runners vanished, a van appeared. Billy took advantage of this, and asked the driver for a lift. He chortled when the chappie told him to hop aboard and make himself at home.

20. No wonder the fat lad thought it funny. That van had a bigger feed than he could ever hope for from Mrs. Goodheart. Billy thought of a good excuse and was soon at the back amongst the grub.

21. A dozen doughnuts helped to knock the edge off his appetite. Two dozen tarts and six pies followed quickly, and Bunter began to think life worth living. When darkness fell he was feeling good.

22. A vanload of grub is good enough for even Billy Bunter. When he'd scoffed the lot he felt like a snooze. He was so happy that he didn't happen to notice that the van was going on for miles and miles.

23. But as the miles went by, Bunter's smiles vanished. The van was at Land's End, and Billy was at his wit's end how to get back to Greyfriars. There was nothing else to do but to walk all the way home.

24. Tramp! Tramp! Tramp! Billy collected a cargo of corns in the first five miles. How he looked forward to a sit-down. Then he groaned—he knew when Quelchy was finished he wouldn't be able to sit down for weeks!

BILLY BUNTER
THE FATTEST SCHOOLBOY ON EARTH!

1. Billy Bunter is in a class by himself when it comes to scoffing grub. When he is in class learning lessons, he soon gets fed-up. He thought more of robbing a pantry than of Robin Hood, but when he heard the word "feast," he sat up and took notice.

2. This was interesting! Anything that had to do with grub always gave the fat lad food for thought. If Robin Hood could have a free feed every night, he could, too!

3. Billy was having thirty-nine winks during the lesson. It was only the magic word "feast" that wakened him. He thought the best thing was to know more about it, so he swotted up a book about Robin Hood.

4. The fat lad was famishing when he read about the greenwood feeds. Robin Hood shot deer with a bow and arrows and Billy knew he could get them in the school museum—and he felt like shooting the old dear who was standing outside the place talking to Mr. Quelch.

5. Miss Jolly was her name, and she was a jolly old nuisance talking there. At last, Quelchy asked her in, and that left the coast clear for Bunter to get the bow and arrows.

6. "Te-he!" tittered Bunter, as he tip-toed into the hall. There was the bow and arrows and also Miss Jolly's feathered bonnet. Billy didn't care whose it was—he thought it a feather in his cap to make a find like this!

7. So Billy snaffled the bonnet, bow and arrows, and all. He beat it to the woods outside the school to do some hunting.

8. But, oh dear, there wasn't a deer to be seen. Billy was stag-gered. Then he thought the next best thing would be a bit of rabbit-pie. Putting an arrow in his bow, Bunter took a pot shot at a bunny.

9. Run, rabbit, run! That bunny didn't need any telling. It got off its mark—but Billy's arrow found a mark all right. That was right in the centre of Farmer Giles' sit-me-down! It was a bull's eye!

10. Billy hadn't meant to hit him, really. But Farmer Giles couldn't be expected to see Bunter's point after feeling the point of the arrow. He came chasing after the fat lad.

11. That arrow had caused a lot of trouble, and Billy had many n-arrow escapes before he reached a cave in the woods. This would do he thought, and dodged through.

12. But that opening was only the front door to an awful lot of other caves. And, although he had a bow and a quiver of arrows, the fat lad was quivering with fright at being lost.

13. Billy was used to being on the rocks, but those rocky caves put the wind up him. Feeling a bit lonely he let out a shout and nearly jumped out of his fat skin when a voice answered him back—in the same words.

14. Billy was about to dash along and have a look at the other bloke. Then he had a think to himself—what was the use of having a dekko when it was only an echo? It certainly took brains to think of a wheeze like that!

15. But Bunter's brainwaves have a habit of going wonky. As usual, he was all wrong. "I like doughnuts and jam tarts!" he shouted, and flapped his listeners to hear what the echo had to say about it.

16. And that echo said a mouthful. "So do I!" it answered, and Bunter nearly swooned with surprise. In fact, he nearly fainted, because the echo wasn't faint any more—it seemed to be right close to him.

17. And what was more, it hadn't said the same as he had—as all proper echoes should do. It had answered him back, and that back-chat was more than Billy could bear.

18. For a moment he stood rooted to the spot with fright, but this was more than he could stand. Yelling like mad, he dashed off through the caves as fast as his fat legs would take him. Behind him the echo kept shouting wise-cracks and giving him the bird.

19. It was a bird, too. In fact, it was the long-lost parrot of Miss Jolly, the old dear whose hat Bunter had snaffled for his Robin Hood outfit. But Bunter didn't know that—he was beating all records for speed.

20. Through the caves, the fat lad ran. Miss Jolly's Polly had put the wind up him proper. Then—SPLASH!—Billy came to the end of the caves and, before he could put his brakes on, he did a dive into a miniature lake.

21. But it wasn't one of those miniature lakes where one minute you're in and the other minute you're out. Billy was in for nearly ten minutes before he was rescued by Quelchy and the boys.

22. You see, they had come to search for the missing parrot. Instead of Billy getting the bird, the bird had got him and it perched on his top-knot. Miss Jolly was jolly glad to see it, as you can guess.

23. She thought that Billy Bunter had found her pet—so did Quelchy. As for Bunter, he thought that he had landed in hot water again. Instead, he had landed in cold water this time, but he was soon fished out and taken up to Miss Jolly's cottage for a tuck-in. So Billy Bunter kept mum—and what's more, he can rely on Polly not to talk and give his game away this time.

109

BILLY BUNTER
THE FATTEST SCHOOLBOY ON EARTH!

1. Harry Wharton got a big surprise, t'other day. He toddled into a tea-room and there sat Billy Bunter scoffing dozens of doughnuts and jam-tarts. The amazing part was that Billy actually had the dough to pay for them. Somebody's money was missing!

2. Harry thought his money-box had been busted. He asked Billy an awful lot of awkward questions, but got no change out of him. Anyway, it was bad manners to talk with your mouth full, thought Billy, and his wasn't going to be empty for ages.

3. But there were quite a few surprises knocking around. Billy got one himself, and you could have knocked him over with a feather bed when he got an offer to go on the stage!

4. At first, the fat lad couldn't believe his listeners. But the gent said that he was Mr. Vardon Variety, the famous manager, and he offered Billy five pounds to appear at his theatre.

5. Bunter had jumped with surprise, now he jumped at the chance. Five pounds' worth of food wasn't to be sneezed at. Also he'd show his chums how good he was.

6. Full of the feed he'd just scoffed, and full of his own importance, Bunter trundled back to school. The boys knew that he was always acting the goat, and they didn't believe him.

7. Then Billy played his trump card—it was the card that Mr. Vardon Variety had given him. When the lads had a look at it, they saw that the fat lad wasn't fibbing, so instead of being a sell, it was a celebration.

8. In fact, when they saw that their legs weren't being pulled, they dumped Billy into an armchair. Then they all stood around with cakes, pies and plates of good things while the news flashed around the school. Getting a good time like this, seemed too good to be true to Bunter, but he shifted the grub just the same. Even Mr. Quelch did his share.

9. Then came the morning of the show. Quelchy asked Billy for a list of food he would like. The little lot that Bunter wanted would have made a ship list if it had a cargo that size aboard. Still, Quelchy supplied it with a smile, because it was the first time he'd ever had a stage star in his class.

10. It was the biggest event in the school since granddad was a boy. Quelchy and some of the boys were going to see the show, but they saw the grub off first. Billy ate enough to feed the B.E.F.

11. What a carry-on there was after that! The lads all carried Billy shoulder-high to where the school brake was waiting. It was Bunter's lucky break, too. Instead of treating him like a silly ass, the boys acted as horses for the brake.

12. At last they all arrived in London. It was in town to-night, and Quelchy was in good form that night, too. He insisted on Bunter having another snack before the show, and the fat lad didn't need to be asked twice.

13. In fact, he heard the first time. He had just been going to suggest a little something or other to keep his strength up for the show, but Quelchy got there first. Still, a feed was a feed to Bunter, no matter whose idea it was.

14. Two dozen doughnuts, twenty jam-tarts and six pies take some shifting—especially after three tuck-ins that day already. Billy couldn't take it—he was really fed up with food.

15. By the time they all reached the stage-door, the fat lad was at the stage when he wanted to lie down and sleep. But the others wouldn't have that—Billy was their star and they wanted to see him shine.

16. Every star has points—they didn't know what Billy's were, but they meant to find out. Quelchy had booked seats in the front and they wanted to go back to Courtfield to tell how great an actor he was. But Billy was already out of action by eating too much.

17. It was all that grub that had got him down. Some of the lads thought that Billy would just have a walking-on part. Billy couldn't even do that—he was shoved on the stage!

18. To his horror he was shoved right up against a table of food. At any other time, Billy would have welcomed the feed with open arms—and open mouth. Now, there was nothing doing.

19. But he had to eat it—that was his job on the stage. He had to scoff and scoff while the other fellow didn't have to eat anything at all. It was supposed to be funny, too.

20. But the funniest part was that Bunter couldn't eat a thing—believe it or not. For the first time he was full of food and couldn't manage any more. The thin man could—and then some. He was as good as Bunter at his best.

21. Gobble! Gobble! Gobble! The way the thin man shoved back the eats was amazing. Still, Bunter couldn't manage anything and that landed the manager into trouble. The crowd didn't half give him the bird—and other things!

22. So Billy Bunter as a star was a black-out. And it was a black look-out for them all when they were all chucked out of the theatre. Then there's a chance that Billy's going to see more stars when Quelchy gets him back to school

BILLY BUNTER
THE FATTEST SCHOOLBOY ON EARTH!

1. Ta-ra-ra-boom-de-ay! Billy Bunter was cantering along Courtfield High Street, when he heard a brass band. Billy paid no attention—he wanted the "brass" to pay for a snack. Then he heard something that sounded like sweet music to him.

2. The fat lad heard food mentioned. There was a recruiting-sergeant actually offering free feeds to all who would join the Army! Billy would have joined the Girl Guides—but he had to draw the line somewhere. So, sorrowfully, he wandered back to school for a drawing lesson from Mr. Quelch.

3. Billy Bunter isn't very good at drawing. That afternoon Billy couldn't draw for thinking of the free feeds that were going in the Army. However, he scribbled down something—and got a shock when Quelchy asked to see it. He had drawn a picture of Quelchy, but his arts didn't cause any 'arty laughter.

4. In fact, Quelchy was furious. That picture of the master was like a pig, and there was nothing Billy could do to save his bacon. The fat lad was in for a 'ean time now, for Quelchy handed him a load of lines to write.

5. Billy thought that it wasn't right, after he had written a few thousand lines. It was hard lines, indeed. He thought Quelchy was rank and vile, and decided he would be better off in the rank and file of the Army. Two ticks later, and Bunter beat it from school—by way of the window.

6. Billy didn't care whether he joined the Army or the Foreign Legion as long as the free feeds were going. The sergeant looked at the fat lad in surprise and didn't know whether he should put him in the Tank Corps as a tank or not.

7. He decided he would wait and see, but when the doctor saw Bunter's weight he had something to say. Billy had to get rid of ten stones in weight.

8. Now the fat lad hates parting with anything—even though it doesn't belong to him. Still the fat was his, and the fat would be in the fire if he refused.

9. Billy will take anything he can get his hands on, but he can't take exercise. The very thought of it made him tired. When he was told to shift the muck, he knew that sergeant wouldn't stand for any mucking about.

10. It was only the thought of the free feeds that kept Billy from collapsing on the spot. He grabbed the barrow and after a few loads he felt as if he was melting into a greasy spot. And Sargy saw that there was no shirking, either.

11. Sixty minutes make one hour—one hour's work makes Bunter sore. Shifting grub was one thing—shifting muck was another. Sargy saw that he did it at the double, too, and by the end of the hour Bunter was doubled up with agony.

12. Sargy then sent him to get tea—that was the stuff to give 'em! Feeling more contented, he tottered away to sample the contents of the grub tent. But though they say an army marches on its stomach, Billy nearly crawled on his!

13. It was a wonder that he had the strength left to get there. It was only the smell of the grub that kept him going. The sight of the huge piles of grub bucked him up a bit—but he forgot there were forty-nine other fellows to be fed, too!

14. Billy could have eaten enough to have fed the B.E.F., and he had no £ s. d. to buy himself a snack at the canteen. But he had something else—a big idea when he spotted the Army food store.

15. Taking a quick look-see round in case anybody was coming, Billy made for the store tent. In the gloom, he looked like a barrage balloon got lost, but Billy didn't lose his way to the store tent—you can bet he didn't!

16. Of course, Billy didn't think he was doing wrong. The Army had promised him free grub—but they hadn't said how much. Billy took that for granted and took as much as he could carry.

17. But Billy never thought there were such things in the Army as sentries. One of them soon spotted that the grub store had been raided and called out the guard, colonel and all! Tut-tut! There was a to-do!

18. That colonel was a crusty old codger, too. He sent Sargy on the hunt, and when he saw Bunter's shadow getting through a pie crust, he nearly threw a fit. Bunter had begun on the buns before he could speak.

19. But when Sargy got his breath back he didn't half say a mouthful. He came charging into the tent, just as Billy finished a pippin in one mouthful. He wondered what could have given Sargy the pip.

20. Billy soon knew. He expected to be shot at dawn, when what Sargy said dawned on him. Instead, he was grabbed and shot along to the colonel. Billy groaned when he saw that Mr. Quelch was with him.

21. Well, Quelchy got Billy—and also a bill for the food he'd snaffled. But though Bunter's Army days were over, he landed into a war of his own when Quelchy got him back to school!

BILLY BUNTER
THE FATTEST SCHOOLBOY ON EARTH!

1. Oh where, oh where can Bunter be—oh where, oh where is Billy? That's what Bob Cherry wanted to know. You see, Billy had borrowed five-bob from Bob and it was Bob's Your Uncle until Billy had to pay it back.

2. Bob wasn't the only pebble on the beach, either! Lots of other lads were stoney, too! They had all lent Billy Bunter boblets, and now they wanted to get their own-back. But Billy hadn't a bean, so he beat it

3. Run, Bunter, run, Bunter, run, run, run! Billy did—he travelled faster than he would have done going to a free feed—and that's saying something! At first he was a furlong in the lead, but he couldn't keep it up for long.

4. Puff, puff, puff! Billy was nearly all in by going all out. Then his peepers lamped a poster. It was all about a lecture on stamps, but it was a let-out for the fat lad. Two ticks later and he was toddling inside.

5. The fat lad at a lecture! That was the last place anybody would dream of looking for him. "Tee-he!" tittered Billy, as the professor took his arm. But Billy wasn't interested in stamps—he was pulling the professor's leg.

6. Grinning, Billy sat down, the chair groaning beneath his weight. Professor Luce-Knutt let off steam, and soon Bunter was bored stiff. But suddenly he sat up and took notice when the prof. nattered on about stamps being valuable.

7. The mere mention of money was enough to start Billy's think-box working overtime. He chortled so loudly that he nearly woke the other blokes at the lecture—he had an idea.

8. It was Bunter's best brainwave for weeks. He knew where he could collar a collection of stamps and get cash for them. At last, the lecture was over, and the fat lad galloped off.

9. Bunter didn't worry about the stamps belonging to Mr. Quelch, the master. They were all gummed down in a book, but Bunter didn't think of the "licking" he would get.

10. Tucking the album under his coat, Bunter ambled out of school again. He would pay back the boblets he had borrowed, and perhaps have a feed, too. Then Quelchy arrived.

11. Billy wasn't half blue at that—just when everything looked so rosy, too! It was just like Quelchy to barge along at the wrong moment and spoil things. Billy did some quick thinking.

12. Billy thought it was a hot idea saying he had a cold on his chest. But it was "chest" too bad that Quelchy didn't really believe him. Y'see, the master knew Bunter's little ways!

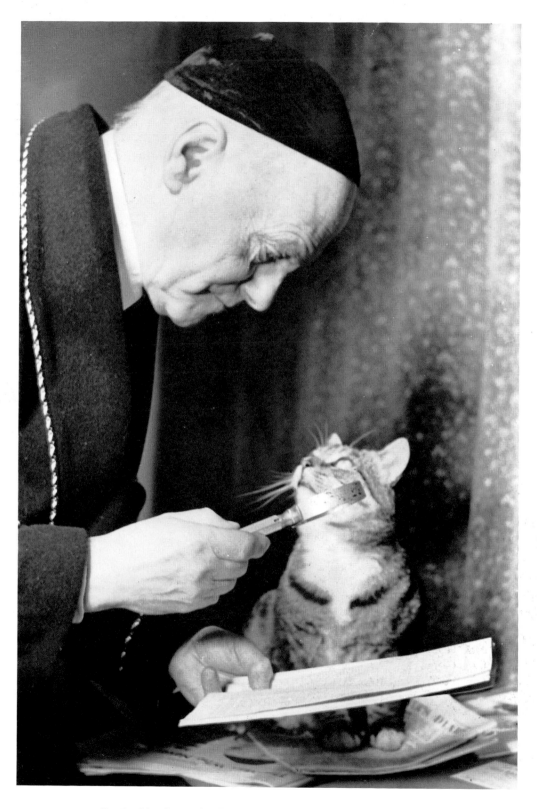

Charles Hamilton alias Frank Richards, the creator of Billy Bunter.

A Plate of Bunter character sketches from the 'Penny Popular', 1919.

II

Colour Plate from the Greyfriars Holiday Annual 1938 by R. J. Macdonald.

Bunter and Mr. Quelch on the cover of Magnet 1937.

Bunter and Bike from the cover of the 1200th Magnet (1931).

'Billionairing with Bunter', Magnet 1385, September 1934.

Bunter's nose takes some punishment on the cover of Magnet 1388, September 1934.

Another Magnet showing Bunter in eavesdropping mood (1937).

BILLY BUNTER'S CHRISTMAS PARTY

FRANK RICHARDS

BILLY BUNTER THE BOLD

FRANK RICHARDS

THE BANISHING OF BILLY BUNTER

FRANK RICHARDS

BACKING UP BILLY BUNTER

FRANK RICHARDS

Billy Bunter hardcover novels published by Cassell.

Billy Bunter at Butlins (1961). This cover features a photo of Gerald Campion, the T.V. Bunter.

THANKS TO
BUNTER

FRANK RICHARDS

BUNTER'S LAST
FLING

The 38th and final story in the splendid saga of WILLIAM GEORGE BUNTER of Greyfriars School

FRANK RICHARDS

BUNTER THE
VENTRILOQUIST

FRANK RICHARDS

BILLY BUNTER'S
BOLT

FRANK RICHARDS

More Bunter hardcovers from the Cassell series.

Bessie Bunter Plate presented with 'School Friend', November 1920.

Top: Bessie Bunter and her Cliff House School chums card set which were giveaways in 'School Friend' in the 20's.
Bottom: A selection of Bunter appearances from a set of Maynards chocolate cigarette cards.

"Billy Bunter scores."
These characters appear each week in the Magnet Library

"Bunter Bumped."
These characters appear each week in the Magnet Library

"Bunter receives a Postal Order."
These characters appear each week in the Magnet Library

"Raiding the Locker."
These characters appear each week in the Magnet Library

Maynards CHOCOLATE CIGARETTES

"Bunter! How dare you smoke in class, come out here," thundered Mr. Quelch. Bunter started guiltily but quickly recovered his composure. "I wasn't smoking, sir" he replied. "Turn out your pockets" rasped the master. Bunter did so, but no sign of a cigarette was found.

Bunter returned to his seat looking as if butter would not melt in his mouth, but a Maynard's Chocolate Cigarette had just done so.

Maynards CHOCOLATE CIGARETTES

"Enclosed I send a box of cigarettes as requested" read Bunter who was prying into one of Wharton's letters. "My hat! I must tell the chaps about this." At first the chaps were jolly fed with Wharton when they heard what Bunter had to say, because Harry was always so down on smoking, but when it transpired that the cigarettes were Maynard's Chocolate ones they all joined the Remove Captain in disposing of them, and then proceeded to bump Bunter for prying and sneaking.

Maynards CHOCOLATE CIGARETTES

"Billy Bunter's actually received his Postal Order at last," chuckled Harry Wharton as he and his chums sauntered through the close at Greyfriars. Just then Bob Cherry looked up towards Bunter's study window and gave a gasp. "My hat!" he ejaculated, "the young idiot 'll be sacked if Quelchy catches sight of him, and he's only just round the corner." Judging from appearances Bunter was engaged in smoking cigarettes and drinking beer, both of which pastimes were strictly taboo at Greyfriars. The chums of Remove set off at a run to warn Bunter of Quelchy's nearness, but when at last, panting, they arrived at his window, it transpired that the beer was of the ginger variety, and the cigarette one of Maynard's Chocolate ones, upon which Bunter had of course expended his Postal Order.

Maynards CHOCOLATE CIGARETTES

"I'm quite certain I saw Wharton smoking in the close the other night" said Skinner, leader of the Gay Dogs of Greyfriars. "I've always thought he was a bit of a blackguard really, in spite of his calling us smoky rotters, so we'll search his locker and see if we can find some cigarettes."

The blades then proceeded to search and after a few minutes Skinner ejaculated "Eureka! I've found him out at last." As he spoke he held up a packet of cigarettes, but almost immediately his joy changed to chagrin, for the cigarettes he held were Maynard's Chocolate ones. Harry Wharton was much too sensible to have any other than Maynard's, as they never damage the wind and in fact help you to keep fit.

XIII

THE ARRIVAL OF BESSIE BUNTER! *(An incident from "The Girls of Cliff House." Complete in this issue)*

"THE SPECTRE OF LYNN'S FOLLY!"

BESSIE BUNTER'S PAINFUL PREDICAMENT!
(An amusing incident from the magnificent long complete tale of the Girls of Cliff House, contained in this issue.)

You must read the wonderful Long Complete Cliff House story "BESSIE'S DREAM COMES TRUE!" inside.

Several appearances of Bessie Bunter. 'School Friend' from 1919 & 1920 plus 'Schoolgirl' 1937 and a 1968 'June & School Friend' Library.

A Frank Minnit drawing of Bunter on the cover of the 'Knockout' annual for 1952.

C. H. Chapman, the best known 'Bunter' Artist.

13. The fat lad needed some knowing too, as he waddled back to the lecture-hall with his haul of stamps. It was the second time he had done that trip at top speed, but he knew that the professor would be pleased to see him.

14. The professor was—there was no doubt about that! His peepers popped wide open when he saw the stamps that Bunter wanted to sell. But it was Billy that was sold, for the prof. wasn't half so potty as he looked!

15. He knew his stamps, that professor did—and he did Billy Bunter and no mistake. Y'see Quelchy's stamps were worth lots of quidlets but the prof. didn't let on to Bunter, when he saw that he knew nothing about them.

16. As for the fat lad, he nearly fainted with surprise when the professor passed over one pound, two shillings and tuppence. He hadn't expected as much as that! He was so pleased that he nearly forgot to take the tuppence!

17. Recovering himself in time, Billy snatched the money and scooted off. He was getting used to going at top speed, but this time he travelled in the direction of the tuckshop. He really needed something to keep his strength up.

18. Billy allowed so much for grub and so much to pay back Bob Cherry and the other boys. But he didn't allow for his own appetite and, before he knew it, he had knocked back a pound's worth of good things.

19. The odd two-and-tuppence wasn't much good now, so Billy spent it on more doughnuts. It was a real beanfeast, and now Bunter hadn't a bean. But he brightened up when he saw a bobby put up a poster.

20. It offered a reward for the return of Quelchy's stamps! At first, Bunter couldn't believe it, then another beauty of a brainwave struck him. That pound reward would pay back the money he'd borrowed.

21. Quelchy got a shock when Billy told his tale. He couldn't believe that the professor had pinched his stamps, but he meant to make sure. Calling a copper, Billy and Quelchy called at the lecture-hall.

22. The professor was poring over the stamps as Bunter and the rest poured into the room. He soon told Quelchy that Billy had sold him the stamps and, to cap the lot, he showed the cap that the fat lad had left behind in his hurry.

23. That cap brought matters to a head. Billy had put his foot in it again, and Quelchy quivered with rage when he saw what the fat lad had been up to. Instead of easy money, there were hard times ahead for Billy now.

24. It was the professor who got the best of the bargain. He sold the stamps back to Quelchy for nearly double he had paid Bunter. As for Billy, he got more than he'd bargained for and, now, if you say "stamps," he shudders!

BILLY BUNTER
THE FATTEST SCHOOLBOY ON EARTH!

1. Billy Bunter is the fattest schoolboy on earth—and the funniest! But it was no joke when Billy was broke, and saw some corking cakes in a shop window. Billy's mouth watered, but his spirits were damped, 'cos he had no money to buy any.

2. There was one beauty marked at two bob and a tanner. Billy wondered if he could borrow the money on the strength of his postal order that never arrived, when a man and a boy came bowling round the corner. The gent was handing out half-crowns.

3. But there was a catch in it. Gently the gent broke the news to Bunter that, before he could get the money, he had to look after his little Egbert. The fat lad was so hungry that he would have taken care of King Kong to get two-and-a-tanner!

4. Little Egbert looked so meek and mild that Billy thought it money for jam. At least, it was money for jam tarts, and the fat lad led Egbert at top speed into the nearest tea-rooms.

5. But the waiter there was a wise guy. He recognised Billy's clock, and so there was no tick. The fat lad had to fork out before he waded into the good things.

6. How the fat lad groaned. He had to go through all his pockets to find that half-crown. The worst of it was that the waiter didn't mind waiting until the fat lad found the money.

7. Billy had to stand up to get it. When he went to sit down again, he got a shock that was more than he could stand. The grub had gone! Egbert had eaten the lot!

8. It was a black look-out for Bunter. "Oh, crumbs!" he groaned, but there wasn't even a crumb left for him. Fuming, the fat lad made for the exit followed by little Egbert.

9. But over in a corner crusty old Colonel Coughdrop was feeding his face. Billy didn't pay attention to him—he was keener on bath-buns than bath-chairs. But Egbert did!

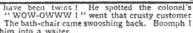

10. That kid was troublesome enough to have been twins! He spotted the colonel's "WOW-OWWW!" went that crusty customer The bath-chair came swooshing back. Boomph! sore foot and sloshed it a beauty with his boot. —and things went all wrong for Billy. Swish! the chair caught Bunter in the back and bumped him into a waiter.

11. And that waiter was carrying a basin of stew! Oopsadaisy—over it went and crowned a customer. Poor Bunter got all the blame—that stew landed him in the soup with everybody.

12. Ding ! Ding ! Ding ! Egbert was having a grand time while all this was going on. He had spotted the cash register and was causing more trouble, by playing a piano solo on the keys that make the money drawer open.

13. Egbert didn't leave that till until he had helped himself to all the money in it. It was a present for Bunter, but the fat lad was being careful of Egbert in the future. However, he had to hold the cash the kid handed him.

14. It was a bad mistake. The manager, finding his cash all gone, called a copper and Billy was copped holding two handfuls of coppers, silver and notes. It was the first time the fat lad had shuddered at seeing money.

15. That copper wouldn't believe Bunter. No wonder !—Egbert looked as though butter wouldn't melt in his mouth—even though Billy knew that half-a-crown's worth of grub had melted there a few minutes before. Away they went to the lock-up.

16. The sergeant was pleased to see him. His cell hadn't had any customers for months, and Billy was given the best one in the place. But sargy should have been keeping an eye on Egbert, that kid couldn't keep out of trouble —he was already after the key !

17. Billy didn't know anything about it as he was given the order of the boot into the cell. It was the worst thing that had ever happened to the fat lad. Living on bread and water was far more than Billy Bunter could ever hope to bear.

18. But the more Bunter groaned, the more Egbert grinned. Suddenly he showed Billy the key he had snaffled, and the fat lad bucked up a bit. Yes, Egbert had taking ways !

19. "Tee-hee ! It's turned out nice again," tittered Billy, as he turned the key in the lock. What a sell it would be to the coppers when they found that their cell was empty !

20. Billy wasn't long in finding the back-door of the cop-shop. Emerging with Egbert, he beetled along the High Street, for it was high time he found the lad's dad again.

21. But he found Egbert's mother instead—and that caused more bother for Billy. The lady thought that her little lamb had been kidnapped, but Bunter thought he'd been acting the goat when the copper chased them again.

22. The copper nearly collapsed when he saw Bunter. He knew that the fat lad couldn't have sneaked through the prison-bars, and, wondered how he had done it. As for Egbert he looked so meek that HE couldn't have done it.

23. So back to the lock-up went Billy. Sargy was surprised to see him again—then in popped Egbert's pa. It was Bunter's turn to be surprised, for the gent gave him enough to keep him in grub until next week !

BILLY BUNTER

THE FATTEST SCHOOLBOY ON EARTH!

1. Billy Bunter had just finished breakfast. He'd scoffed enough to keep six boys from starvation for weeks, but still he wasn't satisfied. He'd been looking round for more, when Mr. Quelch, the master, called the boys together.

2. Billy couldn't help looking round—being the fattest schoolboy on earth. But he had to go with the others. How he groaned—he preferred grub to Quelchy's gas. The master said that Sir Jasper Juniper was to pay a visit.

3. That's all the mean old blighter would pay for anyway—if he'd paid for a feed, Billy would have been interested. All that stuff about a school concert left him cold, so he snaffled some bananas to keep his strength up.

4. Billy parked himself on the top of the school steps to scoff them. He made a big slip when he threw one of the skins over his shoulder. Quelchy made a bigger slip when he came out to welcome Sir Jasper.

5. SWOOSH! The master planted his left beetle-crusher right on that banana-skin. Oopsi-daisy and over he went! ZONK! The master's boot caught Sir Jasper a boot-y right on his schnozzle as he came up the steps.

6. Gosh, old Sir Jasper didn't half make a song and dance about that. Only Quelchy telling him about the school concert saved the situation. Even then, the old codger wasn't so keen, as the master hauled him into the hall.

7. The first on the programme was a recitation by Bob Cherry. He was the apple of Quelchy's eye; the master thought he would get an encore but he gave Sir Jasper the pip!

8. Bob's poem was all about the boy on the burning deck, and Quelchy thought it was hot stuff. He beamed at the first verse, but it was the reverse with Sir Jasper. It left him cold.

9. Two more verses and Bob was finished—even though he had fifteen more to go. Sir Jasper just couldn't stand him. The next turn was Johnny Bull, and Sir Jasper turned purple.

10. Johnny meant to play "There's a Long, Long Trail Awinding," on his trumpet, but he broke down at the first bend. It was a solo, but it was so loud that Sir Jasper got the jitters.

11. At last Johnny struggled wearily to the end of the trail, and Quelchy clapped loudly. He was quite pleased but Sir Jasper would have liked to have clapped Johnny into jail.

12. Little Tommy Brown was next. Quelchy told Sir Jasper that he had a voice like a nightingale. The gale part was right—Tommy nearly lifted the roof off!

13. Then came the big event—Billy Bunter! For the first time, the beam faded from Quelchy's fizzog. The fat lad and trouble were closer than twins, and the master was certain that Billy would get in some mischief or other.

14. Thump! Thump! Bunter bounced on to the stage with the grace of a baby elephant. The fat lad was dressed up like Julius Sneezer, or something. His togs were a bad fit—so bad that the lads went into fits of laughter.

15. "Friends, Romans, Countrymen, lend me your ears," began Billy, and how the boys howled. They knew the fat lad and wouldn't lend him anything, 'cos they never got it back. Then it was Bunter's turn to howl!

16. Two steps astern was an antique aspidistra on a stand. Billy threw out his arm in a dramatic gesture and dotted it one. Everybody thought it funny, except old Gosling who got the job of gathering up the bits and pieces.

17. The most amazing bit was that Sir Jasper liked it. The old codger's face actually cracked into a smile. So Billy began at the beginning again—but you can trust him to put his foot into it.

18. Billy did—he put his foot right into Gosling's bucket! Clatter! Clatter! CRASH! The fat lad slithered to the edge of the stage and did a dive from it—right into the centre of the big drum in the orchestra.

19. BOOOM! Billy struck the right note with Sir Jasper when he struck that drum. Bunter ripped right through the skin, but Sir J. was having a ripping time. He laughed so hard, he nearly bust his own skin.

20. Of course, Mr. Quelch was very annoyed. As shouts of laughter rang out he gave the order to ring down the curtain. He felt like wringing Bunter's neck, too, as he leaped on to the stage.

21. Clonk! The master got there just as the curtain came down. Instead of Billy getting it in the neck, Quelchy got it—the curtain! Next moment, up it went again— taking the master with it.

22. Y'see, chums, there was a hook on that curtain, and it caught Quelchy bending. For a few moments he hung there, like Monday's washing on the line, then his gown gave way. Billy's show was certainly ripping all over.

23. It was a bad let down for old Quelchy! Down into the orchestra he dropped—right into the mouth of a big trumpet. That just beat the band, too, for Sir Jasper. The old codger was now cackling like a cartload of chickens.

24. If Sir Jasper hadn't been tickled pink, it would have been a black look-out for Bunter. The old codger promised Quelchy his chemistry room, but Billy wasn't caring—he had plenty of room for the feed that followed.

BILLY BUNTER
THE FATTEST SCHOOLBOY ON EARTH!

1. You know, chums, Billy Bunter has got a funny idea in his fat head that he's a jolly clever chap—though where he got it from goodness only knows. So when he has a bright idea you can bet something funny will soon happen.

2. Well, this time Billy really thought he'd found a corking wheeze for getting free grub, and there is only one thing Billy likes better than a free meal, and that is two free meals, or more, if he can get them.

3. Billy roped in young Johnny Jingle, who is a bright young spark, to help him with his great idea. It was one of those ideas that need two people to make it work—and even then it may not—if one of the people is Billy!

4. The notion was that they breezed into Poshley's food fill-uppery, ordered a big meal, started a fight over who was to pay—and got thrown out without paying! Bunter had seen it on the pictures.

5. Well, once inside Poshley's, Bunter ordered enough grub to feed the whole B.E.F., and half the F.E.F. if that's what the French chappies call their army. And even if they don't—it'ud still feed 'em!

6. Well, jew know what happened? Blow me if there wasn't another couple in the feedery with just the same idea. They must have seen the same film as Bunter did. They started to fight just as Bunter began to enjoy himself.

7. Making for the door, these two bright bill-swindlers passed Bunter's table still at it. Bunter felt proper annoyed. The cheek! Wheeze pinchers, that's what they were!

8. But what happened next gave Bunter a real scare. The manager of the place, whose name was Horseface Hardcastle, came striding up and, grabbing the two diddlers by the collars, he clonked one with t'other, and t'other with one, both at the same time. Well, this wasn't at all Billy's idea of being thrown out. He'd been hoping that they'd do it nice and gently!

9. Then Billy got a worse shock. Old Horse-face didn't chuck them out at all. He sent for a policeman and chucked them in—in clink. Poor Billy felt like a jellyfish in an earthquake.

10. Still, he thought, perhaps I'm mistaken—perhaps the manager had them arrested for doing something else, like pinching the knives and forks. So he decided to ask.

11. Well, that only made it worse because old Horseface made it quite clear that he knew all about the trick that Billy had been hoping to work. Poooooooor Billy!

12. Johnny Jingle wasn't feeling so chippy about things now. But, anyway, he was much smaller than Billy, so that nobody would ever expect him to pay the bill. Bunter looked like the payer-upper.

13. Nobody took any notice when Johnny Jingle scooted. Nobody, that is except Bunter. Now he was in a fix. Old Horseface was between him and the door, so there was no chance of making a run for it.

14. Bunter was desperate. What could he do? That's what he wanted to know. He thought of hiding under the table—but that wouldn't work—they'd see him. Then at last he made up his mind.

15. There was only one thing for it. Billy would have to fight his way out. And he'd seen summat that would help—a suit of armour behind a screen on the other side of the room. It was the other side to the door, so that Horseface didn't worry when Bunter strolled across.

16. Billy began to convert himself into a sort of super-fatted sardine by strapping on the old tin trousers and so on, just as fast as he could. It didn't fit too well, and by the time he was finished, Billy looked like a cross between a tank and a tin that's been under a bus.

17. Meanwhile other things had been happening. Beefy Bill, the burglar, was in the place, and was planning to steal the day's takings. As a matter of fact he was just drawing his gun as Bunter stepped out from behind the screen, all ready to battle his way out.

18. Before Billy got a chance to do any battling two things happened. The shutter of his tin top-piece went and shut—CLONK!—and Beefy Bill began to do his stuff.

19. But Bunter had a big mace, or knut' walloper and, deciding at this moment to commence his great battle for freedom, he did a spot of walloping. Only he couldn't see!

20. As luck would have it, the chap Bunter walloped was Beefy Bill. And Bunter walloped him so hard that he became just one big head-ache and went down bonk on the floor.

21. And that saved Billy Bunter's bacon. Because old Horseface was so pleased that Bunter had saved his takings from Beefy Bill, that he said all sorts of nice things about him. Also, he said he'd reward him with stacks of free grub, which suited our Billy right down to the ground! Meanwhile the cops turned up again to cart off Beefy Bill.

22. Bunter struggled out of his tin trousers and so-on, and settled down to a real good tuck-in. And never in all his life had Bunter had such a tuck in. Food by the oodle was piled in front of him, and all that Bunter had to do was keep his chin moving up and down and aim his fork. Which was just his idea of heaven! That's what I call luck, don't you?

BILLY BUNTER
THE FATTEST SCHOOLBOY ON EARTH!

1. Billy Bunter is the fattest schoolboy on Earth. He's also a bit of a fathead at times. He didn't know that a sandwich-man carried boards through the streets—he thought it was a man who was wanted to eat sandwiches.

2. Billy was only a boy—but what a boy! He could eat enough sandwiches to satisfy six men. Also it was half an hour since he'd had dinner, and he was a bit peckish. He could do with some sandwiches, so after the job he popped.

3. The thought of a free feed made Billy put his best foot forward—and that's where he started putting his foot in it. Jimmy Puddle was the man he had to see, and Jimmy wanted to be mayor of Courtfield at the coming election.

4. He also wanted somebody to carry his sandwich-boards through the streets. Puddle wasn't half pleased when Billy arrived—so was Bunter when ten bob was mentioned !

5. Ten shillings wasn't to be sneezed at. Billy didn't mind going without sandwiches then. But as he shouldered the boards, Bunter couldn't understand why Puddle kept calling him brave.

6. You see, chums, there was another chappie who wanted to become mayor. His name was Scroggins and his gang's favourite out-door sport was smashing up Puddle's sandwich-boards.

7. They'd been getting a bit out of practice lately, 'cos nobody would carry Puddle's boards. But they weren't bored any longer, when they heard that Bunter had taken on the job.

8. Billy didn't know anything about this—and Puddle didn't tell him, either. Chortling, Bunter cantered along. But around a corner Scroggins' bad lads were waiting for him.

9. Behind Billy was a bodyguard supplied by Jimmy Puddle. Billy didn't know this, either. All he could see was that Scroggins' mob was charging full tilt at him.

10. Behind, came Billy's bodyguard charging to the rescue. Billy groaned. He was a sandwich-man all right—sandwiched between two sets of attacking forces, as the news bulletins might say. This was the end—Billy shut his eyes and shuddered. Tough guys in front of him, tough guys at back of him, tough guys all around him shouted and thundered. Was our Bunter dismayed ? Yes sirs, his knees were soft as marmalade ! They were knocking sixteen to the dozen as Scroggins' men swooped, and Puddle's men pounced !

11. Crash! Bang! Wallop! Then came the offensive on the Bunter eat front—and back as well! The mobs from the two would-be mayors mixed it good and proper. The worst of it was that Billy was right in the middle of the mixing. The sandwich-boards were no good as an air-raid shelter—punches poured on Billy from all sides.

12. Then came the all clear. By this time Bunter was worse than the wreck of the Hesperus. Mr. Jimmy Puddle felt blue at the loss of his boards, but poor old Bunter was black and blue.

13. That meant that he was feeling far from being in the pink. But Billy brightened up a bit when Puddle wanted to reward him. Puddle said he could eat as much as he liked—and to Bunter, that was saying more than a mouthful! A feed wouldn't make him so fed-up, so the fat lad cantered along to the canteen. There was the Scroggins gang but they weren't eating—they were chewing the rag!

14. That didn't sound so good to Bunter. He sidled alongside the counter and gave his order. But Donald, the canteen keeper, was as deaf as a doorpost, so Billy didn't sound too good to him. But Scroggins' lot sat up and took notice.

15. "A FREE FEED! MR. PUDDLE SAYS SO!" Billy was past the peckish stage—he was hungry. He fairly bellowed that order, and Deaf Donald couldn't help but hear. So did the Scroggins gang.

16. They trickled around looking for tasty bits. Deaf Donald had only heard the last part of Puddle's orders, but he did his stuff. He got out a feed for everybody and told them to pile in.

17. They did! Billy Bunter was first off his mark, but he was no match for the Scroggins gang. They were quicker than light—they were feeling hollow themselves and they beat Bunter in their great grab.

18. It was the first time that Bunter had been beaten in a race for grub. It was a bitter pill to swallow—and that was all that the fat lad did swallow. The Scroggins gang swiped all that grub completely.

19. But they thought that Mr. Jimmy Puddle had ordered that feed for them and, by jiminy, they all went along and voted for him. Puddle was as pleased as Punch and presented Billy with a pound note. It was twice what Billy had been promised, but Bunter didn't think twice on where to spend it. So, that day, both Billy and Puddle did plenty of jaw exercise. The mayor making speeches—and Billy feeding his face!

BILLY BUNTER
THE FATTEST SCHOOLBOY ON EARTH!

1. Billy Bunter was fed up. That meant that he hadn't fed his fat face for at least twenty minutes. He was looking forward to his next feed when he looked out of the window. Below was a van—and a hamper was being unloaded.

2. To Billy Bunter, a hamper meant only one thing—GRUB! He goggled as he saw Gosling stagger towards the school with it. It wasn't half heavy—surely there would be some to spare. In a flash, the fat lad was downstairs.

3. That hamper would be for some mean beast who wouldn't give him any—not that Bunter would himself! Still there was a chance of being able to scrounge something. But Gosling told Billy that the hamper was for him!

4. Billy couldn't believe his luck! He couldn't get that hamper into his study quick enough. There was a letter attached, but Billy wasn't to be hampered with that. He tore off the ropes—and got a big surprise!

5. That hamper was filled with—CATS! Billy goggled again, but there was no grub there. Out poured the pussies—dozens of them! It was a let down, so Billy read the letter to see what it was all about.

6. The cats had come from his Aunt Tabitha. The old dear was going away for a day or three, and she wanted Billy to look after them. They seemed a pesky lot of pets, but Billy had to put up with them.

7. There was five bob for doing it—and that meant five bob's worth of food. Billy would have kept a menagerie for that. But the cats had to be fed, so Bunter raided Bob Cherry's hamper.

8. It nearly broke Bunter's heart to hand out grub to a lot of miserable moggies. But the cats couldn't take it. Their miaowing showed that cakes and things weren't on their menu.

9. There was only one thing to do with that grub. You can bet that Billy Bunter did it, too! He scoffed all the good things while the pussies wondered when their turn was coming.

10. But Bunter thought that it was time he turned in. Up to bed he went, and all the cats followed after. There wasn't half a catch in this cat-keeping business—they came to bed, too!

11. But instead of sleeping, the moggies had a sing-song. The cats' chorus echoed through the corridors, and landed on old Quelchy's listeners. He thought it was Bunter tearing his tonsils!

12. Quelchy cut up rough about it, too, so Billy decided that the best thing to do was to cut along and get the cats something to eat. If he got fish he was sure it would be sufficient.

13. Prowling into the pantry, Billy got an outsize haddock and beetled back to his bedroom. This was the stuff to give 'em. The moggies thought so, too—they rushed at Billy, and in two ticks the haddock was no more.

14. The pussies' purring showed that it served the purpose. Packed with best haddock, the cats curled up and went to sleep. Billy had gone to bed with an empty stomach, but the cats didn't care—some of them slept on it !

15. In fact, they slept all over the fat lad. They were here, there, and everywhere, and Billy couldn't get into bed for cats. They didn't half make themselves at home in Bunter's bed-room.

16. Bunter wished that they'd make for their own home, but they wouldn't budge. At last, he managed to shoo them off, then he crept into the sheets to snooze with the cats to keep him company.

17. Morning dawned—and it dawned on Billy that he would have to do something about these moggies. If Quelchy saw them, there was sure to be trouble. Billy thought the best thing to do was to lock them in.

18. After bed, Bunter's first thought was breakfast. In two ticks he was downstairs and sitting at the table. Smacking his lips, he chortled—it was kippers for breakfast that morning.

19. But there were others who thought kippers were good for breakfast—the moggies did, too ! Billy's room was right above the dining-room, and the cats caught a whiff of the fish.

20. That did it. One whiff of kipper and you couldn't keep those cats back. Like streaks of light, they were out of the window and after them—right into the dining-room !

21. Talk about raining cats and dogs ! Those pussies poured in through the open window and made a formation attack on the fish. They made no bones about it—they ate them, too !

22. Of course, Bunter got the blame. Quelchy started quizzing him, but before Billy could say a word, the door burst suddenly open. It was Aunt Tabitha. She had come back a day earlier—and was Bunter glad to see her ?

23. The fat lad didn't care what the cats were doing now. It was up to aunty to see things right, and she left Quelchy with no doubts about how good Billy had been to her homeless moggies.

24. To top it all off, Aunt Tabitha invited everybody to tea at her home. Billy got his five bob, and then tucked into the good things. In fact, he ate so much that he didn't spend a penny on doughnuts until half-an-hour after.

BILLY BUNTER
THE FATTEST SCHOOLBOY ON EARTH!

1. Billy Bunter is the fattest schoolboy on earth—and he's the laziest. T'other evening he was supposed to do a spot of swotting, but did Billy do it? You bet he didn't! That was too much like hard work, so he read a book instead.

2. Billy's favourite books are cookery books—he likes anything that has to do with grub. The next best thing he likes are the advertisements in magazines about food. Billy read them twice over, before he spotted something else.

3. It was an advertisement on how to be popular. Bunter's peepers popped open when he saw it. Since he'd snaffled Bob Cherry's hamper of food he had been very unpopular in the school. Also, popular people were asked to parties.

4. Bunter read the advertisement over again. There were lots of big words, but Billy skipped them. The main idea on how to be popular was to learn to dance. And the cost was ten bob.

5. Billy laughed at that. Fancy paying ten shillings to learn to dance—think of the doughnuts and jam tarts he could get for that! Bunter already had a wheeze how to learn free!

6. Once upon a time, Bunter had been in the library. No, he didn't go there for a book to read—Mr. Quelch, his master, had sent him, and he remembered he'd seen a book on dancing.

7. But that was just like Bunter. The book he got was all about African native dances. But that didn't worry the fat lad. Any dance was all right if it made him popular.

8. Back in his room, Bunter opened the book and got ready for his first lesson. Crash! Clump! Crash! Bunter's dancing was as graceful as a baby elephant with heavy boots on!

9. Now the school had been specially strengthened for air raids—even then, it couldn't stand Bunter chucking his weight about. The floor was the first thing to go!

10. C-R-R-ASH! The floor simply faded away beneath Bunter's beetle crushers. He had put his foot in it with a vengeance—both feet, in fact, for Quelchy's room was below.

11. It was the worst hole that Bunter had ever been in. Not only had he knocked in Quelchy's ceiling, but he gave the master a kick on his dome as well. That meant trouble!

12. Quelchy would have got more than a kick on the cranium, too, if Harry Wharton hadn't heard Bunter's cries for help. Harry called his chums, and they grabbed Bunter and pulled.

13. But down below Quelchy had got busy—he didn't need to see Bunter's face to know who had done the damage. But half of him was no good, so Quelchy gave a pull to get the rest of Bunter down beside him.

14. But that was a bit of a job, for Harry Wharton & Co. were hauling at the other end. Poor old Bunter! He was just like the rope in a tug o' war. Something had to go soon—and it did!

15. Harry Wharton's side won! Suddenly there came a rending crash as another part of the floor was torn apart. This was to make room for Quelchy, for the master was pulled up, too, and there wasn't room for both of them.

16. But there was a w—hole lot more to come. Crash! Bunter bumped safely on to the floor of the room above. But Quelchy didn't stop there—he sailed through the air like the man on the flying trapeze, only he didn't have a trapeze with him on this trip.

17. Bunter blinked as he saw what he had brought with him. Quelchy of all people! He saw the master do a dive into a fire bucket and he beat it. No fire could have made him run faster. The sight of Quelchy in the bucket made him turn quite "pail."

18. Being the fattest schoolboy on earth, it was jolly difficult for Bunter to find a place to hide. The silly ass tried to dodge behind an aspidistra. But it was no good—he had to find another place to plant himself.

19. Ah, there was a wardrobe! Billy barged inside and banged the door. It was a tight fit for Bunter, and Quelchy was having a dozen different kinds of fits by this time. Fuming, Quelchy looked for the fat lad.

20. Suddenly the master's eyes gleamed behind his glasses. He'd spotted the wardrobe doors, and the way they bulged showed that Bunter was behind them. Quelchy grabbed his cane—poor old Bunter was for it again!

21. The next second and the wardrobe doors were open. There was no good of Bunter trying to look like a moth in a coat. Quelchy grabbed him by the listener and yanked him out. Billy was due for another dancing lesson!

22. That cane made him hop! When Quelchy got going, Billy danced harder than he had ever done. He had the African dances beaten to a frazzle, but by the yells, you would have thought that there were savages inside Quelchy's room.

23. The smacking was so hard that Bunter couldn't sit down for a fortnight. Then the first thing he did was to write a letter to the people who wanted to make him popular. What Bunter said, showed that they were unpopular with HIM!

BILLY BUNTER
THE FATTEST SCHOOLBOY ON EARTH!

1. Billy Bunter was feeling blue, but that was nothing unusual. It was impossible for the fat lad to be happy and hungry—and he was always hungry. Worse still, it was Easter, and most of the chaps had gone away for the holiday. There was hardly a soul for Bunter to snitch a snack from to keep his strength up between meals. Mournfully, the fat lad mizzled along Courtfield High Street.

2. He was looking for somebody to stand him a treat, when he suddenly came to a standstill. There was a poster offering five pounds to anybody who would fight Kid Bashem. Billy Bunter would have fought all the Nasties for that!

3. Bunter was thinking what grub he would buy with that five pounds, when a bloke came whizzing through the door. Clump! He caught his chin on the pavement, and pulled up short right at the fat lad's feet.

4. Bunter blinked when he heard what had happened. That chappie hadn't been chucking his weight about. Somebody else had done it! Now, Billy was a bit of a fathead, as well as being fat round the middle.

5. He began to boast about how he could fight. The bloke who'd landed on his listener didn't wait to hear. But somebody else did—the chappie who had done the chucking-out! Billy gulped as the bloke galloped towards him.

6. He was a foul-looking fellow, so Billy did a duck. He didn't want a faceful of fist! Ding! Dong! But it wasn't Bunter's dial that was walloped—it was the fire-alarm!

7. That beefy bloke didn't half dot it one, too! The firemen didn't need the bell—they could have easily heard the smack. But Bunter didn't wait for the charge of the fire brigade, he buzzed as only Bunter can buzz.

8. Meanwhile, the fire brigade had started charging. They charged the beefy bloke five pounds for a false alarm. The beefy one nearly swallowed his false teeth with fury.

9. But Bunter was far from being down in the mouth. He saw the boxing manager and said he was Battling Bunter. Golly, he couldn't even box matches!

10. The manager opened his mouth with surprise, but all the same, he welcomed Bunter with open arms. Why? Because he couldn't get anybody to stand up against Kid Bashem!

11. Before Bunter had the chance to change his mind, he was shoved into a room to change his togs. Then he entered the ring amid ringing cheers.

12. Now, Billy thought there was too much kidding about this Kid Bashem. Nobody could be so tough. Then he blinked when Bashem came bounding into the ring. That bounding bounder was the beefy bloke whom Bunter had seen at the door.

13. The same chappie who'd bust the alarm! Gosh, Bunter never felt so alarmed in all his life. More ringing cheers showed Billy that the crowd were with him, but how he wished he could have been with the crowd—right in the very back row. He tried to sneak off, but in less than a minute his seconds had grabbed him, and shoved him forward. The hour of Bunter's doom was at hand.

14. Billy didn't mind it being at hand—what he didn't like was the look of Kid Bashem's two fists. Billy needed a secret weapon to save him, so he got off his mark and scooted round the ring as fast as he could.

15. Bunter was certainly having a run for his money—but not the way he wanted it. It wasn't any fun playing ring-a-roses with a real tough guy. The referee didn't like it either. He said so, which was just too bad.

16. Boomph! Kid Bashem copped him a beauty on the crust. He was a boxer not a runner, and he wanted to hit something. Bunter not being available, the ref. copped all the clouts that were going.

17. Round and round ran Bunter. He wondered when he could call a halt, when somebody called a copper. He was a copper all right, and he copped something he didn't expect. That was one on the chin that knocked him for six.

18. That naughty Kid Bashem tied him in knots in the ropes. Then he looked round for Bunter, and the fat lad was running round the ring at forty knots an hour. But he just couldn't keep it up for ever.

19. At last Billy had to put the brakes on. He was all in—and there was Kid Bashem all out to give him a hiding. But there was no place where Bunter could hide—so Billy stood ready to do or die.

20. Then suddenly help came. Bunter gasped—he'd heard of it raining pennies from heaven, but here was a shower of coppers. These boys in blue seemed to drop right out of the blue. And they dropped in the right place—all on top of Kid Bashem! The worst of it all was that Bunter was below that big fight.

21. Bunter didn't wait to see the result. He rolled up from underneath and ran for his life. After him came Kid Bashem with a copper still clinging to him—and now our Bunter thinks it safer to spend his Easter in an air-raid shelter!

BILLY BUNTER
THE FATTEST SCHOOLBOY ON EARTH!

HE! HE! HE! THIS'LL TEACH OLD QUELCHY A LESSON!

APRIL 1ST

BLACK INK!

1. It was April First—and believe it or not, but Billy Bunter was first in the class-room. But Billy didn't get in early to do lessons. Oh dear no! He hated school as much as he liked grub —and that's saying something.

NOW, GOSLING, ONE OR TWO BOYS HAVE BEEN LATE FOR SCHOOL LATELY. THEY SAY YOU DON'T RING THE BELL LOUD ENOUGH!

2. Billy had a wheeze on—he meant to play an April Fool joke on Mr. Quelch. Chortling, he scribbled something on a sheet of paper. He would get his own back on Quelchy when he pinned this on the master's back.

WOT I SAYS IS THIS 'ERE—THAT'S FUNNY—THAT IS!

OOH—I SAY!

I'M AN APRILL FOOL A MEEN BEEST A NITWITT

3. Billy got his chance when Quelchy stopped to talk to Gosling, the porter. Suddenly Bunter's hand shot out—faster than if he'd been reaching for a cake—and there was the paper pinned to Quelchy's back!

HA HA! HO HO! I WONDER WHAT CAN BE AMUSING THE BOYS SO MUCH THIS MORNING?

I'M AN APRILL FOOL A MEEN BEEST A NITWITT

4. Gosling gurgled with mirth as the master walked off. Tommy Twinkle twittered a bit, but didn't dare laugh. The rest of the boys did —they simply roared as they read what Bunter had written.

TELL ME, TWINKLE - WHAT IS MAKING THE BOYS LAUGH SO MUCH THIS MORNING?

PLEASE, SIR - IT SAYS YOU ARE A MEAN BEAST AND A NITWIT!

I'M AN APRILL FOOL A MEEN BEEST A NITWITT

5. Not knowing how comical he looked, Quelchy cantered off to the class-room. The roars of laughter grew louder, and Quelchy grew suspicious. There was Twinkle again, so the master asked him all about it.

HOW DARE YOU, BOY— WHAT DO YOU MEAN BY CALLING ME NAMES!

NUNNO, SIR - IT'S ON YOUR BACK, SIR!

6. Now Twinkle was a bit of a twerp. He twittered worse than ever and landed into trouble. At last he managed to babble that there was a paper on Quelchy's back. The master was quite taken aback with that.

GOOD GRACIOUS! WELL - I KNOW WHO WROTE THIS! THERE IS ONLY ONE BOY IN THE SCHOOL WHO SPELLS SO BADLY!

I'M AN APRILL FOOL A MEEN BEEST & A NITWITT!

7. But when he read what was on it—" I'M AN APRILL FOOL. A MEEN BEEST & A NITWITT "—Quelchy blinked unbelievingly. Then knew who had done it—BUNTER!

TWINKLE, TELL BUNTER I WISH TO SEE HIM IN MY STUDY— AT ONCE!

YESSIR!

8. Besides being the fattest schoolboy on earth, Billy was the world's worst speller. There was no doubt that this was Bunter's work—his spelling spelt trouble for him now.

BILLY— MR QUELCH WANTS YOU AT ONCE— IN HIS STUDY!

W-WANTS ME? OH LOR I WONDER HOW HE FOUND OUT I DID IT? I'M OFF!

9. Quelchy told Twinkle to fetch Bunter. Tommy toddled straight to the tuck-shop, where the fat lad was sure to be found. There he was, feeding his fat face at full speed.

OH CRUMBS! OH CRIKEY! I'LL HAVE TO HIDE MYSELF!

10. Billy groaned as he got Quelchy's message. He would get it in the neck, now! He was so scared that he left half a doughnut and scooted off as fast as he could.

GASP! I KNOW WHERE I'LL HIDE—HE'LL NEVER FIND ME HERE!

SCHOOL BELFRY

11. There was only one way to dodge a hiding from Quelchy—and that was to find a safe hiding place. As Billy bounded along, he spotted the school belfry, and in he bolted.

HE! HE! QUELCHY WILL HAVE FORGOTTEN ALL ABOUT IT BY TEA-TIME. IT TAKES BRAINS TO THINK OF A WHEEZE LIKE THIS!

CRACK!

12. A belfry is the tower where the bells hang. Billy didn't give a hang about that as long as he could hide there. He went for a tour round the top of the tower to see what he could see.

13. Billy beamed as he climbed the beams—Quelchy would never find him up here. But these beams were made of wood—they wouldn't bear the weight of a boy as heavy as a baby elephant. Suddenly there came a loud crack!

14. The beam Bunter was on had given way! Bunter gave one loud yell and dived for the bell-clapper to save himself. Down below Quelchy was waiting. He felt like wringing Bunter's neck when the bell began ringing.

15. There was something wrong with it. The ding-donging didn't sound so good to-day. Quelchy flapped his listeners again—then he forgot all about Bunter. The bell had to be seen about first.

16. Along to the belfry beetled Quelchy. Gosling had gone red in the face. In fact, he felt blue what with pulling the ropes and getting the wrong notes from the bell. He told Quelchy that, too!

17. But the master thought that Gosling was pulling his leg when he said he was pulling the rope as hard as he could. He decided to take a hand in the job himself, and grabbed the rope of the bell.

18 Harry Wharton and his chums had gathered that something was wrong. They gathered around to see what their master was up to. Next thing was that they, too, were roped-in to do some rope-pulling.

19. Meanwhile, up above Billy Bunter had caught the clapper of the bell. It wasn't too bad until Quelchy and the boys began pulling. That's when the trouble started.

20. To and fro and back again swung Billy. This was worse than a life on the ocean wave, and Billy hadn't a notion how to get out of it. He was seasick in less than two seconds.

21. By this time Quelchy had forgiven Gosling. The porter certainly needed support if he were to get more than a muffled dong out of that bell. He called on the boys to give a big heave.

22. Quelchy nearly bust his brace-buttons with the beef he put into it. Harry Wharton and his chums heaved as they'd never done before. Old Gosling had bellows to mend trying to make that bell ring, too.

23. Something had to happen—and it did! Suddenly there came a loud crack, and the ceiling of the belfry went bust! The rope of the bell had broken, and down came Bunter with a bellow of fear—and the bell!

24. Quelchy didn't have to put two and two together to find the cause of all the trouble. One look at Bunter under the bell was enough. Now Billy's had his fill of April Fool jokes, 'cos he won't be able to sit down for a full week, now!

BILLY BUNTER
THE FATTEST SCHOOLBOY ON EARTH!

1. Corks, chums, something serious happened at Courtfield Theatre, t'other evening. Romeo Razzberry roamed into Daisy Dewdrop's dressing-room and snitched her string of best Sunday sparklers when she was out.

2. Romeo was light-fingered, but was he handsome? He was—and then some! He was the minstrel of the show, but he liked jewels better than jews-harps.

3. By a bit of fiddling, Romeo managed to ram the sparklers in his fiddle, and off he went to do his stuff in the show. Up in a box, Billy Bunter watched the stage. He was at the stage when he needed a snack, when the manager told about the missing jewels.

4. Now, you'll all be wondering how Bunter managed to get a box, when he's always broke. Well, Bob Cherry happened to leave his ticket on the table, so Billy just "borrowed" it for the one evening.

5. Of course, Billy would've preferred a free feed to a free show, but he was far from feeling fed-up as he watched the play. There was Romeo Razzberry tootling and twanging, and Bunter blinked when he got a bag of gold.

6. Gosh, Billy would have liked to have been a minstrel, he would. He wouldn't mind bags of gold being bunged at him, he thought, as he barged off to the cloak-room. Think of the doughnuts he could buy!

7. But Bunter's dreams of doughnuts were suddenly dashed. Romeo Razzberry came romping round a corner and dashed into the fat lad. He was off to collect the jewels.

8. But he collected more than he bargained for in that collision. Bunter didn't even budge —his twenty stones take some shifting, and Romeo bounced off like a rocket.

9. Crash! There was a sound of wood meeting wood as Romeo's cokernut hit a table. Then over came a vase and bonked the bad lad. Billy didn't wait. He grabbed a ticket.

10. But Romeo had dropped his cloak-room ticket in the collision, too. Billy didn't notice that—he was in too great a hurry to get out. He handed in the one he'd picked up.

11. But you can trust Billy to get things all muxed-up—I mean, mixed-up... He'd picked up Romeo Razzberry's ticket. To cap everything, he got Romeo's hat and fiddle instead of his cap.

12. Billy blinked—this was a bit of luck. The bag looked like the bag of gold the minstrel had got. Putting on the hat, Bunter looked like a covered wagon as he rolled along.

13. Billy Bunter didn't go straight back to school—not likely, when he had been handed a free bag of gold. Into the woods he went to count it up, but the fat lad found something he hadn't counted on.

14. There was no gold in that bag! Billy felt a fool when he saw that fiddle—but he wouldn't if he'd known what was inside, would he, chums? Then Bunter had a brainwave—he'd be a wandering minstrel.

15. Billy didn't expect bags of gold to be chucked at him for a start. Perhaps they would come later when he'd had some practice. He couldn't even play yet, but a little thing like that didn't bother Billy.

16. Chortling, the fat lad cantered off to Mrs. Mimble's tuck-shop. Perhaps he would get some doughnuts and lemonade for his serenade, so he began to warble under the window like the wandering minstrel in the show

17. Billy Bunter was a wandering minstrel, all right. His voice wandered all over the scale, but the tune from the fiddle was lost at the start and had to find its own way. Still, Billy didn't worry.

18. But Mrs. Mimble did. She muttered something about her cat cutting up rough again; and decided to do something about it. Certainly Billy's playing was like a pussy having its tail pulled.

19. Bunter didn't hear the window being opened. The squeaks it made sounded like a few extra notes that had sneaked in from somewhere. But all the more the merrier, thought Bunter, and carried on until—CRASH !

20. Mrs. Mimble had accidentally knocked over the aspidistra that had been on the sill for an airing. It copped Bunter right on the cokernut and cut his second chorus short. This was the re-verse of what he'd expected,

21. SWOOSH ! Before Bunter could get to his feet, down came a shower of wet stuff. It was meant to catch the cat, but it caught Billy instead. It wasn't half a wash-out for the wandering minstrel now !

22. By the time Billy came round, Mrs. Mimble had closed her window again, thinking she had made the cat shut up. But Bunter's eyes opened wide as he saw what was lying on the ground beside his broken fiddle.

23. It was a string of sparklers ! Bunter didn't bother to work out how they'd got there. But he had a good idea that they were Daisy Dewdrop's jewels that had been stolen at the theatre. He had the right idea for once.

24. Along to the police-station, Billy beetled, and in came Romeo Razzberry, wrapped up in bandages. Billy told the cops who he was, and was handed a fat reward. He'd got something for his singing after all !

BILLY BUNTER
THE FATTEST SCHOOLBOY ON EARTH!

1. Billy Bunter is the fattest schoolboy on earth. He can eat six boys' dinners, and simply call them a sample. He is always looking round for grub, and is so fat he looks round, too.

2. T'other day, Mr. Quelch, the master, was giving his class arithmetic—that is some sums. But Billy hated the sight of an exercise book, and longed to exercise his jaws.

3. There was a happy look on the fat lad's dial as he counted off the seconds on the clock. It wouldn't be long now! Quelchy thought there was something too quiet about Bunter.

4. The master was booked for a shock. He blinked when he opened the book, and saw what Bunter had done. Billy had added his sums—and then some! The totals were totally daft.

5. Billy Bunter groaned—now he was for it! But Quelchy gave the worst punishment that Bunter could get. He sent Billy off with a message that would make him late for dinner.

6. Off went the fat lad at full speed. This was a tragedy; not half it was! All the other greedy beasts would get the pick of the grub. Billy bounced along like an energetic elephant.

7. Meanwhile, chums, meets the kids of Courtfield Infants' School. Of course, that chappie with the bald head isn't in the class. He's Mr. Ferdinand Fizzogg, the headmaster.

8. Old Fizzogg was telling his tots that a new teacher was coming, when Bunter tottered into his school. The Head gave a gurgle of joy and came full steam ahead to meet him.

9. The fat lad nearly faded away when he was called Mr. Thinn. Bunter had been called lots of names, but this beat the band. Old Fizzogg thought he was the new teacher.

10. Being mistaken for Mr. Thinn was a bit too thick. But there was nothing he could do about it. Fizzogg fairly rushed into the room and told the tots that Billy was their new master.

11. Before Bunter could get his breath back, the headmaster was heading for the door. Billy was about to beat it—who wanted to teach a bunch of kids, anyway?—when he stopped.

12. Ah, this was something worth looking into. Bunter's peepers had spotted parcels on the desks. His first thought, as usual, was grub! He was right—they were the little lads' lunches.

13. Bunter couldn't teach these boys for toffee. But there was nothing he could be taught about getting free feeds. In a flash, Billy had a scheme—he sent the tots out to play.

14. And while they were playing, Bunter played them a dirty trick. Chortling, he collected the parcels. There were twenty-five of them altogether and they were all full of food.

15. Munch! Crunch! In two ticks, Billy was feeding his fat face at full speed. There was enough grub in the twenty-five parcels to keep his strength up until he got back to school.

16. Tarts and cakes were greedily gobbled by the fat lad. He ate an apple right down to the core and encored it with a brace of bananas. Billy felt a bit better after all that.

17. Now was the time, he thought, to find Fizzogg and give him the letter Quelchy had sent him with. But before Bunter could beetle off, in came the little boys from the playground.

18. They were jolly hungry after their games, but they were jolly angry when they saw the dirty game that Bunter had played on them. But big as he was, Billy wasn't getting off with it.

19. Instead, all the little lads got on to him. Some jumped on his back, and beat him with their fists. Others took the feet from the fat lad and tumbled him over a desk. It was when they got the fat lad bending, that he copped it most.

20. One lad larruped Bunter with a cane. Another made him roar with smacks from a ruler. Another bonked him good and hard with the blackboard until Bunter felt black-and-blue all over. Then in came Fizzogg.

21. In a flash, the tots shot back to their seats. Bunter was too dazed to do anything but to sit on the floor and groan. These lads had certainly taught their greedy teacher a lesson that he wouldn't forget.

22. Of course, old Fizzogg wanted to know what all the fuss was about. But the fust thing Billy did was to say that he wasn't Mr. Thinn, then he showed the headmaster the letter that Quelchy had sent.

23. When Fizzogg saw that Bunter wasn't Mr. Thinn, the fat was in the fire. Billy caught it hot again. There he was shoved in amongst all the kids—but what hurt him most was that there was no dinner for him that day!

135

BILLY BUNTER
THE FATTEST SCHOOLBOY ON EARTH!

HERE YOU ARE, MY BRAVE BOY—HERE IS FIVE POUNDS FOR STOPPING THAT RUNAWAY HORSE!

RAH!

THANKS, YOUR HONOUR!

COO! WHAT A LUCKY CHAP!

OOH! I WISH I COULD DO SOMETHING BRAVE—THEN SOMEBODY MIGHT GIVE ME FIVE POUNDS!

CRUMBS! WHAT AN IDEA! I'LL PUSH THAT CHAP IN THE RIVER—AND THEN SAVE HIM!

1. Billy Bunter is so fat that, when he strolls down the street, folks sing : " Roll out the barrel !" And you can always be sure of a barrel of fun when the fat lad is around. But for once nobody gave him a second glance. They were all too busy watching a hero being handed five pounds reward for saving somebody from a runaway horse.

2. That made Bunter blink—then it made him think. He was so stony he couldn't even buy a rock bun. Five pounds' worth of food would make a nice little snack for him !

THERE! THATS THE FIRST PART DONE!

HELP!

DON'T BE AFRAID, MY MAN—I WILL SAVE YOU!

GUGGLE! GASP! GUG!

CATCH HOLD OF MY HAND. I WILL PULL YOU OUT—'COS I'M BRAVE!

GLUP!

3. Suddenly Bunter gasped—he had a brilliant brainwave ! There was a chappie standing on the river bank staring at the wet stuff. Chortling, Billy went cantering forward and gave the chappie a hefty push.

4. SPLASH ! Into the wet stuff he went. In a flash the fat lad had whipped off his blazer. Now he would rescue the chappie he had pushed in—and get the reward of five pounds for doing it. Billy was licking his lips already !

5. Billy beamed as he bent over the edge of the river bank. This was money for jam—jam tarts and dozens of doughnuts, too ! The other fellow couldn't speak 'cos his false teeth were full of wetness.

THERE YOU ARE - I'VE SAVED YOUR LIFE! CAN I HAVE MY FIVE POUNDS NOW?

YOU NITWIT! I WAS JUST GOING IN FOR A SWIM—TAKE THAT FOR PUSHING ME IN!

YAH! THE MEAN BEAST! HE DIDN'T EVEN GIVE ME A KIND LOOK!

6. So far not so dusty, thought the fat lad as he hauled away. The other chappie was making funny sort of gargling noises, but Bunter didn't care as long as he got five pounds.

7. But Bunter's rescue from the wet stuff was a wash-out. Instead of getting a reward he got a hefty kick. The chappie he'd pushed in had meant to go in for a swim anyway !

8. Poor old Bunter was sunk ! His dreams of the five pounds faded as he footed it for safety. Worse still, all that exercise had made him hungrier than ever. What could he do ?

SCREAM!

OW! HELP!

CORKS! WHASSAT! I WONDER WHATS UP NOW?

HI! YOU! SAVE ME—THE LADDER IS SLIPPING!

OOOH! YES, SIR!

THAT'S RIGHT, BOY—HOLD IT STEADY!

HAVE NO FEAR, SIR! I'M BRAVE AND STRONG!

WET PAINT

9. Billy didn't wonder for long. He was wandering along by a fence when he pulled up short. Loud cries for help came from around the corner. It seemed like Bunter's big chance !

10. There was a paint slapper-onner, whose ladder had slipped. Coo, that painter wasn't half in a tiz-woz until the fat lad bowled forward to the rescue.

11. In a brace of shakes Billy braced himself against the fence and held the ladder firmly. Nothing short of an earthquake could shift that ladder with Billy's weight behind it !

12. Now, some folks say that it's unlucky to walk under a ladder. It certainly was for Billy Bunter! The painter reached the ground safely, but instead of giving Billy five pounds he gave him a nod and walked off.

13. But that was only the beginning of Bunter's bad luck. He tried to follow the painter to say he would take five bob instead, but he couldn't budge. The paint on the fence was wet—and Bunter was stuck.

14. All that paint on his coat didn't half make him feel blue. There was only one thing to do—leave the coat sticking to the fence. But Billy knew it would be a black look-out for him when he reached school without it.

15. Billy was thinking what Mr. Quelch, his master, would do to him, when he suddenly brightened. Thinking of the master had given him another brilliant brainwave.

16. Old Quelchy was simply rolling with money! The mean beast could easily afford five pounds to be saved. Chortling, Billy got some wood and some bricks and clambered on to the roof of the school. He'd managed to " borrow " Bob Cherry's blazer, but took it off again.

17. Billy was laughing like anything now. He laid the boards and the bricks over the top of Quelchy's chimney. The smoke wouldn't get out now. It would blow back into the room. The master would think his room was on fire.

18. At least, that's what Bunter thought he would think, if you know what I mean. He slipped down a rope to rescue the master from the window, but Bunter had made his biggest slip yet. Quelchy knew what had happened.

19. So instead of being fooled, he was full of wrath. He reached the window gasping for breath—and Bunter gasped when he saw that the master had seen through his wheeze. He would catch it hot for that smoke now.

20. Billy was at his wits' end—but he was too far from the rope's end to escape. Roaring with rage, the master grabbed the rope and pulled Bunter in through the window. The fat lad couldn't save himself now!

21. Holy smoke! What a mess that smoke had made to Quelchy's room! There was soot all over the place, which didn't suit the master at all. The look-out was blacker than ever for Bunter, and Quelchy made him get busy cleaning the room up. Worse still, the fat lad won't be able to buy doughnuts for months, because all his pocket money is going to pay for the damage. So, instead of having a five-pound feed, Billy is absolutely fed-up !

BILLY BUNTER
THE FATTEST SCHOOLBOY ON EARTH!

1. Billy Bunter got a big shock, t'other day. Mr. Quelch called the boys together and took them for a ten-mile walk to get an appetite for dinner. Ten miles! Gosh, Billy was almost starving hungry after waddling ten yards.

2. The fat lad is never happy when he's hiking. Soon his corns began to complain. He couldn't even get a berry off a bush to eat. So he gave old Quelchy the razzberry, and sat down to take a load off his poor feet.

3. As Billy sat there, he sniffed the fresh whiffs of the countryside. Suddenly, he shot to his feet—he'd sniffed the smell of something to eat. There on a stile was a yokel having his dinner in style with a monster pie.

4. The moment Bunter spied that pie, he meant to have it. It was a shame that such a lovely pie should be wasted on a farmer's boy when Billy was simply starving.

5. For the next five minutes, the fat lad exercised his jaws at top speed, and talked the farmer's boy into swopping places with him. Of course he had to get the pie thrown in as well.

6. After that it was all change. The farmer's boy put on Bunter's togs and had room to spare. The others were so tight that Bunter could have done with a shoe-horn to get them on.

7. But Billy meant them to be tighter still—when he got that pie tucked into his tummy. Smacking his lips, he squatted down to dig into the pie. This was the life!

8. But was it? Not when Farmer Giles came galloping on the scene! By George, Billy didn't care where Garge was now. He wanted to get on with eating that pie.

9. But Billy didn't even get one bite out of it. Before he could feed his own fat face, he was sent to feed the farmer's pigs. Only the thought of more pies made him do it.

10. Soon Bunter was amongst the pigs. In case you don't know the difference, chums, that's him dressed as a farmer's boy. The porkers weren't half glad to see him, too.

11. They were making a terrible din because their din-din was late. But Bunter made them wait. Farmer Giles had said that he had to stir the grub well, before serving.

12. So Bunter stirred and stirred, but there was an even more stirring time ahead for him. The porkers couldn't wait for their food—they came to get it for themselves.

13. CRASH ! It so happened that the pen wasn't too strong. A couple of pushes from the porkers and their pen burst wide open. Woomph ! Before Bunter could blink, the pigs bowled him over as they charged out.

14. In the meantime, while Farmer Giles was calling Bunter everything, Quelchy had called the rest of the boys to a halt. They rested and waited for the fat lad to arrive, but there was no sign of Bunter.

15. Quelchy was about to start back for school when one of the boys gave a sudden start. " Lul-look, sir ! " he gasped. Billy Bunter was arriving at last—bouncing about on the backs of a bunch of runaway pigs.

16. Quelchy took one look then took to his heels. The boys weren't far behind and they all streaked for the school as fast as they could. But the piggies seemed to have a fancy for the fat lad's schoolmates. They came galloping along. Into Courtfield High Street they charged, and you never saw such a to-do in all your life. It was the charge of the heavy brigade, and what a tiz-waz they made.

17. They cleared the street in no time. Air-raid shelters, lamp-posts, and other places of safety were speedily filled. But the porkers weren't finished yet. They came charging on to school where Garge was waiting.

18. Gosh, Garge wasn't half glad to see his piggy pets again. But Quelchy wasn't so pleased to see Bunter perched on the back of a porker. The pigs had landed Billy in trouble—how could he save his bacon ?

19. Billy tried to gargle out an excuse, but it was no good. Quelchy packed Garge and his porkers back to the farm, and took a firm hold on Billy. The fat was in the fire for the fat lad again.

20. Not only was the master annoyed. The boys were wild with Bunter, too, for their clothes were all dirty and had caught a strong whiff of pigs. It was no posh perfume either.

21. In fact, the scent of the pigs nearly sent them crazy. There was only one cure—the clothes had to be well washed. There was only one person who deserved doing it—Billy Bunter. Ruba-dub-dub, the fat lad scrubbed away like three men at that tub. He can still eat after it though—everything except bacon !

BILLY BUNTER
THE FATTEST SCHOOLBOY ON EARTH!

1. Billy Bunter likes one meal each day—starting from when he awakens in the morning until he goes to bed at night. Of course, he can't get that, so he's always thinking up wheezes to get grub.

2. Billy thought he saw a good chance t'other day in Courtfield High Street. There was a johnny selling hair restorer and making plenty of money at it, too. It gave Billy a brainwave. He would make some himself. Though it looked like being a hair-raising experience, the fat lad didn't care as long as he raised the money.

3. Chortling, Billy rolled off to the school chemistry-room. He hadn't the foggiest notion how to make stuff to make hair grow. But that didn't worry Bunter—for grub he'd try anything once.

4. Billy got a big bowl, and then collected all the bottles he could. Into the bowl he poured their contents, and was nearly bowled over by the awful whiff. The mixture looked gruesome, but as long as it grew some hair, it was O.K.

5. The whiff was so strong that the fat lad could've leaned against it. At last, it was ready. Billy poured the stuff back into the empty bottles without wasting time to get his gas-mask. Now he had to get a case.

6. Along the corridor Billy rolled until he reached Mr. Quelch's room. There was a case to carry his bottles. Bunter "borrowed" it—and the master's cap and gown, too.

7. Now when Bunter gets a brainwave, he never stops to think what might happen. He just goes bald-headed at it. Soon, he had collected a bunch of bald-headed old jossers.

8. A bob a bottle was all that Bunter asked for his hair-grower. It certainly made the crowd grow bigger, and Billy had a busy time. Soon he was sold out, so off he went.

9. But one old josser spotted the name on the case. He hurried home to try Bunter's hair-grower, but when the horrid, sticky stuff squelched on his head he remembered "Quelch."

10. All the other gents had given the stuff a trial, too. Gosh, what a mess it made. The stuff from Bunter's bottles stuck to their heads. They didn't bottle up their wrath.

11. Meanwhile, Billy had taken to his heels with his takings. He'd made twenty-five bob so he made for the tuckshop as fast as he could. Gosh what a feed he'd have now !

12. But Bunter's dream of dozens of dough-nuts, suddenly fizzled out. Behind him, he heard shouts of wrath, and then saw a herd of bald-headed gents coming charging after him. Billy didn't wait—he began to run.

13. Faster and faster went the fat lad. He had seen that the gents were the ones he'd swizzled with his hair-grower. Billy didn't let any grass grow under his feet as he bolted along the lane.

14. The thought that he might have to give the twenty-five bob back, nearly broke Bunter's heart. So he broke all land speed records as he sprinted for safety—and landed into still more trouble.

15. Mr. Quelch was out taking the air. Billy was taking a corner at full speed and didn't see him. CRASH! Billy barged right into the master, and sent him bowling over with a smack on the schnozzle.

16. That bonk from the case nearly made a hospital case out of Quelchy. He fell flat to the ground, absolutely flabbergasted that it was Bunter. But Billy didn't wait. He dropped the case and scooted.

17. In fact, Billy was gone like the wind before the master got his wind back. Quelchy was quite surprised at getting his own case back. But he got a shock when he saw the gents wanting their own back.

18. He knew that Bunter had stirred up some trouble or other—and Billy had when he'd stirred up that mixture. Now, they both looked the same in caps and gowns, so it looked like trouble for Quelchy.

19. So Quelchy scooted, too. The master was fresh, and he soon caught up with the fat lad. He called on Bunter to stop, but Billy didn't put his brakes on. Then Quelchy tripped and his case came curling through the air.

20. WHAM! Billy caught that case right in the neck! It rattled his back teeth and then bowled him over. In two ticks, Quelchy and the bald-headed gents had caught the fat lad. Poor old Bunter was for it again!

21. The gents said it was bare-faced robbery for Bunter to sell them that hair-grower. But they grew quieter when Quelchy made Bunter hand their boblets back to them.

22. But the trouble wasn't over yet. That sticky stuff was still all over the gents' bald heads, but Quelchy wasn't stuck for a way to get it off. He made Bunter scrub them all clean again before dinner. Now, Bunter is hungry and what's worse, he's fed up because five bob is to be taken out of his pocket money to buy turpentine!

BILLY BUNTER
THE FATTEST SCHOOLBOY ON EARTH!

1. Billy Bunter is the world's fattest schoolboy—he's in a class by himself when it comes to eating. He gets four square meals a day, but doesn't call that a square deal. He needs a great deal more, so when the fat lad isn't filling himself with food, he fills in the time working out wheezes to make money to buy it. T'other day Billy saw a parachute jumper, and his think-box began to tick over at umpteen-to-the-dozen!

2. That parachute jumper was making loads and loads of money. Billy worked it out in doughnuts and jam tarts, and it looked like easy feeding for him. It was a wonder wheeze, so back to school he waddled.

3. Billy felt in the pink as he got a pot of paint and began painting posters. All the bills were about Billy being a brave and daring parachute jumper. Bunter splashed-out in real style with that paint and brush.

4. The fat lad meant to stick at nothing to make his wheeze a winner. He stuck the bills all over Courtfield village. The peepers of the passers-by popped open when they saw that Bunter was to jump from the school tower.

5. The next part of the programme was to get a parachute. Billy thought : "Parachute— ah, pair o' sheets !" Off he bunked to get one from his bed, but Bunter beamed when he saw a pile of brand new ones just asking to be taken.

6. It didn't take Billy long to "borrow" one of the sheets. Then he scooted to his room and fixed pieces of cord to the corners of it.

7. The school playground was packed with people. They'd all come to see Bunter do his parachute jump, and they cheered when they saw that he wasn't letting them down. Billy beamed as he came bowling along.

8. Bump, bump, bumpity-bump ! Bunter bounced up the steps of the tower like a baby elephant. He was just in time to miss Mr. Quelch, who was asking awkward questions.

9. Billy's parachute jump meant doing a bit of overtime—jumping over the clock. But he shuddered as he saw the ground so far below. It wasn't half a nasty drop of drop !

10. The thought of the money he would make made the fat lad go on. Fixing on his parachute, he stepped on to the parapet. Billy didn't like the view any better from there.

11. The fat lad was about to change his mind and tell the people to keep their change, when Quelchy suddenly appeared. The shock was too much for Billy Bunter—he slipped !

12. He took a purler off that parapet. Quelchy quickly grabbed at the fat lad, but couldn't hold him. Gosh, Bunter didn't half get that sinking feeling! He toppled from the tower and shot into a lot of nothingness.

13. Going down—going down! Bunter and Quelchy looked a priceless pair of twerps on that parachute. The crowd on the ground gurgled and gasped. They wondered how high Bunter would bounce after hitting the ground.

14. Poor old Billy wasn't half in a state! His wheeze wasn't so ripping now. Suddenly there was a ripping sound from behind, and Billy saw that the parachute had caught on one of the hands of the school clock.

15. It was the first time the fat lad had had anything on "tick," and didn't like it. The school clock was an alarm clock now, for it was certainly alarming to be hung up there with the ground so far below.

16. Bunter remembered that Quelchy called the ground terra-firma. He must have meant that the more firmer the less terror. Luckily, one of the other masters had sent for the local fire brigade to rescue them.

17. The local brigade were a bright lot of lads. They were boys of the old brigade, and the captain was as deaf as a door-post. He looked as if he had helped to put out the Great Fire of London.

18. It would have been quicker and safer to have sent him a postcard. He got all the instructions muxed up—I mean mixed up, but he was determined to do or do.

19. The brigade hadn't had a fire for years. This was just the chance they needed to try out the hose they had bought at last summer's jumble sale. The captain called his men.

20. Meanwhile, time wasn't hanging heavily on Bunter's hands. It was t'other way about—Billy and Quelchy were hanging heavily on the hand of the clock until—SWOOSH!

21. From the very start Bunter's wheeze had been a wash-out. Now it was worse than ever. The bold boys of the fire brigade had a go with their hose, and Bunter and Quelchy got the whole lot of the wet stuff!

22. By this time the master on the ground had got his breath back. He ground his teeth with rage as he roared at the fire chief. Then he told him to get Bunter and Quelchy off the hand of the clock.

23. This was speedily did, but it wasn't a happy landing for Billy Bunter. Both he and Quelchy had caught a cold with their wetting, and Billy is going to catch it hot when the master gets his strength back!

BILLY BUNTER

THE FATTEST SCHOOLBOY ON EARTH!

1. B stands for Billy and for Bunter. When Billy Bunter isn't feeding his fat face, he stands around wondering where his next feed is coming from. T'other day at ten minutes past dinner-time, the fat lad was simply famishing. He was passing Courtfield Reporters' Club, and he nearly passed out when he heard them talking about the grand feed they'd just had.

2. The mere mention of food was enough to make Billy think overtime. He would be a reporter! He fairly galloped to the "Gazette" to get a job—and as many free feeds as poss!

3. Billy beamed as he bounced into the office. Two ticks later and his fat face was like a full moon coming over a mountain. The editor was actually excited at seeing him. He gave Billy a job on the spot.

4. Billy was bunged off to get the life story of a bloke named William Bates. But as well as being fat round the middle, Bunter was a big fathead, too. There was a catch in it—you don't get reporters' jobs so easy!

5. But Bunter didn't give the matter a second think. Not even when he saw that the address was an all-in wrestling club, for he was all out for his feed. Billy wouldn't have minded wrestling with a nice, juicy steak!

6. But from the club came sounds of clouts. Biff! Bang! Wallop! These were followed by groans and gargles of pain. Then out of the door shot a shower of reporters.

7. By the look of them, they had been more than reporting. They'd been in a scrap, but that didn't make a scrap of difference to Billy. He bowled past them and asked for Mister Bates.

8. That was asking for trouble. Bill Bates was the bloke who'd done all the bashing about. Bunter's dream of a steak looked like being the biggest mistake of his life.

9. Bill Bates was pleased to see Bunter. He slapped him friendly like on the back and nearly knocked him through the floor. Then he took Billy along to his pulverising parlour.

10. Billy groaned as the beefy bloke began to tell his life story. It looked like being a dog's life for the fat lad now. He'd a feeling that he'd been sold a pup somehow.

11. Billy had an' all. The reason he'd got the job as a reporter was because Bates had been so rough with all the others. Billy was just beginning to find that out!

12. In a flash Bates grabbed the fat lad by the flipper. Billy expected a gripping story, but he didn't like to be gripped like that—it hurt to much! This Bates was a tough baby—and no kid about it!

13. Bates was a man of few words. There was no beating about the bush with him—he began beating Billy Bunter to let him see how he'd done his stuff. Billy didn't like it one little bit.

14. The fat lad was a mere feather in the hands of the bruiser. Billy's twenty stones seemed like twenty pebbles when Bates began chucking him about. Oopsadaisy, and over went the world's fattest schoolboy as easy as that.

15. BOOMPH! Instead of striking lucky, Bunter struck the floor with a thump that shook the building. But there were no full stops in Bill Bates' life story, even though Bunter was in a state of comma.

16. The bruiser was just getting into his swing. He swung Billy over and grabbed him by the tootsies. It didn't need this to make the fat lad realise that he had put his foot in it good and proper this time!

17. But matters were coming to a head. Bill Bates swung Bunter up above his head to show him his grand slam. Billy wasn't watching—all that he could see now were stars and stars and stars.

18. Then, suddenly, Bates got his share of the stars, too. He was starting to chuck Billy down when the fat lad slipped. Bonk! Bunter bonked Bates and down they both went!

19. Meanwhile, there had been a rally round of all the reporters. They were determined to get Bill Bates' life story, even though it meant risking their own lives to get it. Egged on by the excited editor, they arrived at the wrestling club. To their utter surprise they couldn't hear a single howl being uttered.

20. From inside they'd expected to hear hollow groans, but they were disappointed. The only thing that was hollow was Billy Bunter, who was still dying for something to eat. Then the editor hollered to his men and in they went.

21. Two steps they took, and then they all stopped. They expected to see bits and pieces of the fat lad scattered here and there. But there was Bunter perched on the tough guy's tummy and writing away.

22. To make a short story shorter, Billy had landed right on the top of Mister Bates. Being no featherweight, his twenty stones had rocked the bruiser to his foundations. So Billy got his story—and money for a feed as well!

BILLY BUNTER
THE FATTEST SCHOOLBOY ON EARTH!

1. Billy Bunter had been a bad boy. He'd been sent to bed without any supper, but he suffered so much from night starvation that he couldn't stay there. So, after "lights-out," he lit out on the hunt to ease his hunger.

2. Billy didn't need a torch to guide him through the black-out. He knew the way to the pantry by heart and soon was heartily tucking-in. Nobody can hold a candle to the fat lad when it comes to putting grub away.

3. But when Quelchy came along and held up a candle, there was trouble. The master was amazed that one boy could have eaten so much. Holy smoke, chums, but Billy's "snack" was the whole school's rations for a whole week!

4. Back to bed the fat lad was lugged by one listener. But he could hear well enough with the other—and Quelchy certainly said something! He knew a new way to punish Bunter for pinching grub from the pantry.

5. For the second time that night, Billy Bunter couldn't sleep. First, because he'd been hungry—second, because he was fed up. Believe it or not, but Billy was actually getting a postal-order, and he didn't want to miss it.

6. Things were so bad that Billy actually hurried through his breakfast, the following morning. Then he followed Quelchy from school and saw him post a letter. It was to Billy's dad telling him what had happened.

7. Billy had to get that letter somehow. If it reached his dad, Billy could say tootle-pip to his postal-order. Billy glared at the pillar-box—it was enough to make anybody see red!

8. Billy had once read how Sexton Blake had picked a lock with a nail. It was a wheeze worth trying! Bunter beamed as he trotted along to the post-box with a nifty-looking nail. Picking that lock would be a picnic.

9. But Billy couldn't pick daisies without making a mess of it. The fat lad fiddled and fumbled with the nail, but it was no good. He just couldn't pick that lock and get the letter back.

10. Billy was about to give up, when he saw that the road was up. There would be something there to bust the box with. So Billy tooled over and took some tools.

11. Puff! Grunt! Gasp! Billy had a go with a pick, but his blows were just pecks to that pillar-box. A crowbar just crumpled up like a candy-bar, but Bunter wasn't beaten.

12. Billy likes doing things in a big way. He meant to bust that letter-box, and there was only one way he could do it, now. Chortling, the fat lad scrambled on board the steam-roller.

146

13. By a bit o' luck, Billy pulled the right lever. Clatter-bang! Bumpity-bump! The steam-roller started moving—so did the people in the street. They screamed and scrammed when they saw who was steering.

14. The fat lad let the steam-roller go full speed ahead. Billy looked like a young steam-roller himself, and that pillar-box looked like having a tough time with the pair of them. The more the steam-roller chuffed, the more Bunter puffed. Then—Thud! Bump! Bunter let the letter-box have it. As it bumped, Billy blinked, then he shut his eyes tight. It was a case of weight and see, now!

15. Crash! Bang! Wallop! You never heard such a noise in all your life. The steam-roller bonked the box, then it bounced back! Billy opened his eyes and goggled—after all his work, the letter-box was only bent!

16. Billy was beaten at the post. He felt like stamping with rage. Then along came the postman who was annoyed at seeing his beautiful letter-box all bent and twisted. But Billy was beetling off as fast as he could!

17. Cantering around a corner, Billy stopped and scratched his coconut. Then he got a natty notion! Dash it all, all he had to do was to dash home and take the letter from the postman at the other end.

18. Billy gave a gargle of joy and galloped off to the railway station. Bunter Court was miles away, but Billy didn't care. He mizzled into the mail train that was standing there.

19. That's right, chums—Billy dived into the van and vanished. Sixty minutes later—that's one hour—and our fat lad popped out again. By gum, he wasn't half sticking to the trail.

20. In two ticks, Billy was round at Bunter Court. The fat lad would be round no matter where he was. But what I mean is, that he was waiting at the garden gate for the postman.

21. Of course, Billy wasn't supposed to get the post. The letter was for his parent, but apparently, the postie thought it was all right. He handed the letter to Billy and the fat lad chortled.

22. Billy's sigh of relief rattled the rhode—rhodede—make it rhubarb bushes at the bottom of the garden. He had got the letter at last, and all that was needed was a feed to make him completely happy.

23. Billy's father answered his ring, and he threatened to wring his fat son's neck. Quelchy had had a second think and had phoned Mr. Bunter with the bad news. And for the first time, Billy was glad to go back to school.

BILLY BUNTER
THE FATTEST SCHOOLBOY ON EARTH!

1. Billy Bunter is by far the fattest schoolboy in the world, because he is never far away when there's grub going. T'other day at twenty minutes past dinner-time, he ambled along Courtfield's new avenue. Seeing no one to stand him treat, Billy stood watching a bevy of best bricklayers having their afternoon cuppertea and what goes with it.

2. Billy's walk, or waddle, into Courtfield had made him hungry again. The mere sight of food gave him ideas. He would get a job as a bricklayer and get his lunch in large lumps, too!

3. The fat lad tackled the foreman as he came forth. Billy said he could do six men's work—but he didn't say he meant it at meal-times only. The foreman nearly fell over with surprise.

4. He just couldn't believe his luck when Billy said that he didn't want any wages—that he would work for free feeding only. But that foreman had no idea what it cost to feed Billy.

5. It was a big blow to Bunter that the whistle blew to start work before he had a chance to feed. His first job was to get a pile of bricks then begin at the foot of the ladder and work up.

6. But Billy had to take the bricks with him—right to the top of the scaffold ! It was bad enough having to work like a horse, but the silly ass didn't take anything to carry the bricks.

7. Fumbling and foozling, the fat lad managed to get half way up the ladder. By that time more than half the bricks had been dropped, but the thought of a free feed kept him going.

8. Puff ! Grunt ! Gasp ! Somehow Billy scrambled up on to the scaffold—with one brick ! Still it was better than nothing, and Bunter beamed as he carried it to the bricklayer.

9. That bricky looked tough enough to chew bricks. He'd been waiting for a load to start work, and he started with angry surprise when he saw all that Bunter had brought him.

10. Then the bricky began to get a load off his chest. Bunter didn't wait to hear it all. The first few words were enough to make him scram for safety at full speed !

11. Along the scaffolding he scampered. After him came the bricky breathing fire and slaughter. He was one of these high and mighty men—high on the scaffolding and mighty tough to look at.

148

12. But Bunter had had one look and that was enough for him. But before he could say rhubarb and rhodedondrons, he had reached the edge of the scaffolding and below was a lot of nothing between him and the ground.

13. Billy looked like being up the pole properly until he spotted a pole sticking out from the side. It was a chance and Bunter took it. Shaking like an aspirin—I mean an aspen—the silly ass climbed along the pole.

14. But at the end of the pole Billy turned pale. He would have turned back, but the baffled bricklayer was laying in wait for him. Then his spirits rose again as he saw a rope going down from the pole towards the ground.

15. Gurgling with gladness, Billy grabbed the rope and gave the bricky a fond good-bye—one that didn't make him any fonder of the fat lad! But the rope didn't run through the pulley as Billy expected—it simply galloped! Down went the fat lad—faster, faster, faster! Then—SPLOSH!—he came to a full stop in wet cement.

16. Cement was the last thing Billy meant to land into, but there he was. The stuff had just been put there and it began to harden round the fat lad. It took the whole gang ten minutes of tug-o'-war before they got Bunter out of it.

17. But still some of the cement stuck to the fat lad. It grew harder and harder. In a tick Billy was stuck so stiffly that he couldn't even change his mind if he'd wanted to.

18. But to make a bad mess worser, who should appear but Mr. Quelch! The master spotted Bunter even though he was disguised like an outsized dollop of cement.

19. Poor old Bunter was out of the cement and into the soup! In fact, he was well in the cart now, for Quelchy got the men to load Billy on to a barrow and take him back to Greyfriars.

20. It was the hardest day's work these men had ever done. Pushing Bunter on a barrow was no easy job, but the men meant to make up by chipping off the cement. They didn't mind if bits of Bunter came off, too.

21. But Quelchy didn't let them have their fun just yet—he had other ideas! He rummaged out a base for a statue that had gone for lunch or had got broke or something. On to this base Bunter was placed.

22. Stiff in his cement overcoat, Billy couldn't even struggle. The big stiff just looked like a statue as he stood there, and what's more, he wasn't chipped out of the cement until well after tea-time!

BILLY BUNTER
THE FATTEST SCHOOLBOY ON EARTH!

YAM! FANCY HAVING A HALF-HOLIDAY AND NO MONEY TO BUY ANY GRUB!

WELL BURY THE CASH HERE BY THE OLD POND, BILL! NO-ONE WILL EVER FIND IT!

COO! I WONDER WHAT IS GOING ON HERE? I'LL TAKE A LOOK THROUGH THAT HOLE IN THE HEDGE AND FIND OUT!

1. Billy Bunter's idea of a half-holiday is a hamper full of a week's grub, and all day to eat it in. That's why he felt fed up when there was no feed for him on his half-holiday—he was both broke and broken-hearted.

2. He went for a walk in the woods, wondering if a few nice juicy worms might make a meal. But even Bunter turned at worms. Through the dark, dreary, woods he stumbled —and then he stumbled into adventure.

3. His tummy went all of a jelly as he heard hoarse voices coming through the thicket. He wanted to run for his life, but his feet wouldn't let him. Then he plucked up all his courage and, tip-toed round the tree trunks.

COO! BURGLARS! *HE! HE! HE! WHAT WOULD LORD DISHWATER SAY IF HE KNEW WHAT HAD HAPPENED TO HIS MONEY?*

CUK—CRUMBS! SOMETHING'S GIVING WAY!

CRACK! *CRACK!*

4. And there, through a hole in a hedge, he spied a couple of burglars carrying bags of swag. Billy gave a gasp and a couple of groans, then his ears flapped and his eyes stood out like organ-stops as he watched the wicked burglars.

5. "Coo," he muttered, "fancy those crooked crooks hiding all that money so's no one can spend it! Why, it would keep me in doughnuts for a week!" His voice gave way—and so did Bunter! The fence beneath him folded-up,

6. Crack, crack, crack! Bunter performed his famous tight-rope-walking act—the part where he fell off! His feet went up, his head went down, and his hands clutched frantically at the bushes. But nothing could save him now.

OW! HELP! OOOCH! *? ?* *? ?*

SPLOSH!

GET HIM! HE'S SPOILED EVERYTHING!

7. He came out the other side looking like a cross between a hedgehog and a pin-cushion, and he nearly fainted with fright as he hung over a pool of dirty ditch-water. He didn't know which he feared most, the ditch or the desperadoes.

8. Bunter never did think much of washing, because water is such wet stuff. And when he was forced to take a bath he liked the water to be warm. But as he dropped into the ditch, he was worried about his schoolboy complexion.

9. Everything comes to him who waits, they say. But there was something coming to Bunter that he wasn't waiting for. As he came up for the third time, those crooks told him a thing or two or three about what they though of him.

THAT SILLY CHUMP HAS RUINED OUR FILM!

HELP! THIEVES! ROBBERS! GANGSTERS! RESCUE!

PUFF! GASP! *WANTE* *POLICE*

10. But Billy didn't stop to listen. He darted through the hedge again in two shakes of a cat's whiskers. And Bunter, being the world's prize ass, didn't realise that the two burglars weren't really crooks at all, but were film stars!

11. But Billy had got the idea into his head that they were the real thing, and not the reel thing. He did the next half mile in record time.

12. ¶And he didn't stop running—and puffing—and gasping—until he pounded into the police station. The sergeant had just awakened up from a quiet nap when Bunter barged in.

13. Was Bunter excited ? Between his puffs he managed to gasp out the horrible news of those two burglars and the bags of dough they had buried in *Farmer Giles'* meadow. The sergeant's eyes goggled with excitement.

14. He asked Bunter all sorts of questions, and for once in a way the fat fellow knew most of the answers. Those he didn't know he just made up. And slowly it began to dawn on the sergeant that one of the crooks must be One-eyed Ike.

15. He showed Bunter a picture of old One-Eye. But Bunter, who was studying the words on the picture, saw something about a reward of five pounds for One-Eye's capture. It took him about ten minutes to spell out the words.

16. Then Billy saw that ten pounds reward was offered for the capture of the other crook, and he had visions of becoming rich all of a sudden. He had visions, too, of all the lovely grub he could buy with fifteen pounds !

17. Having wakened up the other cops in the station the gallant men set out on the trail, with Bunter in the lead, feeling like William the Corn-curer at the battle of Tell-em-to-keep-it. Was there a man dismayed ? Well, Bunter wasn't !

18. And then, without stopping even to change step, Bunter and the brave boys in blue arrived on the scene. " There they are, sergie," he shouted. " There are the bad burglars, the—er——" But the men in blue were seeing red now.

19. Headed by the sergeant, they charged into battle. But they charged too much—into the ninepennies instead of the fourpennies—and the film stars and staresses were struck all of a heap. Because Billy Bunter's bungling with burglars had completely ruined a posh film scene.

20. But the police weren't going to let a little thing like that spoil a real good round-up. They plunged into the fight, collared and cuffed the film stars until they looked like a scene from Donald Duck. Even Bunter lent a bit of weight to the fight.

21. Then, after everybody had had enough, including the black-eyed boys in blue, the film producer told the sergeant just what a prize twerp he was. And that went for poor old Bunter, too, until—

22. The camera-man stepped in, grinning all over his face. He'd taken a picture of that lovely scrap—and told the producer that it would do nicely for their next film, the Battle of Hastings, ten-clicketty-click. Bunter was hailed as a hero.

23. They gave him a scrumptious spread, with all the grub he liked best, and some over. It all seemed like a lovely dream to the fat fellow, but he woke up all right when they told him he could start in on the sergeant's second helping, too !

BILLY BUNTER
THE FATTEST SCHOOLBOY ON EARTH!

1. Believe it or not, but Billy Bunter actually had some cash. True, it was only threepence, but it was all he could get for the fountain-pen he'd found in Quelchy's corridor. Still, it would keep him from starving until dinner-time.

2. The fat boy thought it was funny being in the money. In fact, Billy felt quite proud of himself as he bowled along to blow-in his wealth on buns. But pride comes before a fall—and, Billy didn't half come a purler.

3. Bunter's tootsies trod on Young Sammy Smiff's marbles. SWOOSH! His feet went one way, while his fat carcass went the other. The result was he tried to tie himself in knots as he took a free flight.

4. Coo, what a calamity! The pennies flew from Bunter's flippers and fell right into the hands of a tough-looking egg who was taking the air. He took the pennies as well and passed Billy a ticket for a prize draw.

5. Bunter didn't want tickets—he wanted buns! This certainly took the biscuit, and he began to cut up rough. But that was before he had a good look at the tough lad. Billy looked—and changed his mind.

6. Gargling with grief, Billy blinked at the ticket. He couldn't eat that, but when he tried to get his money back the tough lad told him to eat coke. Billy was getting all the things he didn't like that day.

7. The only thing that the fat lad could see that was free and for nothing was a seat. Billy parked his pants on it and began to ponder. But though his think-box ticked over, he couldn't think of a wheeze to get grub on tick.

8. Billy was desperate—so desperate that he decided to go back to school, even though it was his half-holiday. He was just getting his courage up when he heard something that made his listeners flap.

9. Two gents passed with a paper—and they read out the winning number of the prize draw. Bunter blinked at the number on his ticket, then he beamed. To his surprise, he'd won the first prize!

10. Bunter beat all records on his way back to school. It was two miles, but Billy didn't mind. He was all smiles as he borrowed Quelchy's best bike to carry home his prize.

11. Billy hoped that his prize would be just one thing—a hamper of grub! He bounced into the prize draw place as elegant as a baby elephant. There was no mistake—Billy was the winner!

12. The prize was in a monster packing-case. Billy gurgled with gladness. If that was full of grub the fat lad could feed his face for an afternoon—so chums you can guess the size it was!

13. Billy was so sure it was grub that he wanted to open it there and then. But he didn't open the case in case the other chappie wanted some. There was just enough for one—that is, one Billy Bunter.

14. Billy had gone flat out to get his prize—he was nearly flattened out when he got it. It didn't half weigh heavy, but somehow he got it on to his back and then got the whole lot on to the bike.

15. Puff! Puff! Puff! Billy pedalled for all he was worth to reach a place where he could open his prize. He looked like a barrage balloon with the lid on it, and on he pedalled until something went pop!

16. It was the back wheel of the bike. Bunter's weight was bad enough, but the case had caused a complete collapse. The back wheel was buckled so badly that the bike wouldn't go without it.

17. Billy was all of a do-dah. It was Quelchy's bike and he'd gone and broken it. The fat lad was down in the dumps until he spotted a rubbish dump at the side of the road. There were some wheels there!

18. All the wheels belonged to broken-down barrows. Bunter didn't care—he picked the biggest and fixed it to the bike. Somehow Bunter managed to scramble aboard the bike and off he rolled like a covered wagon.

19. There were no smiles in the next two miles for Bunter. Bump-bump-bumpity-bump went the bike. Billy's grins turned to groans as the front wheel folded up. Quelchy's bike looked like one of the ruins that Cromwell knocked about!

20. But it takes more than that to keep Bunter from a feed. He pedalled and he puffed and somehow he got the broken-down bike back to school. It was a feat that kept him off his feet, for he was on his hands and knees all the way.

21. Back in the bike shed, Billy couldn't control himself. He just dived at the packing-case and tore it to pieces. But there was no peace for him—Quelchy had arrived and seen his bike, such as it was now.

22. The master nearly shed a tear as he saw the ruins of his bike outside the shed, then gathering his gown about him he galloped in. The culprit was copped—it was Billy Bunter in the act of pulling out his prize!

23. Meanwhile, the fat lad had the miseries. There wasn't even a crumb of cake in the box. Instead there was a bike—a brand new bike, but he couldn't eat that. Bunter was fed up with it all.

24. The worst of it was that Billy couldn't even sell the bike to buy buns. Quelchy took it in place of the one that Bunter had changed into old iron, so his prize was a nasty surprise to him after all.

BILLY BUNTER
THE·FATTEST·SCHOOLBOY·ON·EARTH!

1. With Greyfriars school at its summer camp, Quelchy, the Head, naturally wanted the boys to get plenty of outdoor exercise. So he had arranged for several entries from the school in the local cross-country walk.

2. As the only exercise William George Bunter cared for was jaw exercise, our fat chum didn't think much of this idea of Quelchy's —until he heard there were to be free packets of grub for the competitors from the school.

3. One packet of grub was no good to Billy, of course, so he very quickly worked out a scurrilous scheme which, by writing out a phoney list of names, would put him in possession of all the packets that were to be made up.

4. Hustling off to the cookhouse with his phoney list, he had little difficulty in persuading the cook that he had been sent by Quelchy to collect all the rations.

5. It was unfortunate he bumped into Bob Cherry on his way back, because Bob grabbed a packet—and that meant Billy would have to do without that much grub.

6. He was wondering, too, how he was going to walk in the race and carry all those packets as well—until he spied Jones Minor. "Come on," he ordered. "You've got to help!"

7. And it was no good Jones Minor protesting because—well, because it just wasn't any good arguing with Billy when he was on a grub trail. Jones Minor ought to have known better.

8. But Billy was quite ready to be helpful, and, spotting a small handcart, he told Jones Minor to dump the grub in that. "You can push that along behind me," he beamed.

9. So when Billy was changed into a more suitably streamlined costume, he marched off to the starting post with Jones Minor and the grub barrow tailing behind.

10. But a little caution was necessary here. It wouldn't do for some suspicious rotter to think Billy was taking more than his share. "You catch me up presently," said Billy.

11. And Billy took his place at the start with the local sportsmen, apparently, without any grub at all. Much to everyone's surprise. Could Billy be slimming?

12. But Billy hadn't gone far along the road before he drifted to the rear and Jones Minor, complete with grub cart, came lumbering up behind. Billy soon started stoking.

154

13. In fact, Billy was paying far more attention to the business of shovelling away his supply of food than to the direction in which he was walking. It was Jones Minor who realised they were alone on the moors—and lost.

14. And Jones Minor decided at last he had had enough, and time to put his foot down with a firm hand. He insisted on trying to find his way back to camp while there was a chance. "Selfish little beast!" snorted Billy.

15. And as Jones Minor made his way back across the moor, he was alarmed to see dark, forbidding storm clouds coming up over the horizon. But Billy's mind was still concentrated on food.

16. Time passed. Darkness fell—and so did the rain—and poor little Jones Minor, covered in gloom and muddy wetness, staggered at last into camp.

17. And what a shock for Quelchy when his small, dripping figure appeared in his tent and reported that somewhere out on the murky moor was Bunter, lost.

18. Well, even Bunter could not be allowed to perish alone in the storm-swept darkness, so Quelchy rallied the boys in a search party and sallied forth.

19. But it takes a lot to get a Bunter down and having scoffed all the grub, our fat pal had set off on his own trek for home, and wet, weary and once more hungry, he came plodding into camp just after the search party had left.

20. It was the turn of Jones Minor to get a shock now as Billy oozed into Quelchy's tent and stood blinking unhappily in the light. "Ow!" gasped Jones Minor. "A search party has gone to look for you!"

21. But Billy wasn't put out by that at all. His gloom had vanished at the sight of Quelchy's table loaded with food and he hurried forward joyfully. "If Quelchy's gone out, he won't need his supper," he chortled.

22. It was nearly an hour later when the very soggy and browned-off search party returned to camp. "Alas, poor Bunter," murmured Quelchy. "Vanished without trace of even a crumb. We may never see him again!"

23. But the biggest moment in Quelchy's day was still to come for, as he entered his tent, there was the fat, useless form sprawled in bovine slumber at his empty table, his snores shaking the tent. "Bunter!" gasped Quelchy.

24. But there was still one more scene in the drama—and a very painful one it was for Billy. "A little exercise will warm us both up," said Quelchy grimly, and Bunterish yells of anguish proceeded to rend the night.

BILLY BUNTER
THE·FATTEST·SCHOOLBOY·ON·EARTH!

1. Greyfriars had been having a spell under canvas, but now it was time to return to the famous old school building, and as the Head, the one and only Henry Quelch, was going by road, each boy was given his fare.

2. "And don't get lost!" said Quelchy as he handed out the cash, but the idea of wasting so much money on a railway ticket was too much for Billy Bunter. Money should be spent on grub, thought Billy—and he soon spent it.

3. Well stoked-up and licking the last spot of jam from his lips, Billy sauntered out of the grub shop and begun to wonder just show he was going to get back to Greyfriars. "I'll stow away on a goods train," he decided.

4. And prowling round the goods yard, he soon found a train which would be going in the right direction. And there was an empty truck with the door open.

5. "Just the thing!" thought Billy as he clambered in. There was plenty of straw, too, so he could have a nice snooze. Yes, he had been pretty smart!

6. Billy settled down in a corner with a self-satisfied chuckle. Ha, ha! The other silly rotters had had to pay their fare and wouldn't get any grub until they got to Greyfriars.

7. But our fat chum's peaceful ponderings were suddenly disturbed by the sound of approaching footsteps and voices outside. "Oh crumbs!" he thought. "An inspector!"

8. But it was no railway official who appeared in the open doorway, and Billy scowled as a weather-worn wanderer of the road heaved himself aboard.

9. And the new arrival was not alone, for as the train began to gather speed three more trampish travellers tumbled into the van on top of Billy.

10. "Yaho! Leave me alone!" growled our chum, as the gentlemen of the road gathered round him, beaming. "Must be one of us," cried one. "Though he looks too well fed!"

11. "And those clothes are much too good for a tramp," grinned another. "If you are going to be a tramp you must look like one," he went on to Billy.

12. "You'd look much better in my coat. I'll take yours." And before Billy could do anything about it the change was made. "I'll swop trousers." said another.

13. Billy howled and spluttered, but it was no good, and in no time he was rigged up and looking more like a tramp than the tramps themselves. "Gimme back my clothes!" he bawled, shaking with rage.

14. But when the tramps only grinned the Bunterish wrath stirred to action, and with a yell he launched himself at the jacket pincher. "You rotten crook!" he cried angrily. "I want my coat!"

15. But the gentlemen of the road weren't going to part with their trophies, and the next moment the truck shook with the thud of bouncing bodies and the cries of battle as Billy went down under their mass attack.

16. Four to one was too much for Billy and he was soon gasping and helpless. "The train's slowing," cried one of the tramps. "Chuck him out!"

17. And poor Billy was seized, hustled to the door, and the next moment was flying through the air with the greatest of ease. "Ow!" he yelled. "Help!"

18. Thud! Billy had cleared the fence and landed on the hard, unsympathetic ground, and howls of Bunterish agony filled the air as the train vanished into the distance.

19. And there was Billy, spoofed, robbed, dished, and well and truly stranded. And it was fifty miles to Greyfriars! Worse still, he hadn't even the price of a bun to cheer him up. It was a black and gloomy outlook.

20. Next day Billy still had not reached Greyfriars, and Quelchy was on the war-path. "Where can the foolish boy be?" he growled, when Jones Minor tugged his gown. A familiar figure was tottering over the horizon.

21. It was Billy! A battered, tattered, starving, beaten, and browned-off Billy, and as Quelchy bore down on him and started to vent his wrath, he staggered weakly. "Please, sir," he gasped. "I think I'm going to faint!"

22. And with an expiring gasp the famous fat form keeled over and collapsed on the ground. "G-good gracious!" cried Quelchy, and his anger vanished. "Carry the poor boy inside at once!" And Jones Minor was very upset.

23. "The stupid boy really must be starving," murmured the shocked and amazed Quelchy, as the boys carried Billy off to the school sick-room. Billy really was out to the wide and for once everyone felt sorry for him.

24. But Billy quickly recovered. A plentiful supply of his favourite medicine administered by the pretty nurse soon revived his cheerfulness. "Just get him strong enough for some of MY medicine, nurse," said Quelchy grimly.

BILLY BUNTER
THE·FATTEST·SCHOOLBOY·ON·EARTH!

1. Billy, as usual, was broke and hungry, but as he wandered gloomily through the village he suddenly spotted Sir Eustace Goldbags counting a wad of pound notes. And while he looked a gust of wind caught one and whisked it away.

2. And Sir Eustace never even turned to look and see where it went. "Pooh! What's a pound note to me?" he chortled, and hurried on his way. But Billy had great respect for a pound note. It meant a lot of grub.

3. He saw it waft towards a barred window and sail gaily through. Well, if old Goldbags didn't want that note Billy did, and he started thinking very hard how he could get it. He'd got to peep through that window.

4. He made it with much heaving and grunting, and as he peered through the opening he saw the note lying on the floor of the room beyond. "I must get in there," he said.

5. But when he scuttled round to the front of the building to see what were his chances of getting in, his heart dropped to boot level. For the place was a police station.

6. But Billy wasn't going to give up. A quid's worth of grub was worth fighting for, and Billy began to scheme a scheme to get himself pinched by the law.

7. And when he wandered off his grey matter groping for inspiration, instinct took him towards the nearest restaurant. "Got it!" he beamed. "I'll have a good feed and refuse to pay."

8. This was a real inspiration, thought Billy. He'd get a free tuck-in, and, when he was arrested, the quid note as well. But the manager was watching him warily.

9. And when Billy sat back, feeling full up and pleased with himself, and announced he couldn't pay, the manager was ready for him. "I shan't call a policeman," he said.

10. "If I do that I shan't get my money, I'll inform your headmaster—and as you've had a free meal, we'll throw in a throw out!" And the hefty doorman seized Billy.

11. Woosh! Billy hurtled through the air, looped the loop neatly, and landed with a resounding thump on the hard and hurtful pavement outside. "Ow!" he yelled painfully.

12. But Billy wasn't done. Oh, no! There were other ways of getting copped by the cops, and a large notice outside Courtfield Park gave him another Bunterish brainwave.

13. "If I take a dog in the park they're sure to pinch me," reasoned Billy, and at that moment a likely-looking bow-wow appeared on the scene without its master and almost asking to be taken for a run.

14. "Come on, doggie," beamed Billy, tying a piece of string to its collar. "We'll go and have a romp over the grass and annoy the park-keeper. I only hope he hurries up and catches us and fetches a policeman."

15. But though they chased over flower beds and ignored "Keep Off the Grass" notices, not a park-keeper appeared. "Lazy rotters," grumbled Billy. But doggie didn't mind. He spotted the duck-pond.

16. Ducks were meant to be chased according to doggie ideas, and with a couple of loud Woofs! away went Fido straight for the duck pond, dragging Billy after him.

17. Billy was taken completely by surprise and before he could get control he found himself flying through the air in a graceful swallow-dive straight for the pond.

18. Wallop! Splash! Doggie, ducks and Billy churned up the water in a young tidal wave and then, as our fat pal came up spluttering he saw two irate figures on the bank.

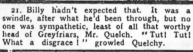

19. He was copped all right this time, but his wet woefulness soon vanished when P.-c. Pinchem pushed him in the cell and he saw, still lying on the floor, the elusive pound note. "Got it at last!" he grinned.

20. But alas, there was a large legal fly in the ointment, for when Billy was brought up in court the magistrate had some very unkind things to say, the most unkind being that he was going to fine Billy fifteen bob.

21. Billy hadn't expected that. It was a swindle, after what he'd been through, but no one was sympathetic, least of all that worthy head of Greyfriars, Mr. Quelch. "Tut! Tut! What a disgrace!" growled Quelchy.

22. So Billy had to pay up. And he only got five bob change. Five bob—after all that skilful scheming! Billy was disgusted. But he was due to be a lot more disgusted before long. Quelchy had an eye on that five bob.

23. In fact, Billy held on to his hard won cash for just two minutes, and then Quelchy whisked it away. "I will take this," he snapped. "It will go towards the restaurant bill for which you couldn't pay." Billy was speechless.

24. But our chum had plenty to say when Quelchy struck his final blow. At long last Billy's famous postal order had arrived. For two years he had waited for it, and now Quelchy was taking that, too. "T'isn't fair!" howled Billy.

159

BILLY BUNTER
THE·FATTEST·SCHOOLBOY·ON·EARTH!

1. It was too good to be true, chums! There was William George Bunter, hungry, penniless, and friendless—except for Jones Minor, and he was penniless, too!—when up ran the little chap with a letter for our fat chum.

2. Coo, how Billy's eyes gleamed! At last! A postal order, just when he needed it. 'Twas too good to be true. Too true, it was! 'Cos when Billy opened the letter there wasn't a sausage in it—not a ha'penny!

3. It simply said that Billy's Uncle Bertram, who used to go to school with old Quelchy, would be arriving to see how little Billy was getting on. As if Billy cared! He was starving —on the border-line of a famine!

4. And as he plodded down the passage, ted-up with not being fed, what should he see but cakes and buns and doughnuts, and more cakes, all piled high in Quelchy's study!

5. Well, chums, that was not only too good— it was true! And before Jones Minor could say "Don't!" our Billy was inside making sure the buns were good enough for Quelchy.

6. Jones Minor was awfully upset. He said it wasn't right and he'd tell Quelchy. But Billy was too full for words! You can't argue with luvverly grub once it's down!

7. And Billy didn't argue! He sat down to get over it, and promptly fell asleep. And that's how Quelchy found him when he turned up. There was Billy in the chair—full up! And there was the cupboard—empty!

8. It was too true to be good, chums! And it put Quelchy in a real bad temper. He stood there and remembered all the bad things our Billy had ever done in his life. Never before had Quelchy remembered so much!

9. 'Twas the last straw, chums! It was the outside edge—the pink limit—and more than flesh and blood could stand. And there was only one thing Quelchy could do—expel Billy Bunter—once and for all!

10. Think of it! William George Bunter kicked out of Greyfriars! What a let-down! What a show-down! Kicked out in the middle of the afternoon before he'd had his tea! Could any punishment be greater?

11. Poor old Jones Minor was sobbing his lickle heart out, he was! But Billy would have liked to sock him on the nose! The die was cast! There was no escape. Billy was stood on the platform to be expelled!

12. But while this was going on in the Hall, something else was going on at the gates, and coming in, too! 'Twas Uncle Bertram, asking to see that lad Bunter! And he was told that Bunter was then in the Hall.

13. So into the Hall went Uncle Bertram. There he saw our Billy on the platform, with Quelchy telling the whole school the sort of chap our Billy was. "Never," he cried, "has there been such a boy as Bunter !"

14. That's what Quelchy said, but the words, as they left his mouth, meant something different from what they meant when they hit Uncle Bertram's ears. In fact, chums, Uncle Bertram thought Billy was a wow !

15. "Hurrah for Bunter !" yelled the silly old chump. Quelchy was most annoyed and began again. "Never have I had in my care such a boy as William George Bunter !" Whereupon Uncle Bertram let himself go again.

16. "Up the Bunters !" he bawled. "Three cheers for Billy !" And so he went on until he realised that of all the cheerers there he was by himself. So he stopped a bit.

17. And that gave Quelchy a chance to explain that he was indeed expelling William George Bunter. Old Uncle Bertram was awfully upset and pleaded for his lickle nephew.

18. Quelchy ought not to do it, he argued. Think of Greyfriars without a Bunter ! You can't ? Well, there you are ! Besides, did Quelchy remember his own distant youth ?

19. If he didn't, Uncle Bertram reminded him. That he did ! Reminded him of how he put glue in the Headmaster's slipper when he was a nipper—that is, when Quelchy was a nipper ! Quelchy began to go all awkward.

20. "And what about the time you put a cake of soap in our Form-master's cheese-dish !" quacked Uncle Bertram. And he laughed his silly head off. But Quelchy didn't like to be reminded of his dark deeds.

21. Our Billy was peeved. He couldn't hear what Uncle Bertram was saying, but Uncle Bertram seemed jolly pleased about something. And Billy couldn't see anything to be pleased about. Neither could Quelchy.

22. He wanted to wipe out the past, but Uncle Bertram wouldn't let him. "Remember when you spotted your face with red ink and said you had the measles, Quacker ?" he asked. And Quelchy went redder than the spots !

23. He thought that if his boyhood skylarks were ever found out he'd lose his job. "Let us forget everything !" he said. And Uncle Bertram beamed broadly. "That's the spirit !" he cried. "Forgive and forget !"

24. So Quelchy forgave and said he'd forget, and our Billy stayed where he was, at Greyfriars. And just to show there was no ill-feeling, Uncle Bertram stood the whole school a good feed ! Hurrah for the Bunters !

BILLY · BUNTER
THE · FATTEST · SCHOOLBOY · ON · EARTH !

1. It's a well-known fact, chums, as every schoolboy knows, that to be well known is to be known well. But if you think it's a good thing, ask William George Bunter. Why, even the new gym master knew him !

2. At least, Professor Pummel had heard of our Billy. So when he got a job at Greyfriars, "gymming," he was ripe and ready to tackle the task of getting a bit of weight off the fattest schoolboy on this or any other earth !

3. Quelchy beamed at the idea—the old meanie ! He called for Bunter, and up popped Billy, thinking he was going to get an extra spud for dinner. But all he got was orders to let Professor Pummel do things to him !

4. Coo, what a shame, chums ! If our Billy wants to be fat—well, it's a free country, isn't it ? Professor Pummel suggested a nice pleasant time together in the gym !

5. Billy couldn't think how anybody could be nice and pleasant in a gym, but he had to toddle along. The Professor got out the box-horse and told Billy to jump over it !

6. The Professor was so nice and kind, too ! He said he could catch Billy—yes, even if he turned a couple of cartwheels in midair. But our Billy wasn't too sure about it !

7. Anyway, it takes a lot to daunt a Bunter ! If the chump thought he could catch a Bunter —well, let him try, thought Billy. So Billy took a good run and leapt over the box-horse. That is to say, Billy leapt !

8. "Here I come !" he cried valiantly. And how he came ! Billy turned a somersault all right, but he didn't want to. 'Twas just one of those things, chums. When Billy hurled himself in the air he lost control !

9. He hurtled through space like a rocket gone nuts ! He somersaulted, did a victory roll, looped the loop, did a tail spin, spun on his axis, and just zoomed all the time, straight for the stalwart Professor.

10. And did the Professor catch him ! He most certainly did ! He caught all of him, right in the bread-basket. The impact was terrific. Never before in the history of Greyfriars had so much schoolboy been caught !

11. Professor Pummel was flattened against the wall. 'Twas real kind of him to get in the way. If he hadn't, our Billy might have hurt himself. But the Professor didn't take it kindly. "I've had enough !" he growled.

12. "Let's see you swarm up that rope, as nimbly as a monkey !" he said. Now Billy knew very well that monkeys don't swarm, but the Professor wouldn't listen to reason. He said Billy had to swarm like a monkey !

13. So Billy swarmed. "'Swarm work!" he muttered, as he swarmed. Up and up he went, while the Professor stood below to guard him from all harm. But Billy was an awful weight to support on that rope!

14. That's where it wasn't fair, chums! Billy wasn't strong enough to hold himself up. And suddenly he wasn't holding himself up. Nothing was! Billy let out a yell and fell! Down—down he dropped, like a stone!

15. About twenty stones, in fact! And, of course, Professor Pummel had to do something about it. If he hadn't, the gym floor might have got chipped! So the noble gent broke Billy's fall with his spine—whoof!

16. 'Twas too much for Professor Pummel. To be knocked out of puff twice in ten minutes was more than too much. "You're too fat!" he said crossly. "I'll take you for a run."

17. That was his idea to get some of the fat off our Billy. And this time the Professor thought he'd mastered Master Bunter at last! 'Cos Bunter couldn't fall on him running!

18. But Billy fell on his feet, all the same. 'Cos while the Professor went sprinting through the school-gate, Gosling, the gate-keeper, reminded him of the strict rules.

19. Quelchy's orders, see, chums? No lad to go out without a cap. So Billy stayed behind while the Professor went cantering all over the scenery, up hill, down dale, and round the corners, till he was all in!

20. He had an idea our Billy was behind him all the way. And Billy was behind him—right behind him—until he turned to come back. Then Billy was in front of him, but Billy was careful to hide in the gateway.

21. But when the Professor cantered in, Billy took up a position behind him as fresh as a newly-watered daisy. But the Professor—well, two good turns deserve another, so Billy held him up and stopped him falling!

22. 'Sfact, chums! Our good Billy nobly saved the Professor from denting the playground. Jolly good show, what? And just then up came Quelchy. "Dear me," he said. "Carry the Professor to bed, boys!"

23. Of course, our Billy didn't do any carrying. Quelchy sent him to fetch assorted vitamins to get the Professor back to health and strength again! Billy was good at grub gathering. Quelchy knew that!

24. Unfortunately, Professor Pummel was too tired even to eat. It looked as if all the vitamin stuff would be wasted. Our Billy hated waste, and so he had a good time getting his weight down—eating!

BILLY BUNTER
THE·FATTEST·SCHOOLBOY·ON·EARTH!

1. Up till now the Bunter brain had devoted itself almost entirely to ways and means of getting hold of food, if possible, without paying for it. So it wasn't surprising he always came bottom of the class.

2. But when he discovered Jones Minor tucking in to a free tea in Quelchy's study as a reward for coming top, Billy began to think there was something to be got out of this learning business after all.

3. "If Quelchy's going to dish out free grub just for swotting up a few beastly dates and sums and things, I'll soon show 'em what a Bunter can do," snorted Billy, wiping the dust off his books and settling down to study.

4. Shooing Jones Minor away, Billy was soon deep in a history book, and grunting disgustedly over King Alfred burning the cakes. "Careless rotter!" he growled. "Wasting good grub!"

5. But all this sudden unaccustomed brain work made Billy restless, and, his fat head deep in a maths book, he ambled down the corridor, as Quelchy approached from the opposite direction.

6. Thud! Wallop! Quelchy and Billy met on the corner, and Quelchy coming off second best against the Bunter bulk, bounced backwards to the floor. "Clumsy youth!" roared the Head.

7. But Quelchy's anger soon changed to beams of delight as he picked himself up and studied the book Billy had been reading. "My boy!" he burbled. "I am delighted."

8. Well, chums, you can guess that was quite a shock for Quelchy. But if it was possible to improve Billy's grey matter, Quelchy was more than ready to help.

9. So Billy was led off to the Head's study, and when next he appeared, he was loaded with some of Quelchy's best books. "There is hope after all," beamed Quelchy. "Amazing!"

10. And, to give Billy credit, he really settled down to some honest swotting. "If I can soak up these books as easily as I can soak up grub, I'll soon be top boy," he chuckled.

11. But alas for Billy's good intentions! His solitude was soon shattered by some rowdy Remove rotters who appeared, yelling and shouting over a game of catch.

12. "Jealous beasts!" grumbled Billy. "Won't let a chap work. Why the—— Wow!" And Billy's mumbles changed to a howl of anguish as the ball hit his eye.

13. "Why didn't you catch it?" someone called. But the Bunter wrath was roused and, seizing the heaviest of Quelchy's books, Billy flung it with all his strength. It scored a bull's eye, too, on the biggest of the ball throwers.

14. That did it! "Want to play rough, eh?" roared the smitten one. "All right!" And as Billy bent to pick up another book, back came the first one, smacking him Thump! against the tree. "Bash him!" came a yell.

15. And poor Billy was well and truly bashed—and biffed—and beaten up. And when it was all over, our fat chum lay gasping beneath the ruin of Quelchy's books. Those heavy tomes had certainly left their mark on Billy.

16. Any more swotting was out of the question now. And what would Quelchy say when he saw the wreckage of his precious books? Billy groaned miserably. Now, he'd have to hide the battered books, somewhere.

17. But as he wondered what to do with the battered books, he came on an old junk man by the school gates, and fortune smiled on Billy at last. "I'll give you a couple of bob for those torn books," said the man.

18. Well, chums! A couple of bob can still buy quite a lot of grub, and Billy's world was smiling again. Why bother to swot, anyway? This was a much quicker way to a free feed. And perhaps Quelchy wouldn't miss his books.

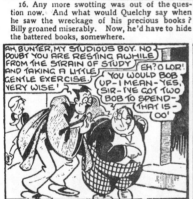

19. But just as he was about to enter the village cafe, Billy jumped guiltily as a familiar hand patted his shoulder. "Ah, my studious boy," waffled Quelchy. "A little relaxation from your labours." And Billy groaned.

20. But Quelchy suspected nothing, and was so delighted with the new studious Bunter that he insisted on paying for Billy's feed. "You will return to school all the more determined not to be beaten," he beamed.

21. Billy felt this was all too good to last—and so it was, for when they left the cafe and rounded a corner, there was Billy's junk man, and Quelchy quickly spotted his battered books laid out on the counter.

22. And now Quelchy beamed no longer. No, indeed! He scowled stonily at Billy and demanded the two bob. "I wish to make a purchase," he said grimly. "Something you need more than books."

23. And Billy watched anxiously as Quelchy stalked off into the general store. What could he need more than books—if it wasn't grub? And they didn't sell grub at the store! Trouble brewing, said Billy's instinct. O crumbs!

24. And when Quelchy appeared again with a long swishy cane, Billy didn't need a fortune-teller to tell him what the future held. And he was supposed to be returning to school determined not to be beaten! Poor old Billy!

BILLY·BUNTER
THE·FATTEST·SCHOOLBOY·ON·EARTH!

1. It was a beautiful morning. The sun shone, the birdies twittered and the Head of Greyfriars, as he flung open his window, felt all joyous and juvenile. "Ah!" breathed Quelchy. "I must get the boys up, too!"

2. But when he reached the dormitory, he beamed with greater delight, for the beds were all empty. It seemed the boys had thought his own thoughts and had already gone out to frolic in the early morning sunshine.

3. But did we say all the beds were empty? Well, not quite! For there was one which still held a human shape—or almost human—for the heaving mound beneath the sheet belonged to William George Bunter.

4. "Lazy, wretched youth," growled Quelchy, as he whisked away the sheet and gave Billy a severe shaking. "Outside at once and let the fresh morning air bring the roses to your cheeks." But poor Billy felt anything but rosy.

5. In fact Billy just couldn't wake up, and though he tottered out to the playing-fields, where the other boys were playing leap-frog, he could only collapse limply against a tree and blink dreamily at the others' unnatural antics.

6. But Quelchy wasn't going to let Billy go to sleep again. Oh no! "Come, Bunter. Rouse yourself and join in the leap-frog," he urged, while Jones Minor dragged him from the tree and pushed him towards the waiting "frog."

7. But it was no good. Billy tottered forward a few feet and, in the act of trying to heave himself off the ground, he collapsed completely in deep sleep.

8. Bunterish snores scared the birds for miles round, but Quelchy wouldn't give in. Heaving the sleeping Billy from the ground, he ordered the other boys to fetch a skipping rope.

9. For a moment Billy almost awoke—at any rate, long enough to stand upright while Jones Minor and Quelchy swung the skipping rope. "One, two, three, jump!" cried Quelchy.

10. But as the rope whizzed round, there was no jump from Billy. With a loud and shattering snore, he rolled back over the rope and was asleep again before he hit the ground.

11. Quelchy had just about had enough by this time, and as he glared at the slumbering Billy, he decided he must take desperate measures. "Fetch a pail of water," he ordered.

12. And presently Jones Minor returned with a brimming pail, raising it cautiously above Billy's head. "Bunter must be roused," snapped Quelchy. "A few drops should do!"

13. But at that moment Billy in his sleep decided he would do a little exercise on his own and his arms stretched out in a terrific yawn, upsetting the water all over Quelchy.

14. Damp, dripping and determined, Quelchy strode off towards the school. "Come with me, boys," he growled. "We will change and then at all costs Bunter must be wakened."

15. And later, dressed and breakfasted, Quelchy and the boys sallied forth again. This time armed with a blanket and determined to shock the still sleeping Billy into wakefulness.

16. Getting the Bunter weight into the blanket was a big job and only after much heaving, pushing and shoving was he manœuvred into position. "Reminds me of my school days," said Quelchy. "This is certain to succeed."

17. And then they all gathered round the blanket, Quelchy joining the boys in taking a grip on the edge. "Get ready," Quelchy cried. "Now! All together—HEAVE!" And up into the air sailed Billy like a barrage balloon.

18. And in mid air Billy woke up. This time, he really woke up. And finding himself in the middle of nothing, he let out a yell for help. "Ow!" he bawled. "What's happening? O gosh! Where am I? What's up?"

19. Well, Billy was up all right, and what goes up has to come down! And Billy coming down at full speed was altogether too much for the blanket, and with a loud ripping noise it split, while Billy crashed through.

20. With a dull thud, Billy struck the ground and his yells of pain and anguish even had Quelchy worried for a moment. But it is difficult to damage a Bunter, though Billy was shocked to hear he had missed his breakfast.

21. But later, in class, the energies of the early morning began to have their effect. Sighs and yawns filled the room and even Quelchy's eyes drooped, as one after the other everyone fell asleep. Everyone, that is, except Billy.

22. "Sleepy lot of rotters," snorted our fat chum, who had never felt so wide awake. "Whatever is the matter with them all? Even Quelchy." And Billy blinked round in astonishment at the strange scene of the sleeping class.

23. Indeed, they were sleeping so soundly, that they never heard the lunch bell, and Billy wasn't going to waken them. Not he! Here was a chance to get some of his own back and he lost no time in making for the dining-room.

24. When, at last, Quelchy and the boys did wake up, they found that Billy had got the laugh of them after all. Not a crumb of food remained on the tables. Billy had scoffed the lot and was resting.

BILLY BUNTER
THE·FATTEST·SCHOOLBOY·ON·EARTH!

1. A nice day on the river with a picnic lunch sounded pretty good to the Greyfriars lads, and the picnic part especially appealed to Billy Bunter. Already Billy was thinking how he might get more than his fair whack of the grub.

2. He even hoped that he might have charge of the picnic basket, but he should have known Quelchy would take care not to risk any chance like that. But Billy started thinking hard when he heard Jones Minor was to be the grub guard.

3. Jones Minor was to row up the river, with the lunch basket, ahead of the main party, and Billy gave a Bunterish chuckle as he thought of a wily wheeze to spoof his little pal and get his own fat hands on that picnic hamper.

4. Down to the river he ambled just as Jones Minor was about to load the basket into a rowing boat. "Quelchy wants a chap he can trust on this job," he said loftily.

5. But Jones Minor was taking it pretty hard. He was really hurt to think Quelchy trusted Billy more than him, and he wandered away glumly as Billy grabbed the grub basket.

6. Billy wasn't wasting any more time over Jones Minor's feelings. Dumping the basket in the row-boat, he seized the oars and went floundering happily away down the river.

7. It was some time later that the Greyfriars motor-boat set off with Quelchy at the wheel, and the Head was so full of sunshine that he did not see poor Jones Minor creep aboard.

8. And away they went while Quelchy pointed out the wonders of Nature, the stooging sticklebacks, the nesting newts, still unaware that Jones Minor was not where he should be.

9. And little Jones Minor still huddled in a corner of the boat, nursing his hurt feelings and determined to have nothing to do with the Head who wouldn't trust him.

10. But suddenly Quelchy found something else beside the wonders of Nature to study, for slowly trickling past the boat came a familiar biscuit tin bearing a Greyfriars label.

11. And following it more empty tins, bottles, jam jars and paper came drifting by. And at sight of it, Jones Minor suddenly realised the Bunterist trick that had been played on him.

12. "Oh, sir!" he gasped. "I fear we are the victims of a Bunter prank!" But Quelchy, at the thought of Billy and the basket alone together, waited no longer and put on speed.

13. Alas! They were too late, for as Billy hove in sight, he was just in the act of throwing the last tin overboard. Billy had fed well and now he was ready to sleep well. "I'll just drift along and have a nice little snooze," he beamed.

14. But there was to be no snoozing for Billy now, for just as he was settling down, up roared the Greyfriars launch and, leaning over the side, Quelchy grabbed the row-boat and began to give Billy an idea of what he thought about him.

15. But so occupied was Quelchy in what he had to say that he did not notice the two boats drifting apart—until he found himself stretched across a growing gap of water. His feet were slipping, but he dared not let go of Billy's boat.

16. "Help!" gasped Quelchy. "I shall fall in the water. Quick, Bunter, use your oar. I insist you save me from this uncomfortable situation." But as Billy dived an oar into the water, the boats kept drifting further apart.

17. And then Billy heaved on his oar. He wasn't sure what he was supposed to do, but what he did was to catch a mighty big crab—and Quelchy at the same time. For with a terrific whump! up came the oar!

18. Quelchy let out a yell as he did a double jack-knife dive and then with a loud splash disappeared into the river. "O lor!" groaned Billy. "Why does the old fathead want to look down there for the picnic basket?"

19. But when the bubbles which came to the surface were not followed by Quelchy, the boys began to get worried, and even Billy peered down over the edge of his boat. "He'll get his feet awfully wet," he mumbled.

20. In fact it began to look as if Quelchy had gone for good, and big tears began to ooze from Billy's eyes as he thought it was all his fault. But if he had looked behind him, he would have seen a very wrathful Quelchy climbing aboard.

21. And as Billy went on thinking his sad thoughts and wondering how he could live in peace without Quelchy, the object of his wonderings had climbed quietly into the boat and had taken his stance with the second oar.

22. "Ah! This reminds me of when I stroked the Greyfriars crew," murmured Quelchy. "And now I will stroke Bunter as I have never stroked before. One, two, three——" And a mighty swipe struck Billy astern.

23. But Billy's sudden departure over the side suddenly upset the balance arrangements of the boat and, before he could save himself, Quelchy felt the floor beneath him heave upwards, and over he went.

24. So the Greyfriars day down by the river had a damp and dismal ending, but as Quelchy glared wetfully at our fat pal he promised grimly that there was a warm spell ahead. In fact, Billy caught it hot!

BILLY BUNTER

THE·FATTEST·SCHOOLBOY·ON·EARTH!

1. William George Bunter was prowling through the school orchard the other day in search of windfalls to ease the pangs of hunger, when, suddenly, peering round a bush, he spotted a strange and whiskery gent burying a big tin.

2. And as the tin had a label on it bearing the word "Biscuits," Billy was very interested. Just why this queer cove should bury a tin of biscuits was beyond Billy, but he wasn't going to see good grub going to waste like that.

3. If the Whiskery One didn't want them, Billy did, and he promptly hared off to the school toolshed for a spade. And he wasn't stopping for any interruptions from his little pal, Jones Minor. Billy was on a hot scent.

4. Jones Minor wasn't used to seeing Billy move so quickly and when our fat chum appeared again carrying a spade and dashing off towards the orchard, Jones Minor decided to follow.

5. And from behind a tree he watched Billy wielding his spade as if his life depended upon it. "Very [strange," muttered Jones Minor. "Surely Bunter is not slimming."

6. No, it was all very suspicious. Billy was up to something, he felt sure—and it would be something that was no good to anyone except Billy. Jones Minor meant to watch.

7. In fact, at last Jones Minor decided to ask Billy outright just what was going on and Billy jumped guiltily as his little pal came marching up to him.

8. But Billy wasn't going to share his secret with anyone. He meant to keep this find all to himself and, waving his spade, he shooed Jones Minor away. "Hop it!" he ordered.

9. Well, chums, Jones Minor duly "hopped it" over the orchard wall, but he still kept watch and he was surprised when, after more furious digging, Billy hauled out the biscuit tin.

10. But as Billy made off with his prize, Jones Minor sat on the wall to think it out. And as he puzzled over the mystery, he heard voices coming round the corner.

11. Jones slid out of sight while the owners of the voices came into view. They were Quelchy and Colonel Bracebutton, and the Colonel was telling about his stolen jewels.

12. Jones Minor was shocked. The fact that the jewels had been in a biscuit tin certainly made it look as if Billy was the thief. Jones Minor decided he must act at once.

13. Billy Bunter might be a fat, greedy so-and-so, but Jones Minor wasn't the one to see his pal arrested for theft. But when he came upon our chubby chum, he found Billy wasn't to be easily parted from his newly won prize.

14. "Buzz off, you nosey little rotter," growled Billy. But Jones Minor refused to buzz and going suddenly into action, he gave Billy a hefty shove which bowled him clean over the log on which he was sitting.

15. "I regret this violence," apologised Jones Minor, "but it is for your own good." And seizing the biscuit tin he dashed off towards the school, leaving Billy helplesly howling with rage and agonized despair.

16. Straight to Quelchy's study went Jones Minor with his tin and when he explained that he had found it in the wood, the Colonel was delighted. "Ah, the Bracebutton Biscuit Tin, and the jewels safe—I hope," he beamed

17. But just as Jones Minor was patting himself on the back for having saved Billy's reputation, that fat fraud came bowling down the corridor and burst into Quelchy's study. "Hi ! My biscuit tin !" he blurted wrathfully.

18. Poor little Jones Minor turned away in despair as Quelchy fixed Billy with an accusing finger. "Explain, wretched boy !" he growled, and Billy, realising that he had put his fat feet well and truly in it, duly explained.

19. But Quelchy knew Billy's explanations of old and as the whole thing smelt of typical Bunterish roguery, he meant to check up with the police. Finding himself involved in criminal crookery, Billy trembled fearfully.

20. "O Lor !" he groaned, as Quelchy telephoned the police, and our pal heard that he was to go with the Head to the police station to identify the whiskery one. He felt sure that months in a deep, dark cell were in store for him.

21. But down at the police station he felt a little more hopeful. If he could recognise the right set of whiskers perhaps the real thief would go to prison and he would be let off with a warning.

22. And to Billy's great relief, amongst that imposing array of black face fungus, he spotted the growth he had seen in the orchard. "That's him,", cried Billy, wagging a thick finger at the culprit. "That's the rotter !"

23. And so it was, but Sam the Swizzer wasn't stopping and with false whiskers flapping, he dived for the door. But a big cop quickly copped him and Sam was marched off to where he wouldn't have to worry about whiskers

24. And Colonel Bracebutton was so braced at getting back his jewels and the biscuit tin which had been handed down through generations of Bracebuttons, that he stood our chums a slap-up feed—in spite of Quelchy's frowns.

BILLY·BUNTER
THE·FATTEST·SCHOOLBOY·ON·EARTH!

1. The labour shortage had struck Greyfriars and Quelchy was forced to ask for one of the boys to help clean up the school. "We will all go for a ramble," quoth the Head, "and leave the school to the splendid lad who volunteers to do the cleaning."

2. But there seemed to be an absence of splendid lads that day and as no hands were raised willingly, Bob Cherry decided to try a little encouragement. Taking a toy pistol from his pocket he jammed it suddenly into Billy Bunter's back.

3. "Stick 'em up!" he breathed in Billy's ear and so startled was our fat chum that he flung his arms up in the air with a yell. Of course, Quelchy thought he was volunteering for the job and was delighted. "Ah, noble boy," he beamed.

4. But Billy felt anything but noble, indeed, he felt hopping mad at being diddled into the beastly job. "O lor!" he groaned. "I hate any sort of cleaning."

5. But there was no getting out of it now, and Billy was led to the cleaners' room and armed with pails, mops and brushes. "Make the old school shine like new," said Quelchy.

6. So the ramblers rambled off and Billy was left to do his charring. And it was a very disgusted and disgruntled Billy who clattered off to set about his lonely task.

7. But when he entered Bob Cherry's study, the Bunter spirit suddenly revolted. It was Bob Cherry who had landed him into this, and Bob Cherry ought to pay for that.

8. Billy had remembered that Cherry had just received a large cake, and our pal felt that this was a first-class chance to get his hands on it and his teeth into it.

9. But Bob Cherry had hidden that cake too well and Billy's frantic searching brought not a crumb of it to light. "Greedy blighter!" he stormed. "Fancy keeping it all to himself."

10. By the time Billy had turned the study inside out and still found no cake, he was quite exhausted. He had been looking forward to that grub and was really hungry now.

11. A hungry Bunter was something to be reckoned with, and Billy made up his mind that the next study he tackled should produce some food. Bolsover wouldn't let him down.

12. He would tidy Bolsover's study up and then the rotter wouldn't mind him helping himself to the grub in his cupboard. There was sure to be something good to eat in it.

13. But when Billy got there, the cupboard was bare, and once more he groaned at his bad luck. "Anybody would think the suspicious rotter expected someone to come looking in his cupboard," growled Billy.

14. And then he remembered having helped himself to sweets before from a hoard he had found in Bolsover's box and next moment the contents of that box were flying all over the room. But there were no sweets to be found.

15. Poor Billy was dished again. Bolsover's study looked as if a cyclone had hit it. Every nook and cranny, every drawer and cupboard that might have held hidden grub had been scoured—but there was no sign of eats.

16. Completely disgusted, Billy grabbed up his cleaning tools, which were still unsoiled by any dirt, and marched off in the direction of Quelchy's study. He had to find some food somewhere, and surely Quelchy would keep something in store.

17. But Quelchy's room had nothing better to offer than the other rooms. Not so much as a packet of chewing gum came to light and Billy decided he was the victim of a conspiracy. "I really think the mingy rotters don't trust me," he moaned.

18. And then inspiration hit Billy in a lightning flash. Of course! He had the whole school to himself. Why was he wasting time scratching round the studies when he could go and help himself to all the goodies that must be in the pantry?

19. So down to the cook's quarters he scurried, but still the luck was against our chum. For the pantry was locked and without a doubt, Quelchy had gone off with the key in his pocket. But now Billy's endurance was at an end.

20. There was an aching void inside him which was crying out to be filled and a mere locked door wasn't going to stop him filling it. Billy gave himself room for a good long run, then flung all the Bunterish force at the door.

21. Wham! Crash! No door could stand up to such an onslaught, and as the door burst open, Billy sailed through to land on the pantry floor. But as he looked up eagerly his face turned pale with rage. The pantry was bare!

22. Meanwhile, Quelchy and the other boys had finished their rambling and wearily and happily wended their way back to Greyfriars. "We shall find the school clean," beamed Quelchy. "And Bunter shall be rewarded."

23. The cheery Head had been true to his word, and had brought back the picnic basket filled with tasties which had been saved especially to reward Bunter. "Enjoy this repast, my splendid boy," burbled Quelchy.

24. But Billy's enjoyment was very short lived, for he had barely started on the grub when windows were flung up and angry voices told of the discovery of the wrecked rooms. "O lor!" groaned Billy. "Nobody loves me!"

173

BILLY BUNTER
THE·FATTEST·SCHOOLBOY·ON·EARTH!

1. "Coo!" said Billy Bunter, as he and Jones Minor ambled down the village High Street. "Look at all those girls carrying pies. I'm going after them. The greedy rotters can't be as hungry as I am!"

2. So off cantered Billy after the day-school girls, determined to find out just how he could get his fat hands on one—or more—of those pies. And the girls got quite a shock as our fat chum came plodding after them.

3. But Billy was due for a shock, too, for he soon discovered that the dishes were empty. "We're going to cooking lessons at the village hall," said one of the girls. "We're learning how to make apple-pies to-day!"

4. Well, that made Billy sit down and do some deep thinking. Crisp and crusty apple-pies were the sort of things Billy dreamed about, and he soon hit on a plan.

5. Leaving a worried Jones Minor, Billy hurried back to the school, and after raiding the Dramatic Society's prop. basket, was soon seen again in the High Street strangely disguised.

6. Billy made a fine bouncing girl, and as "she" marched into the village hall bearing an enormous pudding-bowl, the Cooking Mistress almost lost her eyebrows.

7. "Please, I'm the new girl!" burbled Billy coyly, "and you don't know how keen I am on apple-pies." Well, the mistress grumbled a bit, but told Billy to sit down.

8. Billy sat there gazing longingly at the picture of a nice juicy apple-pie which was put on the blackboard, and wondered why they didn't have lessons like this at Greyfriars.

9. "This is something I can really get my teeth into!" grinned Billy, as he gaily sliced up apples into his outsize bowl. Indeed, he was using up all the apple ration.

10. And even then he hadn't enough apples to fill his dish, and he was soon raiding the other girls' supplies. This was going to be a real Bunter pie, and Billy licked his lips in anticipation.

11. Next came the crust-making, and Billy's girlish pigtails fairly flapped with joy as he kneaded and rolled the dough. "Must keep it nice and thick," he chuckled.

12. And soon the masterpiece was finished, a pie to beat all pies. "Come, dear," quoth Miss Twiddlefit, the mistress. "Pop it in the oven." And Billy "popped" it in with gusto.

13. But when he turned away from the oven, Billy started with surprise. For there, surely, was Jones Minor also dressed up like himself in girl's clothes and wearing a wig. This was too much!

14. He thought Jones Minor was pinching his idea, and he grabbed one of the hanging pigtails. "I'll pull your wig off and show you up!" said Billy angrily. "Jones Minor's sister, indeed! I'll teach you!"

15. But it really was Jones Minor's sister, and Billy's mighty heave nearly scalped the little girl. "Ow!" yelled Minnie Jones painfully. "You rough girl. Please desist! I demand you let go my pigtails this instant!"

16. And tearing herself free, Minnie ran to Miss Twiddlefit for protection. "Oh please, miss," she gasped, "did you see what that horrid fat girl did?" And Miss Twiddlefit glowered.

17. But Bunter realised that he really had made a mistake and, seeing trouble looming, he decided that at all costs he must make sure of his beautiful apple-pie.

18. So, grabbing it from the oven, he made a dive for the door. But as he did so, down came one leg of the familiar Bunter trousers. "A boy!" cried Miss Twiddlefit. "After him!"

19. But Billy was away, and a Bunter protecting its food takes some catching. Out of the village and down the country road raced Billy with the girls in pursuit. Bunter decided to hide.

20. And Billy's ruse worked, for the girls went dashing past his hiding-place. He chuckled happily as he watched them go, turning to gloat over his loot. Pockets full of apples and a wonderful pie! He was in luck!

21. Billy scoffed the apples and then thought about getting back to Greyfriars. It was a long walk, and he wanted to eat the pie in the comfort of his study. And then as he sat by the roadside a car came into sight.

22. "Ah!" Billy thought. "I'll cadge a lift. They're sure to help a lady in distress!" And when the car came up, Billy told his tale to the driver. "This pie is a present for a very clever boy at Greyfriars, named Bunter," he said.

23. And no sooner were the words out of his mouth than down banged the car window and out through the opening, like a jack-in-a-box, popped the head of Quelchy, the Greyfriars Head. "Step inside, Bunter," said Quelchy meaningly.

24. Well, that was a nasty surprise for our Billy, but he had to climb into the taxi—and was his face red? So there was to be another painful interview in Quelchy's study—and Quelchy had both eyes on that pie, too! Poor Billy—he was fed-up instead of being filled up!

BILLY BUNTER
THE FATTEST SCHOOLBOY ON EARTH!

1. The latest adventures of our hefty hero were certainly hair-raising. Yet it was all because Billy Bunter had to have his hair cut. Sounds funny, doesn't it? But it's the bald truth, so to speak.

2. Now three times Billy had been given money to have his top-knot trimmed. And three times he'd bought buns instead! But another Bunter brain-wave burst forth. Jones Minor would fork out the fourpence.

3. Jonesy didn't like this a jot, but William George had his way. Off they canteed to Courtfield, but Billy stopped when he saw a bill about a beard contest. Gosh! Fancy five pounds for a forest of face fugus!

4. By the time Billy had worked out what five pounds meant in food, the chums had reached the barber's shop. But, oh, what a surprise! The barber had cut off to the pictures.

5. The fat lad was furious! All this walk for nothing and not even a tart to keep his strength up. Then, suddenly, Billy beamed. The side window was open . . . . . !

6. If the barber was away, then there was no need to pay! Billy chortled as he saw the clippers lying ready . . . Jones Minor would do the job! Gosh what a wheeze!

7. But Jones Minor didn't think so, still he followed Billy through the open window. He should've sheered off, but found himself with shears instead. That was the Bunter way!

8. And as Jonesy snipped, Billy gently snored. But for once the fat lad's dreams were not on food. He was dreaming of the bill he'd seen. Five pounds for the longest beard!

9. Suddenly Bunter bounced right off the chair. Gosh, the Bunter wheeze-box was working overtime that day. The barber's shop had given him his biggest brain-wave!

10. Oh gosh! Oh golly! What a wheeze—the wheeziest wheeze that ever wheezed! Billy saw a way to win the five pounds with no bother at all. Chortling, the fat lad gathered up a bag of hair-clippings.

11. Again, it was a time when Jones Minor should've mizzled. But the little lad waited and that was his mistake. Billy grabbed some clippings and stuck 'em on his chum's chin with paste. The beginning of a beard!

12. Never had face fungus sprouted so speedily! Billy slapped on the clippings. Jones Minor open his mouth to protest, but the paste brush stuck there. Jones said no more after that. All he could do was to gurgle.

13. But even if he had been able to shout his head off, Billy wouldn't have paid any attention to his pal's protests. Soon he had slapped on a false beard that fell to the floor. It was just the job!

14. Beaming like a harvest moon with floodlights, Billy led Jones Minor off to the fair—and the five pounds! But even the best pasted-up schemes can come unstuck. It was the breeze that spoilt this wheeze!

15. Yes, as Billy cantered round a corner, the wind whipped the end of the beard out of his hand. Next sec. it was wrapped round his neck! This was more than Billy had bargained for—the paste was still wet.

16. Gosh, what a carry-on there was in Courtfield High Street! The beard stuck to Billy, too, and a tug-o'-war went on between him and Jones Minor. None of them wanted the whiskers, but Billy got them.

17. Yes, the stuck-up hair clippings suddenly snapped off short, and Billy was left with the biggest part. This was unexpected, and so was the gent who grabbed him by the beard. He was one of the judges.

18. So you can judge Billy's surprise at finding himself being led off to the contest. That was to have been Jonesy's job, but the little rotter had wangled out of it. The fat lad fumed as he was led away.

19. But a Bunter is never down for long. Up bounced Billy's spirits like a sorbo ball. Perhaps he'd win the five pounds himself, Billy chortled. It would serve Jones Minor right—the greedy little rotter!

20. Billy's hopes soared to dizzy heights—but there was a dizzier time coming. Before our fat friend realised what was happening, the judge jerked on the beard. Round and round spun Billy.

21. Crash! Bonk! Billy and his beard suddenly parted. No paste was ever made to hold a weight like Bunter's. Billy hit the ground with such a wallop that another earthquake was recorded in China.

22. For a moment the fat lad didn't know what was happening. But he soon learned. The judge jumped into the air with wrath when he saw that Billy's chin covering was false. How the crowd roared, too!

23. For the next half-hour it was Hares and Hounds with the now hairless Billy as the Hare. Howsomever, he dodged the angry crowd and doubled back. But he nearly doubled up when he saw what was happening.

24. The judge was jawing away to Jones Minor and was handing him a pound note. He had won the booby prize as some of the hair clippings were still stuck on his chin. And Billy stuck to him till the quid was spent!

BILLY BUNTER
THE FATTEST SCHOOLBOY ON EARTH!

1. Hallo, what's going on here? It's Bunter giving Jones Minor a piece of his mind. And, mind you, that's the only thing Billy gives away. It was all 'cos Jonesy was overjoyed at Bessie Bunter's visit to Greyfriars.

2. Was Billy jealous of Jonesy? Of course, he was! Big-sister Bessie would bring some grub and Billy didn't want to share it with a greedy, little rotter. There was only enough food for one when Billy was there.

3. Half-past two . . . and Billy wasn't half hungry. Where had that silly ass of a sister got to? Then, suddenly, he was all smiles. There was Bessie beetling up the path with a bag. Billy galloped forward.

4. It was a jolly good job that Jonesy stayed behind. As Billy greeted his sister it was like two hippos meeting head-on. There was such a crash that a pippin popped from the bag.

5. Poor Bessie was in a proper pickle. She'd had a snack, but had saved the apple for her brother. Now there was no apple, but Billy certainly had the pip. The fat lad was furious!

6. Billy was about to send Bessie back on the next bus when a nifty notion came into his noddle. He was suddenly glad to see his sister again. Gosh! . . . She'd help him with a wheeze!

7. Billy beamed. He might be fat, but he wasn't a fathead. His doting sister thought ditto as Billy spilled the beans. Like her brother, Bessie was always a sure starter for the Grub Stakes.

8. Beaming, the brace of Bunters barged along to Billy's study. Here, the fat lad fished out his Sunday best suit and sister changed into it. This was the beginning of Billy's wonder wheeze.

9. Did the suit fit? It was just like a marquee made-to-measure, because Bessie and Billy were built like twin elephants. Billy capped the disguise by covering Bessie's long hair. Now there was hardly any difference.

10. So far, not so dusty, and now for the grub! That's not surprising, for when Billy uses his brains, it isn't food for thought. No, it's food for eating. Now, the wheeze unfoldeth! Watch Bessie!

11. Bessie barged into Bob Cherry's study and helped herself to a big jam tart. She let herself be seen . . . but not by Bob Cherry! A junior saw this daring dollop of daylight robbery. He was meant to!

12. Off he bolted to tell Bob that, if he didn't hurry, his tart would be bolted by Bunter. But what a shock was in store! There was Billy in the flesh—twelve stones of it—talking to Bob!

178

13. The junior just couldn't believe his peepers, but there was no doubt about it. So that was that, and the next one to fall for the wheeze was Jones Minor. There was Bessie in Quelch's study !

14. Bessie was following the famous Bunter tradition of helping herself to more food. Jonesy jumped three feet in the air, then was off at the double to tell Quelchy. The Head had come out of the library.

15. But who should come out after him . . . Billy Bunter ! Jonesy's horn-rims nearly turned up with horror. Here he was telling tales, and there was Bunter with a book. Quelchy glared . . . he took a dim view !

16. Meanwhile, Bessie had got clear again and had bowled along to Bolsover's study. There was a barrel of biscuits just asking to be taken and Bessie obliged. Once again she was seen in the act.

17. And, once again, the fellows who saw it fell for the Bunter wheeze. Off they went in a body. Serve Bunter right ! He wouldn't half catch it hot because Bolsover was a bit of a bully.

18. But was William George worried ? He certainly wasn't, for there he was bowling along the passage with Bolsover. The juniors just couldn't believe their eyes. This was too much of a mystery for them !

19. Bessie was in fine form. There wasn't a scrap of food left in the whole of the Fourth Form, for Bessie had had it. Satisfied with her successful scrounging, off she went to Billy's study for a snack.

20. But while Bessie was feeding her face, the Fourth were yelling their heads off. They went to the Head in a body and said that Bunter had snaffled their snacks. They were wrong this time.

21. At least, Quelchy thought so and for once he was on the fat lad's side. It certainly was a mystery, but the master couldn't do anything about it. For once, Billy Bunter had a cast-iron alibi !

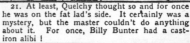

22. But alibis are not for eating, and Billy was beginning to feel hungry. Then, satisfied that he wouldn't be blamed, Bunter made to make off. Good old Bessie ! What a sister to assist him like that !

23. Billy only stopped long enough to make sure that he wasn't being followed by any greedy rotters like Jones Minor. Then he shot off; but when he got there, his study was bare. No grub was in sight.

24. No, but it was all inside Sister Bessie. Not only was Bessie like Billy in looks, but in appetite as well. Her mere snack meant scoffing the lot, and all Billy had was a fond farewell in writing !

179

BILLY BUNTER
THE FATTEST SCHOOLBOY ON EARTH!

1. Believe it or not, but Billy Bunter was happy! Yes, he was eating! Billy had managed to bag a bag of buns. What's more, he'd dodged footer practice. Jaw exercise was what the fat lad liked best.

2. But what was this going on behind the bushes? Billy heard a murmur of voices above his bun-munching. Two nasty bits of no-good were planning to rob Greyfriars' library of some very valuable books.

3. Billy Bunter hated books as much as he liked grub. The crooks could have them. Then, suddenly, Billy sat up. There would be a reward for saving the books. That meant money for more buns!

4. Off hared Billy to the Head's study. Quelchy quizzed at him . . . was his colossal scholar up to his tricks? On second, third and fourth thoughts he began to believe Bunter.

5. While Quelchy was having all these thinks, Billy had only one thought . . . the reward! Well, if that greedy rotter, Quelchy, thought he was to have it, then he'd another think coming.

6. The fat lad loped along to the library. He would lie in wait and catch the crooks. It wasn't easy to find a hiding-place for Billy's bulk, but there was a statue with a hollow base.

7. It was a tight squeeze, this game of weight and see. But, in the meantime, Quelchy had pondered and produced a plan. He, too, would lie in wait in the library.

8. Quelchy's plan was quite a wheeze. He climbed into an empty hamper and had himself carried into the library. Our hero saw the hamper arrive and his hopes rose.

9. Billy thought that hampers were only for holding grub. He groaned when he saw that this one was labelled "Books." What a swizz when he was just in the mood for a snack.

10. The fat lad was really furious now. These book-baggers were certainly a brace of rotters. Why couldn't they hurry up and be caught, so that he could collect the reward. But whassat?

11. Sensation! A loud sneeze had suddenly come from the hamper! Billy blinked. He didn't need three guesses as to who was in the hamper. It must be one of the crooks after the books!

12. Billy moved with the speed he used for dashing after doughnuts. That meant he moved mighty quickly. In two-and-a-half ticks, Billy was fastening down the lid of the hamper. He'd caught the crook!

13. Inside the hamper, the Head was getting into quite a state. He yelled and nearly tore his tonsils loose, but Billy took no notice. "He! He!" chortled Bunter. "That crook can't kid me he's Quelchy!"

14. Next, Billy had to take steps to get the hamper downstairs. That was easy. Billy dragged the hamper to the head of the stairs and pushed. Bump! Bump! Bumpity-bump! Down crashed the hamper.

15. The howls from the hamper were heart-rending. But Billy didn't let that hamper him. The more Quelchy groaned, the more Bunter grinned. He grabbed the phone and dialled Courtfield Backyard 1212.

16. Our hefty hero was all smiles when a brace of bobbies arrived. That was a jolly good job jobbed, and soon he would be collecting the reward. Billy thought of all the buns he would buy!

17. But once again, another Bunter dream was busted! One copper tipped over the basket . . . and out came Quelchy! Billy blinked. It was just like that old rotter to try to keep him from getting the reward.

18. Then Billy suddenly remembered the way he had heaved that hamper downstairs. Gosh! Quelchy would be sore . . . in more ways than one. The fat lad didn't wait for more. He faded as fast as he could.

19. The chase was on! Billy made a bee-line for the library to hide in the hollow statue again. But the fat lad never got that length . . . there was a ladder in the way which he didn't see.

20. And on top of that ladder was one of the bad lads. The crooks had come to collect the books, and the one on top was passing the valuable volumes to his mate below. It was then that Billy barged in!

21. Crash! The fat lad hit the ladder with a mighty wallop. Down came the crook in a shower of books, but the other was there in fighting form. Billy blinked at the big burglar. He hadn't bargained on this

22. Billy tried to do a bunk, but was too late. The crook collared him and the fat lad had a hot five minutes. The most alarming wails were coming from the library when, luckily,

23. That saved Billy's bacon, but the fat was in the fire as far as the book-baggers were concerned. The cops collared them and carried them off to the local lock-up while Quelchy

24. And so Billy Bunter was happy again. Next to grub, he likes bed best. And to have a feed in bed was just what the doctor ordered! Poor old Quelchy. The master had messed-up

BILLY BUNTER
THE FATTEST SCHOOLBOY ON EARTH!

1. Brrrr! The winter night was dreary, but Bunter was somewhat cheery. He didn't care if the wind whistled in the trees. He was whistling happily to himself. William Geo. was on the trail of treasure!

2. No wonder Billy whistled with pleasure at thought of the treasure. He didn't dream of doubloons or gleaming joo-els. Oh no! What he pictured was a plate, piled with doughnuts that he'd buy with the reward.

3. Billy had heard that the treasure was hidden in a haunted house. What's more . . . ooo-er! . . . it was guarded by a ghost! Jones Minor said there were no ghosts, and didn't enter into the spirit of things.

4. But off they went to Spookery Nook. The fat lad took the lead, but not for long. Billy wasn't as barmy as all that. When they reached the house he pushed his pal ahead.

5. Billy thought he was being decent letting Jonesy get the first look at the ghost. But he didn't see what was happening. A slate slipped from the roof and smacked his sit-me-down!

6. The ghost! . . . That silent slap certainly startled Billy. He bounced into the air, then got off his mark. Into the haunted house went the fat lad at full steam ahead.

7. Jones Minor went with him—he couldn't help himself! When Billy pushed, he shoved like a steam-shovel. Suddenly, Billy stopped and had a second think. He couldn't see a ghost.

8. And he couldn't see Jonesy, 'cos the little lad had fallen through a trapdoor. That was another thing Billy didn't see. He stepped forward into the wide open space . . .

9. Luckily, Jones Minor made a more or less happy landing. He landed in a box of sheets and such things. But the mighty weight of Bunter was on its way downwards!

10. But Jonesy's luck held. Billy caught the edge of the opening and held on. Gosh, what an escape! If his fat pal had landed, he would've been flatter than a Pancake Tuesday special! with all that weight on top!

11. Meanwhile, Billy was swinging about like the man on the flying trapeze. But not with the greatest of ease. He shook at the knees! The fat lad looked round and saw a sinister shape arise!

12. That ghost again! Billy let out a yell like a Sioux savage taking a top-note. But there was really no need for the fat lad to be frightened. It was only Jones Minor, arising from the laundry he'd landed in.

13. But as Billy let out his yell, he let go his hold. Thud! The haunted house shivered to its foundations as the fat lad landed. Jonesy shivered, too! A ghost, plus Bunter in a bad temper, was too much for him.

14. But there were more goings-on than ghosts! A brace of bad lads had squatted in Spookery Nook. They were a couple of convicts using the haunted house as a hide-out. They heard Billy hit the floor—who wouldn't!

15. By this time Billy was trying to get through the trapdoor. Suddenly, the box he was standing on began to shake. Gosh, that silly ass Jones was trembling again. He couldn't see what there was to be scared about.

16. But the only reason that Billy couldn't see was because his back was turned. Then the fat lad looked round and . . . Ooo-er . . . there was a ghostly object. Billy blinked — this was too bad!

17. The fat lad thought it was Jonesy up to his larks again. But if he'd known that a convict was under that cover, he'd never had the courage to tackle him. But in Billy Bunter's case, ignorance was certainly bliss.

18. Meanwhile, Mr. Quelch, the Head, was getting worried. The most unusual thing had happened in the history of Greyfriars. Billy Bunter hadn't appeared for supper! Something serious must have made him go astray.

19. So Quelchy called at the local cop-shop, and, being a regular customer, was supplied with a bobby. Off they beetled in the search for Bunter and heard sounds coming from Spookery Nook. Nasty noises they were, too.

20. It was Bunter doing battle with the convict. Jonesy had scrammed to shelter and Billy didn't know who was behind the sheet. It was a good job, too, because Billy wouldn't have been so brave as all that.

21. But, in spite of his good fight, Billy wasn't getting the best of the battle. In fact, the fat lad was all in when the copper fell in. The man in blue had found the open trapdoor just too late. In he dropped!

22. Thud! The copper crashed on the convict, but help was at hand. The other bad lad rushed to the rescue, and then Quelchy arrived. He toppled through the trapdoor, right on top of the rescuing rascal.

23. Gosh, what a free-for-all followed! But Billy Bunter wasn't having any. The sight of Quelchy had scared him more than any ghost, which goes to prove many things. But the master was too busy for the moment.

24. In a brace of shakes the bad lads were bagged. There was a reward for their capture, too, but Quelchy decided to buy books with it. Billy groaned and staggered off to supper. **They could keep their haunted houses!**

BILLY BUNTER
THE FATTEST SCHOOLBOY ON EARTH!

1. It was a cold and frosty morning. Court-field Pond was frozen hard and Billy Bunter was bored stiff. It was the annual skating competition between Mr. Quelch and Colonel Bracebutton. And Bunter had to be there.

2. Now, Billy Bunter likes to see icing, not on ponds, but on cakes. What made matters somewhat worse was the fact that the fat lad had to roast chestnuts. But he wasn't allowed to eat any of them!

3. The chestnuts were for competitors only. It was a sad blow to Billy. It made our William writhe in agony to cook chestnuts for other people. In fact, it nearly drove him nuts. How could he collar a couple or so?

4. But Quelchy seemed to read his thoughts. He forbade Billy to consume any of his cooking. What's more he had counted the nuts and, being a headmaster, he could count.

5. Billy hadn't counted on that. What he said about Quelchy was nobody's business except Bunter's. In fact, his thoughts sizzled so much that they nearly cracked the ice.

6. Meanwhile, the competition had started and Quelchy was doing his stuff. As Billy moaned, Jones Minor got on with the job of roasting the nuts. Billy sniffed. It was a nifty niff!

7. At last Billy could stand it no longer. He leaned his fat against the notice-board with a handful of roasted nuts. Yes, they were silly asses to skate when nuts could be eaten.

8. Cr-r-a-ack! The sound suddenly drowned out the noise of Billy munching the nuts. Bunter's weight was too much for the board. The pole snapped and Billy fell flat on his fat back.

9. But he was flat on the board and the board had fallen on the ice! Swoosh! Away shot Billy like a seal on a sledge, straight in the path of the oncoming Quelchy!

10. What was to be did? Quelchy gathered his wits . . . and his legs . . . together at the same time and jumped. The master did an amazing dive, then landed with a terrific clump on the cold stuff. That ice didn't feel so nice!

11. Quelchy was really rattled. Every bone in his classical carcase had been jarred and he charged at Billy in fury. The fat lad thought it just nice time to fade away. But how could he keep his feet on the ice?

12. It was a proper problem, but there was no time to ponder. Off went the fat lad in a frantic effort to escape from the furious Quelchy, but there's many a slip. In fact, Billy started slipping straight away.

13. THUD ! Billy hit the ice and shot across it like a two-ton toboggan. He was right in the path of the oncoming Quelchy again ! Billy groaned. Why couldn't the rotter keep out of his way at a time like this !

14. Quelchy was thinking the same thinks. Once again, the master did a nifty bit of manoeuvring, and just managed to miss Bunter. A crowd had gathered on the bank, but hadn't banked on seeing such skating.

15. In fact, there was a proper funny turn going on. But it was nothing to the turns that Billy was having. Bunter had often twisted others, but this time he was twisting himself. Round he twisted on the ice.

16. Talk about a pivoting porpoise ! Billy tried to get to his feet . . . a very difficult feat on ice. Swoosh ! Billy slipped again and away he careered like a catherine-wheel. One good turn seemed to deserve another.

17. But the master was madder than a hatter —or even a mortar-board-maker ! He thought Billy was acting the giddy goat. Billy was giddy ! He was so dizzy he didn't know whether it was Boxing Day or Pancake Tuesday.

18. But, even though he was in a dizzy dream, Bunter automatically went towards the eats. Round he spun, straight to where the chestnuts were roasting. Crash ! Bunter hit that brazier with a bang !

19. Next second, Quelchy was caught in a shower of sizzling chestnuts. The fat lad had bumped the brazier so badly that it shot in the air, scattering the nuts. Billy groaned as he saw the goodies going west.

20. It was sad to see these lovely nuts making the ice sizzle. But, at the same time, Quelchy was nearly boiling over with wrath. There he stood, surrounded by the roasted nuts, and giving Bunter a proper roasting, too !

21. Crr-rr-a-a-ck ! Suddenly, there came the nasty noise of ice breaking. Quelchy, giving vent to his wrath, didn't see the ice giving way where the hot chestnuts had melted it. Down, went the master into the wet.

22. Brrrr ! That water was more than wet, it was mighty cold as well. But it didn't cool off Quelchy's wrath . . . it made him grow more hotter under the collar than ever. Of course, Bunter got the blame for it all.

23. But that was just until the judge of the skating competition arrived. He had seen all Quelchy's sensational skating in his attempts to avoid his porky pupil. The result was that the master won the first prize.

24. Five pounds was the prize, but all that Billy got was the job of carrying five pounds of chestnuts back to school. What's more, he had to roast them for Quelchy as he lay in bed . . . which was just too bad for Billy !

185

NOBODY WANTS BILLY BUNTER!

 GO!  OW!

BUNTER'S EXERCISE BOOK! WHAT A DISGRACE! BLOBS AND BLOTS - JAMMY FINGER MARKS - AND CAKE CRUMBS BETWEEN THE PAGES!

 I HAVE TRIED - I HAVE BEEN PATIENT - BUT - ALAS -

 HOWEVER, I WILL ATTEMPT TO REASON WITH THE STUPID YOUTH ONCE MORE -

WHY - WHAT AN UNTIDY STUDY! SUCH DISORDER - SUCH LITTER -

 WHERE IS BUNTER? I AM LOSING MY TEMPER!

 MR. QUELCH - SIR! WILL YOU PLEASE COME ALONG TO MY PANTRY -

 WITH MY VERY OWN EYES I SAW THE THIEF SNEAK FROM THE PANTRY, SIR -

 TWO DOZEN CAKES STOLEN FROM THIS TRAY, SIR! I WAS JUST IN TIME TO SPOT THE YOUNG VARMINT - MASTER BUNTER -

 BUNTER AGAIN!! IT'S ALWAYS BUNTER! BUNTER! BUNTER!

 PLEASE COME - MANY APPLES HAVE VANISHED FROM THE STORE IN THE SCHOOL SHED!

 THE SHED DOOR HAD BEEN FORCED - BUT I SAW THE CULPRIT LEAVE - YOUNG BUNTER, SIR! O LOR! IS COOKIE TELLING TALES?

 THERE IS THE PROOF, SIR - AND THAT FAT BOY IS GUILTY OF THE THEFT!

 TEE! HEE! WHAT A JOLLY FINE SNACK! CAKES AND APPLES! I'LL SNOOP AROUND FOR SOME MORE GRUB - THE ROTTERS CAN'T PROVE IT WAS ME!

 FIND BUNTER - IT IS MOST URGENT! I WILL SEE HIM IN MY STUDY, JONES MINOR! YES, SIR.

 COME IN! TAP-TAP-

 OH - ER - MRS. MIMBLE OF THE TUCK SHOP - ENTER, DEAR LADY. I EXPECTED -

 I HAVE NO WISH TO TROUBLE YOU, MR. QUELCH - BUT I THINK YOU SHOULD KNOW THE AMOUNT MASTER BUNTER OWES ME FOR CAKES AND LEMONADE. HE WOULD BE MY BEST CUSTOMER - IF HE PAID, SIR! F-FOUR POUNDS FOURTEEN SHILLINGS AND SIXPENCE!

 THANK YOU, SIR. I WILL ACCEPT BUNTER'S DEBT FROM YOU. I HOPE YOU GET IT BACK FROM THAT DREADFUL BOY!

 NO SIGN OF BUNTER YET! DOES THE BOY DEFY ME? ALAS! THAT I SHOULD SUFFER SO!

 MEANWHILE COO! I SPY A CAKE ON TODDY'S TABLE!

PLEASE SIR-I LOOKED FOR BUNTER IN HIS STUDY-AND FOUND MY BAG OF SWEETS-AND ONLY TWO LEFT!

ENOUGH! THE BOY IS A MENACE TO THE WHOLE SCHOOL! MY MIND IS MADE UP! YES-- I HAVE DECIDED!

CORKS! HERE'S QUELCHY! I'LL TELL HIM IT MUST HAVE BEEN SOME OTHER ROTTER-

WILLIAM GEORGE BUNTER- I CANNOT TOLERATE YOUR BEHAVIOUR A MOMENT LONGER! I HAVE REACHED A STERN DECISION, AND NO PLEADING WILL INDUCE ME TO ALTER IT!
I WONDER WHAT ALL THAT MEANS?

YOU ARE EXPELLED FROM GREYFRIARS!
EH? YOU CAN'T-- THAT IS-- ER-- FATHER WILL WALLOP ME--

W.G. BUNTER WILL BE EXPELLED FROM GREYFRIARS SCHOOL
FATTY BUNTER IS IN DISGRACE!

OW! THE ROTTER! I'D BETTER GO AND PACK MY BAG!

BLUB! ALL THE ROTTERS ARE AGAINST ME-JUST 'COS I'VE GOT A JOLLY GOOD APPETITE-BLUB! I'LL BET THAT BEAST QUELCHY FEELS PECKISH AT TIMES!

JUST LOOK! THAT FAT, GREEDY OWL IS ABOUT TO SNAFFLE MY FRUIT CAKE! I'VE CAUGHT HIM IN THE ACT!
YUM!

WHAT ROWDY SCENE IS TAKING PLACE IN TODD'S STUDY?
THUMP!
BUMP!
OUCH! OW!

BUNTER WAS ABOUT TO SCOFF MY CAKE, SIR!
BUNTER-- AGAIN!

TO MY STUDY! I CANNOT ALLOW YOU TO ROAM THIS SCHOOL ANY LONGER! AWAIT MY RETURN, BUNTER!
O LOR'! WHAT SNEAKS-

OH-BUNTER-GLUB-THIS IS GUG-GOODBYE. I SHALL MISS YOU, DEAR B-BUNTER! GUG-GOODBYE-GLUP-
GULP!

WILLIAM GEORGE BUNTER BIDS A SAD FAREWELL TO HIS OLD STUDY-
GLUB!

-AND SLOWLY-SADLY-WADDLES INTO THE MAIN HALL OF GREYFRIARS-
BLUB!

ESCORTED BY MR. QUELCH TO THE SCHOOL GATE-

GO!
OW!

-THE DUMPY, FAT FIGURE PASSES ON TO-WHO KNOWS WHERE?

BILLY HAS BEEN EXPELLED.

O CRUMBS! EXPELLED FROM GREYFRIARS! IF I GO HOME PA WILL WALLOP ME—OW! WHAT CAN I DO?

I'M GETTING HUNGRY, TOO—AND QUELCHY TURNED ME AWAY WITHOUT EVEN A SANDWICH! O LOR! WHERE CAN I GO?

WHY—BESSIE! DEAR SISTER BESSIE WON'T LET ME STARVE IN THIS COLD, CRUEL WORLD! I'LL TODDLE ALONG TO HER SCHOOL—

THANK GOODNESS I'VE GOT SOMEWHERE TO GO—AND SOMEONE TO FEED ME!

O JOY! HERE COMES DEAR, KIND SISTER BESSIE! HOW LUCKY! SHE CAN CARRY MY BAG!

WILLIAM! WHAT ARE YOU DOING? WHERE ARE YOU GOING? WHAT'S IN THE CASE—

I'VE BEEN EX—

EXCUSED LESSONS FOR THE DAY? GOODY! AND YOU'VE GOT A BAG OF FOOD FOR A PICNIC—

HOW LUCKY WE MET, WILLIAM YOU MUST BE TIRED—SO I'LL CARRY THE FOOD!

BUT—ER—

DON'T LAG, BROTHER. LET'S ENJOY YOUR DAY'S HOLIDAY!

THAT IS—LISTEN TO ME, BESSIE—

HERE'S A NICE SPOT FOR A PICNIC—LET'S GET BUSY!

A PICNIC—GUR!

NOW LET'S SEE WHAT NICE GOODIES YOU HAVE FOR ME TO SAMPLE! I'LL OPEN THE CASE—

YOU CAN HAVE ALL THE GRUB YOU FIND IN THAT CASE—AND I HOPE YOU ENJOY IT!

OH! WILLIAM!

OF COURSE—IF YOU INSIST, I WILL SCOFF THE LOT, WILLIAM!

GO AHEAD—TEE! HEE!

TE! HE! HE! A FAT LOT BESSIE WILL FIND IN THAT BAG!

COO! RIGHT ON TOP! A JAM SPONGE! OH, THANK YOU, DEAR BILLY!

EH?

A JAM SPONGE! GIVE IT TO ME! THAT MUST BE JONES MINOR'S PARTING GIFT—

GREEDY! YOU SAID I COULD HAVE IT!

HI! BESSIE! KEEP YOUR TEETH AWAY FROM THAT SPONGE—IT'S MINE! IT'S ALL I'VE GOT TO EAT! HI!

O CRUMBS! OO! THE GREEDY ROTTER! I'LL TELL FATHER—I MEAN—COME BACK BEFORE YOU SCOFF THE LOT!

MUNCH!

I'M SAFE NOW! WILLIAM DARE NOT FOLLOW ME INTO MY SCHOOL!

WHAT A MEAN TRICK TO PLAY ON HER UNLUCKY BROTHER! HOW COULD BESSIE BE SO CRUEL—

O LOR! SHE'S SCOOTED INTO SCHOOL WITH JONES MINOR'S PARTING GIFT! A LOVELY JAM SPONGE—OW!

CORKS! I'VE LOST ALL MY TOGS, TOO! THIS IS ALL BESSIE'S FAULT! I'VE NO GRUB—NO MONEY—NOWHERE TO GO—NO NOTHING—

BESSIE MUST HELP ME—AND I'VE GOT A JOLLY GOOD WHEEZE HOW TO GET IN!

GIRLS SCHOOL NO ADMITTANCE EXCEPT ON BUSINESS.

I HAVE TO DELIVER THIS CASE TO THE—ER—HEADMISTRESS MYSELF! MOST IMPORTANT, YOU KNOW—

ON YOUR WAY.

THAT'S THAT! NOW TO FIND BESSIE—AND CADGE SOME GRUB—ENOUGH TO LAST ME A FEW WEEKS!

COO! I'M LUCKY! THERE'S MY SISTER—COO-EE! BESSIE!

BE A SPORT AND FILL THIS CASE WITH GRUB FOR ME—YOU SCOFFED MY JAM SPONGE!

NO!

SLAM!

OW!

O LOR! WHAT CAN I DO NOW? EVEN BESSIE HAS TURNED AGAINST ME—I'M ALONE IN THE WORLD!

COO! I'M NOT ALONE NOW! THERE'S SOME LOVELY GRUB THAT CAN JOIN ME—HERE GOES TO FILL MY CASE!

HEE! HEE! I'M JOLLY GLAD I CAME ALONG TO BESSIE'S SCHOOL—I WAS LUCKY TO BE EXPELLED BY QUELCHY!

NOW I'LL SLIP OUT AND SETTLE DOWN TO A NICE SNACK! I'M GOING TO ENJOY THESE CAKES!

AH! THE PORTER TOLD ME ABOUT AN IMPORTANT CASE—HAND IT OVER, MY DEAR BOY!

EH? O LOR!

THANK YOU!

HERE, THAT'S MINE—ER—THAT IS—I MEAN—OW! I'D BETTER BEAT IT!

FOOD?

CRUMBS! I'VE LOST MY GRUB! WHAT A BEASTLY SWIZZ!

OH MY! NO ONE TO HELP ME NOW! NO FOOD—AND NOWHERE TO LAY MY WEARY HEAD!

IT'S GETTING DARK—AND IT'S COLD! OH DEAR! HOW I WISH I WAS IN MY WARM, COSY BED AT GREYFRIARS. NOBODY WANTS ME!

OW! NOW IT'S BEGINNING TO RAIN!

BLUB!

BILLY BUNTER FINDS HIS BREAKFAST

"O CRUMBS! I CAN'T STAY HERE—I MUST FIND SHELTER!"

"QUELCHY HAS EXPELLED ME FROM GREYFRIARS—BESSIE TURNED ME AWAY—I'M LONELY AND JOLLY HUNGRY!"

"AND I'VE NOWHERE TO SLEEP! NOT A FRIEND IN THE WORLD—"

"COO! SHELTER AT LAST. I CAN TAKE COVER UNDER THIS ROOF— GULP!"

"OW! WHAT A LIFE! I AM UNHAPPY!"

"OO-BLUB-UG! BOO-HOO!"

"WHAT'S ALL THIS SHINDY OUTSIDE MY BARN?" THUMP!

"SORRY! I DIDN'T KNOW—ER—I THOUGHT IT WAS A SICK ANIMAL!" HOWL!

"P-PLEASE—I'VE NOWHERE TO SLEEP—N-NOTHING TO EAT—I'VE BEEN EXPELLED—AND—OW! I'M COLD AND WET!"

"YOU CAN SNUGGLE DOWN IN THIS OLD BARN FOR THE NIGHT. MAYBE A BIT OF BREAKFAST IN THE MORNING—" "BREAKFAST? COO!"

"I CAN PUT UP WITH THIS—IF I'M GETTING A JOLLY GOOD FEED IN THE MORNING!"

ZZ-Z-

"OW! W-WHAT'S THAT?" OO-WOO—

"GUR! NOW THAT HOOTING OWL HAS GONE-ILL TRY AND SLEEP!"

SLAP!

"OW! I'VE GOT A BEASTLY HORSE FOR A NEIGHBOUR! GO AWAY!"

"O LOR! WHAT A NIGHT! I'LL TRY AND SNOOZE OVER IN THIS CORNER—"

"THERE'S NOTHING TO DISTURB ME NOW. I'LL SETTLE DOWN FOR A GOOD NIGHT'S SLEEP!"

"WAKEY! WAKEY! IT'S BREAK O' DAY! LET'S GET MOVING, SON!" "EH? I HAVEN'T SLEPT A WINK—"

"JUST SWEEP OUT YOUR SLEEPING QUARTERS—THEN WE'LL START THE DAY'S WORK!" "WHAT? WORK? I WANT BREAKFAST!"

"NOW—NOW! WORK FIRST—THEN BREAKFAST!" "W-WORK! OW! IT'S A SWIZZ!"

191

BILLY TAKES THE CAKES

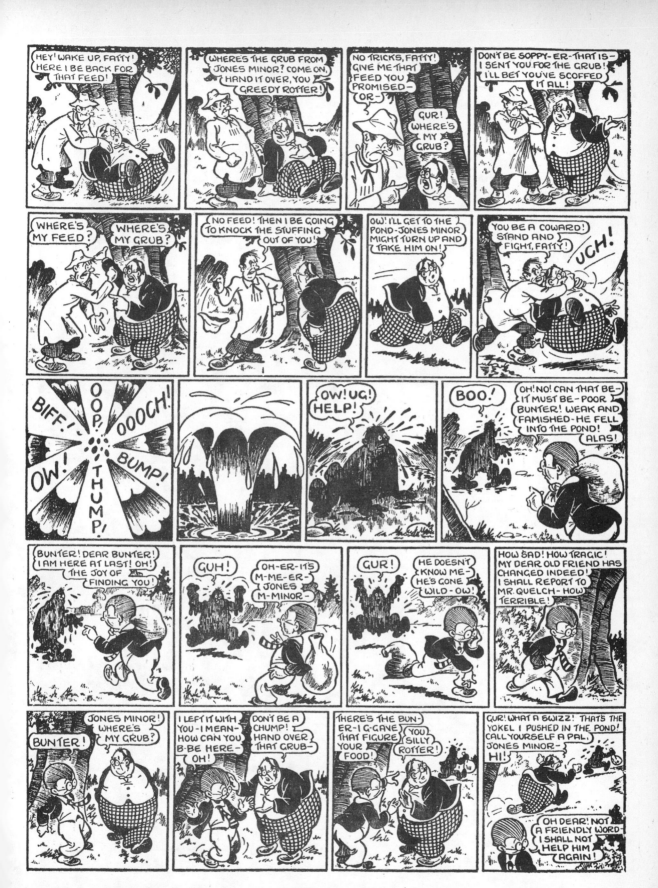

195

BILLY BUNTER HAS BEEN EXPELLED FROM SCHOOL

O LOR! I CAN'T BEAR TO THINK OF ANOTHER NIGHT IN THE OPEN - AND SLEEPING ON AN EMPTY TUMMY!

CRUMBS! WHEN I THINK OF ALL THE LOVELY CAKES AND JAM TARTS - AND WHAT WOULDN'T I GIVE TO BE IN THE GREYFRIARS PANTRY ONCE MORE!

THIS KID LOOKS LIKE A COLLEGE BOY. I WONDER IF HE COULD TELL ME HOW TO GET TO WHERE I WANT TO GO?

AH! YOU LOOK A LIKELY LAD. HAVE A CHOCOLATE. YOU BELONG TO GREYFRIARS SCHOOL, DON'T YOU? I WENT THERE ONCE - HAVE ANOTHER CHOC!

CHOCS! COO - TA!

YOU KNOW, MY BOY - THERE'S NOTHING I'D LIKE BETTER THAN TO LOOK ROUND THE OLD SCHOOL AGAIN. AH! WHAT HAPPY DAYS I SPENT THERE!

MUNCH! YES, SIR. HAVE YOU GOT ANOTHER CHOCOLATE?

I DON'T SUPPOSE THERE'S ANY HOPE OF GETTING INTO THE SCHOOL, IS THERE? I'D GIVE THIS BOX OF CHOCS TO ANYONE WHO COULD HELP ME!

THE WHOLE BOX! OO! I'LL HELP YOU, SIR!

I DON'T WANT TO GET THERE BEFORE IT'S DARK - SO WE WON'T HURRY! TELL ME ABOUT THE SCHOOL - CAN WE GET IN QUIETLY IF THE PLACE IS LOCKED - WITHOUT DISTURBING ANYBODY?

COO! THAT'S EASY!

THERE'S GREYFRIARS SCHOOL. CAN I HAVE THE CHOCOLATES NOW?

SORRY, MY BOY! YOU CAN HAVE THEM WHEN WE'RE SAFELY INSIDE!

A LITTLE LATER

HE! HE! THIS IS A BIT OF LUCK! I'LL GO IN WITH THIS CHAP - AND WHILE HE'S LOOKING ROUND THE OLD SCHOOL, I'LL PAY A QUICK VISIT TO THE PANTRY!

THE GATES ARE LOCKED, SO WE'LL HAVE TO GET OVER THE WALL. THAT'S EASY!

I'LL GO FIRST, CHUM!

THEN YOU CAN PULL ME UP!

PUFF! POOF!

OO! I'M LOSING MY BALANCE! DON'T LET ME FALL!

OW-W!

WHAT A BEASTLY TRICK! THE ROTTER'S BUNKED - AND LEFT ME ALL ALONE!

QUIET, YOU CLUCK!

OOW!

NOT SO MUCH NOISE! LEAD ME TO AN OPEN WINDOW OR AN UNLOCKED DOOR -

YOU SCARED ME!

YOU SHIN UP THIS DRAINPIPE AND SEE IF THERE'S AN OPEN WINDOW ABOVE!

BUT THE PANTRY'S NOT UP THERE - I MEAN -

O CRUMBS! I WISH I HADN'T MET THAT ROTTER! QUELCHY MIGHT SEE ME AND THINK I'M A BURGLAR!

197

BILLY BUNTER

THE FATTEST SCHOOLBOY ON EARTH!

UNUSUAL ANNUAL STRIPS WITH ONE ARTIST DOING THE MAIN ILLUSTRATIONS AND FRANK MINNITT'S VERSION OF BUNTER ADDED.

BILLY BUNTER BARGES IN
He's the Fattest Schoolboy on Earth!

IT WAS THE DAY OF THE JUNIOR SPORTS TROPHY RACE AT GREYFRIARS SCHOOL, AND A LARGE CROWD WAS GATHERED IN THE QUAD TO WATCH THE WHOLE OF THE REMOVE FORM SET OUT ON THEIR CROSS-COUNTRY RACE. WINGATE, THE HEAD PREFECT, FIRED THE STARTING-PISTOL~~ AND THE RUNNERS STREAMED OUT OF GATES AMID LOUD CHEERS!

GO IT, THE REMOVE!

KEEP IT UP, BUNTER! ONLY FIVE MORE MILES TO GO! HA, HA, HA!

HARRY WHARTON AND INKY SOON TOOK THE LEAD.

THE ESTEEMED QUELCH HAS GRANTED THE REMOVE LATE PASSES FOR TO-NIGHT, OLD CHUM! THE BINGEFULNESS WILL BE TERRIFIC!

SAVE YOUR BREATH, YOU ASS!

MEANWHILE, BILLY BUNTER GASPED ALONG IN THE REAR~~

OOF~~ THE BEASTS~ I'D JOLLYWELL RUN RINGS ROUND THEM IF I WASN'T FEELING A BIT OFF-COLOUR~

BILLY BUNTER PUFFED AND GROANED AS HE STAGGERED ALONG AT A SNAIL'S PACE.

THEN HIS LITTLE EYES GLEAMED AS HE DREW NEAR TO THE GATEWAY OF THE OLD DERELICT FRIARDALE GRANGE. ~~

I'LL TAKE A SHORT CUT ACROSS THE GROUNDS OF THE OLD GRANGE. THAT SHOULD BRING ME OUT ON THE ROAD AHEAD OF THE OTHER BEASTS! HE, HE! I'LL SHOW THEM!

BUT AS BUNTER PASSED THE OLD RUINED HOUSE, HE SNIFFED CURIOUSLY~~

SNIFF~~ THAT'S JOLLY STRANGE! SNIFF SNIFF~~SMELLS LIKE GRUB! BUT THE OLD HOUSE HAS BEEN EMPTY FOR YEARS~~

PERHAPS SOME PICKNICKERS~~ I WONDER IF THEY'D SPARE A CHAP A SPOT OF GRUB ~~ I'M SIMPLY FAMISHED ~~ NO HARM IN ASKING ~~

MY HAT, WHAT A FEAST! JUST WHAT I DESERVE AFTER ALL THIS ROTTEN HARD WORK ~~

BUT AS BILLY BUNTER TUCKED IN GREEDILY ~~

THUNDER! WHAT IS THIS! I'LL HAVE THAT FOOL KRALEK FLOGGED FOR THIS ~~

THEN BUNTER GAVE A WILD YELL AS THE MAN SPRANG.

YOU SHALL NOT LEAVE HERE ALIVE, FAT FOOL!

YAROOH! HELP! WHAT IS IT! LEMME OUT OF HERE!

IN DESPERATION, BUNTER HURLED THE PIE FULL IN THE FOREIGNER'S FACE, AND RAN FOR DEAR LIFE.

OUCH! HELP! MURDER!

CURSE YOU!

BUNTER STREAKED AWAY ACROSS THE FIELDS, RUNNING AS HE HAD NEVER RUN BEFORE.

HELP! HE'S AFTER ME! POLICE! FIRE! MURDER!

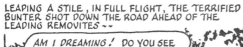

LEAPING A STILE, IN FULL FLIGHT, THE TERRIFIED BUNTER SHOT DOWN THE ROAD AHEAD OF THE LEADING REMOVITES ~~

AM I DREAMING! DO YOU SEE WHAT I SEE, WHARTON?

BUNTER! BUT IT CAN'T BE, SMITHY!

BUNTER TORE IN THROUGH THE GATES OF GREYFRIARS ~~ AHEAD OF THE FIELD.

MY ONLY SAINTED AUNT! IT'S BUNTER! BUNTER'S WON THE JUNIOR TROPHY!

BLESS MY SOUL!

I CAN HARDLY BELIEVE MY EYES! THIS IS INDEED A GREAT PLEASURE, MY BOY! HERE IS YOUR WELL-DESERVED TROPHY!

OUCH! I SAY, IS THAT BEAST STILL BEHIND ME?

THE WHOLE GIDDY LOT ARE BEHIND YOU, OLD FAT MAN! YOU'RE A GIDDY HERO!

THREE CHEERS FOR BUNTER!

BUT LATER, IN THE REMOVE CORRIDOR ~~

JUST A MINUTE, YOU SWINDLING FAT ROTTER! WE'RE GOING TO FIND OUT HOW YOU WON THAT TROPHY ~~

YAROOH! HANDS OFF, BULL, YOU BEAST! YOU CAN HAVE THE ROTTEN TROPHY FOR ALL I CARE ~~

BUMP THE TRUTH OUT OF THE FAT TOAD!

YAROOH! LET ME GO, YOU ROTTERS!

OUCH! YOU ROTTERS! ROTTEN JEALOUSY, JUST BECAUSE I WON THE TROPHY ~~

BOYS! IS THIS INDEED TRUE? YOU DARE TO BULLY BUNTER BECAUSE HE BEAT YOU AT SPORT. THIS IS DISGRACEFUL!

THE WHOLE FORM WILL REMAIN IN GATES TO-NIGHT, EXCEPT BUNTER! YOUR LATE PASSES ARE CANCELLED!

BUT SIR, WE'D ARRANGED TO SEE A SHOW. WE'VE BOOKED OUR SEATS ~~

WITH A SWISH OF HIS GOWN, MR QUELCH SWEPT AWAY ANGRILY DOWN THE CORRIDOR ~~

IT'S JOLLY UNFAIR! WHY SHOULD WE BE GATED BECAUSE OF THAT FAT ROTTER ~~

THERE'S NOTHING WE CAN DO ABOUT IT, BOB ~~~

OH YES, THERE IS! I VOTE WE GO OUT TO-NIGHT, ANYWAY! BLOW OLD QUELCH! WHAT DO YOU FELLOWS SAY?

COUNT ME IN, BOB! I'LL JOIN YOU!

THEN THE BEDTIME BELL RANG, AND THE SURLY REMOVITES MADE THEIR WAY TO THE DORMITORY ~~

SO IT'S JUST YOU AND ME, HAZELDENE! THE OTHERS HAVE GOT COLD FEET ~~

DON'T TALK ROT, BOB ~~

YOU'RE ASKING FOR THE SACK. QUELCH WILL BE WATCHING LIKE A HAWK!

I'M GOING ~~ AND THAT'S THAT!

MY ESTEEMED BOB, YOU WILL GET IT WHERE THE ESTEEMED CHICKEN GOT THE CHOPPER ~~

NO-ONE ELSE COMING? LAST OFFER!

YOU BLITHERING CHUMP! YOU DON'T REALLY MEAN TO BREAK BOUNDS, DO YOU ~?

BOB AND HAZELDENE STARTED DOWN THE IVY, AS BUNTER ROLLED INTO THE DORMITORY ~~

I SAY! WHERE ARE THOSE CADS GOING? I BET IT'S A FEED, AND THE BEASTS ARE TRYING TO HOG IT FOR THEMSELVES! GREEDY ROTTERS!

HA HA HA!

I'M JOLLYWELL GOING AFTER THEM ~~ THEY CAN'T SWINDLE ME OUT OF A FEED ~~~

YOU'RE STAYING HERE, YOU FAT IDIOT!

AS HARRY WHARTON GRABBED AT BUNTER, THE FAT OWL OF THE REMOVE LASHED OUT ~~

SHAN'T! KEEP YOUR HANDS OFF ME, YOU BEAST! TAKE THAT!

OUCH! OW! MY NOSE!

COME BACK, YOU FAT FROG, AND I'LL BURST YOU!

YAH! GO AND EAT COKE, WHARTON! I'D JOLLYWELL MOP THE FLOOR WITH YOU IF I CAME BACK!

THERE THEY GO, THE BEASTS! WELL, THEY'RE NOT GOING TO LEAVE ME OUT OF A FEED ~~ BETTER NOT LET THE ROTTERS SEE ME ~~

THEN BOB AND HAZELDENE NEARED THE OLD GATES OF FRIARDALE GRANGE ~~

LET'S TAKE THE SHORT CUT TO FRIARDALE. IT'LL SAVE US QUITE A WALK ~~

I ~~ I SUPPOSE IT'S ALL RIGHT? LOOKS A BIT SPOOKY IN THE MOONLIGHT ~~

ROT! THE PLACE IS EMPTY AND THERE'S NO SUCH THING AS GHOSTS ~~

WAIT! LOOK THERE, BOB! THAT LIGHT, IN THE WINDOW THERE! WHAT ~~ WHAT IS IT?

MY HAT, YOU'RE RIGHT! THERE'S SOMETHING QUEER GOING ON HERE! IT'S BEEN EMPTY FOR AGES ~~~ I'M GOING TO TAKE A LOOK ~~

I DON'T LIKE IT LET'S GO, BOB ~~

MEANWHILE, A FAT FIGURE WAS CREEPING UP THE WEED-COVERED DRIVE BEHIND THEM ~~

DON'T BE AN ASS! COME ON!

OH CRUMBS, THEY'RE GOING INTO THE OLD GRANGE! THAT FOREIGN ROTTER MIGHT STILL BE THERE ~~

THEN BUNTER SNORTED AND HIS LITTLE EYES GLEAMED.

OF COURSE! I GET IT NOW! THAT FOREIGN ROTTER MUST HAVE BEEN CHERRY OR HAZELDENE IN A DISGUISE. IT WAS JUST A TRICK TO SCARE ME AWAY FROM THEIR MOULDY FEED! THE BEASTS!

MEANWHILE, BOB AND HAZELDENE HAVE REACHED AN OLD GALLERY OVERLOOKING THE OAK-PANELLED STUDY ~~

MY HAT! LOOK DOWN THERE! SO THAT'S WHAT'S GOING ON!

WE'VE GOT TO GET OUT OF HERE! QUICK!

AT MID-NIGHT, KRARK WILL BE HERE WITH THE FINAL SECRET DOCUMENTS. THEN WE LEAVE FOR HOME FROM OUR SECRET AIRFIELD. BY TO-MORROW, THE LATEST BRITISH ATOM SECRETS WILL BE IN OUR HANDS!

GOSH, THEY'RE ATOM SPIES! THEY'RE STEALING DOCUMENTS FROM THE NEW ATOMIC STATION NEAR COURTFIELD, I'LL BET!

COME ON! THEY'LL MURDER US IF THEY FIND US HERE! WE'VE GOT TO GO ~ ~ ~

MEANWHILE, A FAT FIGURE TIP-TOED WARILY INTO THE OLD HOUSE ~ ~

THE BEASTS MUST BE IN THERE! THE GREEDY ROTTERS! MEAN BEASTS, TRYING TO KEEP A FELLOW OUT OF A FEED ~ ~

BLOWED IF I CAN SEE ANY GRUB. PERHAPS THEY HAVEN'T BROUGHT IT OUT YET. THE BEASTS HAVEN'T HAD TIME TO SCOFF IT ~ ~ ~

THEN A GRIP OF IRON FELL ON BUNTER'S SHOULDER AND HE WAS PUSHED FORWARD INTO THE ROOM.

I FOUND HIM LISTENING AT THE DOOR, PROFESSOR!

WELL DONE, MARCOVITCH! WE KNOW HOW TO DEAL WITH HIS KIND! BRING HIM HERE!

THEN BUNTER PULLED FREE, AND LEAPED AT THE PROFESSOR.

I KNOW YOU, HAZELDENE, YOU ROTTER! OFF WITH THAT SILLY BEARD!

AAGH! SEIZE HIM ~ ~ YOU FOOLS!

GREAT SCOTT, IT'S BUNTER! WE'VE GOT TO DO SOMETHING, HAZEL! THE FAT ASS WILL GET MURDERED!

203

THEN WITH AN OMINOUS CRACKING SOUND, THE OLD GALLERY TORE LOOSE ~~

SHE'S GIVING WAY! JUMP FOR IT, HAZEL!

TOO LATE - WE'RE FALLING!

WHOOPS!

OH, C-C-CRIKEY! THERE'S CHERRY AND HAZEL. THESE BEASTS MUST BE REAL FOREIGNERS. YAROOH!

BUNTER STREAKED OUT THROUGH THE OPEN DOOR AS HIS CAPTORS WERE SENT SPRAWLING.

YAROOH! HELP! MURDER! FIRE! POLICE! LEMME OUT OF HERE!

MORE SPIES! GRAB THEM QUICKLY, FOOLS!

BIND THEM SECURELY! THEY MUST NOT ESCAPE!

IT'S NO GOOD, HAZEL~~ THEY'VE GOT US ~~ I ONLY HOPE THAT FAT ASS BUNTER GOT AWAY~~ HE MIGHT BRING HELP~~

MEANWHILE, BUNTER FLED IN TERROR TOWARDS GREYFRIARS AS FAST AS HIS FAT LITTLE LEGS WOULD CARRY HIM ~~

HELP! MURDER! YAROOH!

AH, IT'S BUNTER, OF COURSE! I ALLOWED YOU A LATE PASS! I TRUST YOU HAD AN ENJOYABLE EVENING, MY BOY!

HELP! THEY'RE AFTER ME! SPIES! BEASTS WITH GUNS AND KNIVES AND THINGS! HELP!

IT'S T-T-TRUE, SIR! HONEST! THEY TRIED TO K-K-KILL ME!

RUN ALONG TO BED, YOU FOOLISH BOY. YOU HAVE FRIGHTENED YOURSELF WITH SOME STUPID CINEMA FILM. AWAY YOU GO!

BUNTER WAS DRAGGED DOWN THE STAIRS~~ PROTESTING LOUDLY~~

THE JUNIORS SWARMED INTO THE QUAD~~

THE BOYS CROUCHED LOW AS QUELCH SWEPT PAST LIKE A RAGING TORNADO!

BUT LITTLE DID THE JUNIORS KNOW, THAT MR QUELCH WAS AWARE OF THEIR DESTINATION.

MEANWHILE, INSIDE THE OLD HOUSE ~~

THEN, AS BOB CHERRY AND HAZELDENE WERE DRAGGED THROUGH THE HALLWAY, STRUGGLING FIERCELY ~~

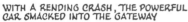

MARJORIE HAZELDENE AND HER FRIENDS PULL UP AS HARRY WHARTON, CAPTAIN OF THE REMOVE, SINGS OUT A GREETING ~~

COMING TO SEE THE REMOVE PLAY FOOTER THIS AFTERNOON, GIRLS?

RATHER! WOULDN'T MISS THE CHANCE OF SEEING YOU WHACKED BY THE UPPER FOURTH!

HA! HA! HA!

WHAT'S MORE WE'RE INVITING OURSELVES TO TEA AFTER THE MATCH ~~ AND WE DON'T WANT ANY OF YOUR STALE BUNS THIS TIME ~~ I'VE MADE A CAKE FOR THE OCCASION.

CRIKEY! SOME CAKE!

SEE YOU AT THREE O'CLOCK! CHEERIO!

I SAY, YOU ROTTERS ~~ DID SOMEONE SAY CAKE?

SO LONG, GIRLS!

211

AND OUTSIDE THE DOOR -- BILLY BUNTER IS LISTENING --

ROTTEN SUSPICIOUS BEASTS! AS IF I WANT THEIR MEASLY CAKE! I WONDER HOW I CAN GET HOLD OF IT?

THE FAMOUS FIVE SET OUT FOR THE GAME - AND BILLY'S FAT LEGS TWINKLE AS HE DODGES OUT OF SIGHT --

GOOD! NOW'S MY CHANCE!

THEN THE FATTEST SCHOLAR IN GREYFRIARS GETS TO WORK WITH A POKER!

SUSPICIOUS ROTTERS! MAKING A CHAP WORK LIKE THIS! THEY NEVER TAKE A FELLOW'S WORD OF HONOUR!

THE WRECKED DOOR SWINGS OPEN AND BUNTER'S MOUTH WATERS ~~

I-SAY! THIS IS A SMASHING CAKE *!*

AT THAT INSTANT BOB CHERRY'S CHEERFUL VOICE FLOATS UP FROM THE QUADRANGLE ~~

WON'T BE A MINUTE *!* LEFT MY SHINGUARDS IN THE STUDY *!*

HURRY UP, BOB ~~ YOU ASS *!*

OH, LOR *!* HE'S COMING BACK *!* I'LL TAKE THE CAKE WITH ME *!*

OOOOF *!*

WHOOOOPS *!*

213

M-MRS MIMBLE ~~ IT-IT'S MY BIRTHDAY TODAY ~~ AND I'M EXPECTING A POSTAL ORDER ~~

NOT ANOTHER THING DO YOU GET, MASTER BUNTER, UNTIL YOU PAY WHAT YOU ALREADY OWE !

BUNTER'S FAT LEGS TAKE HIM TO LITTLE-SIDE WHERE THE REMOVE ARE PLAYING SOCCER ~~

JOLLY GOOD MIND TO REPORT HER ~~ HULLO ! THERE'S THE CLIFF HOUSE GIRLS ~~ I WONDER IF ~~

LOOK OUT, GIRLS ~~ HERE COMES THE PRIZE CADGER OF GREYFRIARS !

GO IT, REMOVE ! ON THE BALL !

AS BUNTER SCUTTLES AWAY IN TERROR, HE RUNS INTO THE HEADMASTER AND MR QUELCH.

BUNTER! WHERE ARE YOUR LINES? TAKE THEM TO MY STUDY IMMEDIATELY!

OW! OH! YES, SIR! RIGHT AWAY, SIR!

BLESS MY SOUL!

BUNTER HURRIES OFF TO MR QUELCH'S STUDY.

LOT OF STINGY BEASTS -- WHERE CAN I GET A CAKE?

BUNTER PUTS HIS LINES ON THE TABLE.

COO! THE PHONE! THAT GIVES ME AN IDEA! I ONLY HOPE OLD QUELCHY DOESN'T BUTT IN!

HULLO! IS THAT THE COURTFIELD CAKE SHOP? I'D LIKE TO SPEAK TO THE MANAGER --

A SONG ABOUT BESSIE BUNTER. SHEET MUSIC GIVEN FREE WITH 'SCHOOL FRIEND' IN MARCH, 1924.

BESSIE - THE PRIDE OF THE SCHOOL

Music by Toni Farrell.   Words by Tom Richards.

Bessie the Pride of the School!

Music by TONI FARRELL. Words by TOM RICHARDS.

Waltz time.

PIANO.

1. We have good look ing girls, we have girls that are plain, We have dark and fair a-

-gain and a-gain! But one of them's diff'rent fr'm an-y we've seen, Need I tell you her

name? You all know whom I mean!

Chorus.

Bes-sie, the pride of the school, girls!.........

Bes-sie, the light of our eyes!.............. When first you meet Bes-sie the bux-om.......

rall.

You get a tre-men-dous sur-prise—she's a char-ac-ter! Watch her par-take like a hunt-er,........... Perch'd on the old tuck-shop stool!.......... But we must not af-front her—she's our Bes-sie Bun-ter! Our Bes-sie, tho pride of the school!..........

2.

Bessie likes nothing better than "telling the tale,"
And the deeds she boasts would make heroines quail!
And when you hear laughter, you'll easily guess
We are chaffing and laughing at fatuous Bess!

Chorus.—Bessie, our champion eater!
Bessie, our Queen of Romance!
Her wonderful, non-stop adventures
She details whenever the chance she can pounce upon!
Hear her hold forth on her home life,
At Bunter Court and then you
Will all laugh till you're stutt'ring, 'midst furious splutt'ring
From Bessie, the pride of the school!

3.

Bessie thinks she's a wonder at all forms of sport,
A marvel at games of every sort.
And if you but saw her I'm sure you'd agree
She's a wonder and marvel—for causing you glee!

Chorus.—Bessie, the duffer at lessons!
Bessie, who earns all the lines!
As dense as she thinks herself clever,
There's only one time when she shines—when she's eaten well!
Bessie's got faults by the dozen,
Some girls dub her "Just a fool!"
But there's none more good-hearted—we'd hate to be parted—
From Bessie, the pride of the school!

BILLY BUNTER

THE FATTEST SCHOOLBOY ON EARTH!

I'LL TODDLE OVER TO BESSIE'S SCHOOL AND CADGE A FEW CAKES FROM HER.

I'LL BET SHE'S GOT PLENTY OF LOVELY GRUB THAT I COULD HELP HER SCOFF!

WHY-COO! THAT'S BESSIE - AND SHE'S CARRYING A LARGE BAG - BESSIE!

HI! BESSIE! STOP! IT'S WILLIAM CALLING!

CRUMBS! PUFF! SHE WON'T STOP! IS MY SILLY SISTER DEAF -

I'M BEING FOLLOWED - I'LL PUT ON SPEED! BESSIE! STOP!

GUFF! GASP! PUT THE BRAKE ON - IT'S WILLIAM!

I MUSTN'T BE CAUGHT - SO I'LL GO EVEN FASTER!

WHAT ARE ALL THESE PIECES OF PAPER? IS BESSIE THROWING 'EM AWAY -

OW! IT'S A TOFFEE PAPER! HOW MEAN! THAT BAG MUST BE FULL OF TOFFEES!

AN EMPTY BAG - THERE'S BISCUIT CRUMBS IN IT! OW! BESSIE!

HERE'S A WRAPPING FOR A LOVELY CHOCOLATE CREAM - IT'S EMPTY! WHAT A MEAN SWIZZ!

OW! I'M GOING THE WRONG WAY! BESSIE IS TRYING TO LOSE ME - SHE WON'T!

O CRUMBS! MY GREEDY SISTER IS STILL EATING TOFFEES - HERE ARE MORE WRAPPINGS!

THAT WILL DIDDLE THEM - THEY'LL THINK I'M UP THE TREE!

B-BESSIE! YOU GREEDY ROTTER - LET'S GO SHARES!

I'VE BEEN TO THE TOP OF THE TREE - AND BESSIE'S NOT TO BE FOUND!

PHEW! I'VE NEARLY EMPTIED THE BAG - AND I HAVEN'T BEEN CAUGHT!

THERE'S BESSIE! I'VE CAUGHT HER AT LAST! NOW I'LL GET SOME OF THAT GRUB!

I'VE NABBED YOU NOW, BESSIE, YOU GREEDY THING! LET ME DIP INTO THAT BAG - I'M FAMISHED!

OW! WHAT A SWIZZ! IT'S EMPTY! I'VE BEEN TRICKED!

WILLIAM! STOP! YOU'RE NOT IN THIS GAME - IT'S ONLY FOR GIRLS!

SILLY! IT'S OUR GIRLS SCHOOL ANNUAL PAPER CHASE! YOU'VE BEEN CHASING THE WRONG HARE, WILLIAM! HE! HE!

OW! N-NO!

231

BESSIE GOES CAMPING

THE GIRLS OF CLIFF HOUSE WERE STAYING FOR A LONG WEEK-END AT THE COAST. THEIR HEADMISTRESS, MISS STACKPOLE, HAD DECIDED THEY WOULD SPEND THEIR HOLIDAY UNDER CANVAS, BUT BESSIE BUNTER, THE FAT GIRL OF THE FORM, WAS NOT VERY KEEN...

BESSIE BUNTER'S STRIP FROM 'JUNE & SCHOOL FRIEND' LIBRARY.

235

236

237

243

THE HUNGRY GIRL LOST HER TEMPER...

BLOW THAT PERISHER PEACHEM AND HIS PERISHING PAINT!

PEACHEMS QUICK DRYING PAINT

UNKNOWN TO BESSIE, THE LARGE CAN HIT THE ROW-BOAT, SPILLING PAINT IN ALL DIRECTIONS

GET ON, MARY! LET'S FIND THE KITCHEN—THERE'S BOUND TO BE GRUB THERE!

I HOPE THERE'S NOTHING ELSE— GHOSTS, FOR INSTANCE!

245

IT WAS MUCH LATER WHEN THE CHUMS CAME ON DECK...

TIME TO UNTIE OUR BOAT AND GET BACK TO SHORE, BESSIE!

I'M IN NO HURRY, MARY!

THEN YOU'D BETTER BE! THE SHIP IS SINKING!

O LOR!

OVER THE SIDE — QUICK!

WOMEN, CHILDREN AND BESSIE FIRST!

THE EERIE NOISE BOOMED THROUGH THE FOG...

WHOOOOOOOOOOO

DID YOU HEAR THAT, BESSIE?

YOU MUST BE JOKING! I RECKON THEY HEARD IT IN TIMBUCTOO!

THEN A VAGUE SHAPE LOOMED THROUGH THE MURK...

L...LOOK!

LUMME! IT'S A SEA MONSTER! I'M GETTING OUT OF THIS!

AT THE SAME TIME, THE LITTLE VESSEL WAS SIGHTED...

EEEEEEK! IT'S A ROW-BOAT— I MEAN, A GLOW-BOAT!

'TIS THE LOCAL LEGEND COME TRUE!

257

OTHER ARTISTS ON BUNTER

BILLY BUNTER STRIP BY ERIC ROBERTS.

THIS IS MORE LIKE IT! A PICNIC PARTY! I THINK I'LL JOIN IN!

EEEKK! LOOK, IT'S A THING FROM 50,000 FATHOMS DEEP!

RUN FOR YOUR LIVES! SOUND THE ALARM!

THOSE SILLY OLD ROTTERS HAVE GONE OFF THEIR FOOD!— AND THEY LEFT ME TO FINISH IT OFF! WHACKO!

A GREAT BLACK MONSTER ALL SLIMY AND GLISTENING,— ABOUT TEN FEET ROUND THE MIDDLE!

IT CAME UP FROM THE DEEP LOOKING FOR FOOD!

CALAMITY!

I AM NOT AFRAID! LEAD ME TO IT AND I SHALL ATTACK THE MONSTER SINGLE-HANDED!

BRAVE MAN!— COME THIS WAY, SIR!

I FEEL A BIT TIRED AFTER ALL THAT GRUB! I THINK I'LL HAVE A LITTLE FLOAT AND SLEEP IT OFF!

AH! THERE IS THE CREATURE BASKING ON THE SURFACE! I SHALL CREEP UP ON IT AND USE THIS WEAPON!

LOTS OF CHOCOLATE FOR ME TO EAT...LA.LA. CRUMBS! I WISH I COULD REMEMBER THE REST OF IT!

AIM! FIRE!

YAROOGH! I'VE BEEN TORPEDOED OR SOMETHING!

GRACIOUS! THE MONSTER HAS MADE A TREMENDOUS LEAP INTO THE AIR! I MUST SURFACE AND CAPTURE IT!

OH CORKS! WHAT HAVE I LANDED ON NOW?

EEEKKK!!!

COME BACK HERE, BUNTER!

O CRUMBS! IT'S NOT ME, SIR! I'M A SWANNEL CHIMMER— ER, I MEAN A CHANNEL SWIMMER, ER, OH CORKS!

BILLY BUNTER

THE HEAVYWEIGHT CHUMP OF HIS SCHOOL

THE FAT OWL SKIDS ON A SEA OF MUD... AND HITS THE HEADMASTER WITH A NASTY THUD!

BILLY BUNTER

THE HEAVYWEIGHT CHUMP OF GREYFRIARS

BUNTER WAS INTERESTED WHEN HE SAW JONES MINOR WITH A MYSTERIOUS BOX IN THE LOCAL WOODS!

I BET IT CONTAINS GRUB!

GOING TO HAVE A PICNIC ON YOUR OWN, EH, YOU GREEDY LITTLE BEAST? I'LL HAVE THAT!

HI!

I'LL SHUT MYSELF IN MY ROOM AND SCOFF IT!

SQUELCH   SQUELCH

WHOOPS

OOF!

MUDDY SLITHER

YOU'VE MADE EVERYWHERE MUDDY!

AND WHAT HAS HE GOT IN THIS BOX?

EEK! A HEDGEHOG!

OOER! IT'S NOT MINE, SIR! IT BELONGS TO JONES MINOR!

YOU KNOW ANIMALS ARE NOT ALLOWED IN SCHOOL, JONES MINOR! LET IT LOOSE, THEN REPORT BACK TO ME!

AND YOU CAN CLEAN UP ALL THE MUD!

WE REALLY NEED A CEMENT PATH HERE SO THAT MUD ISN'T BROUGHT INTO THE HALL!

YES, HEADMASTER! I'LL GET JONES TO MAKE ONE AS A PUNISHMENT!

SO JONES MINOR WAS SET TO WORK...

WE'LL INSTRUCT YOU! FIRST MIX THE SAND AND CEMENT WITH WATER—!

CEMENT

SAND

BAH! THIS IS ALL BUNTER'S FAULT!

LATER...

IT'S FINISHED! WELL DONE, JONES! YOU MAY GO NOW!

I'LL GO, ALL RIGHT— AND SORT OUT THE FAT OWL!

THERE HE IS!

EE! LOVELY GRUB! COOK'S NOT LOOKING SO I'LL BE EVER SO QUIET AND PINCH SOME!

KITCHEN

TAKE THAT, FOR GETTING ME INTO TROUBLE!

YOW!

URG!

KITCHEN

AFTER THE FOOD, EH? YOU'RE GOING TO GET MORE THAN YOU BARGAINED FOR!

BILLY BUNTER
THE HEAVYWEIGHT CHUMP OF GREYFRIARS

269

WHAT A SOPPY BRANCH! IT CAN'T TAKE MY WEIGHT!

TEE, HEE! WHAT LUCK! NOW I'LL GET BACK QUICKER TO THE TUCK SHOP!

THEN MR. QUELCH SAW THE MISSING CLOTHES... SOME RASCALS ARE WEARING THEM!

GIVE ME BACK MY PUPILS' SUITS! —OOER! MONKEYS!

CHATTER! HELP! CHATTER!

I BOUGHT THESE UNIFORMS TO DRESS UP MY TROUPE OF PERFORMING MONKEYS! A FAT SCHOOLBOY SOLD THEM TO ME!

BUNTER!

THEN THE RICH RAG TRADE GENT ARRIVED...

I'M TAKING SOME EXTRA CLOTHES FOR MY BOY! HOP IN, MR. QUELCH! I'LL GIVE YOU A LIFT BACK TO SCHOOL!

OH, BLOW! THE TUCK SHOP'S NOT OPEN YET! OPEN UP! THUMP

IT'S THAT FAT BOY AGAIN! HE'S ALWAYS STANDING IN THE WAY OF MY CAR!

I'LL BUY THOSE EXTRA OUTFITS FOR MY OTHER PUPILS, SIR! YOU CAN TAKE THAT CASH IN PAYMENT!

OKAY! I'LL SEND MY SON SOME MORE!

AND SEEING YOU'RE INTERESTED IN OLD CLOTHES — YOU CAN REPAIR MINE! GET STITCHING!

YAROO!

BUMPER STITCH BOX

CHRISTMAS WITH BUNTER

"My hat!" murmured Billy Bunter. "This is ripping! They can put it down to the cat in the morning."

"KNOCKOUT" COMIC
BILLY BUNTER
THE FATTEST SCHOOLBOY ON EARTH!

1. Billy Bunter had a secret—a bag of sweets! He was keeping it dark 'cos he meant to keep them all to himself. But the whole school knew that he was having a good time. The sound of succulent sucks echoed everywhere.

2. Mr. Quelch quivered with indignation. When his porky pupil smacked his lips, it was like a round of applause with wet hands. At last, the Head couldn't stand it any longer, and, through sound, found the fat lad.

3. Billy's lip-smacking ceased suddenly and changed to a wail like a whale with toothache. It was a smack in the eye to him when Quelch bagged his bag of bullseyes. Just like the greedy rotter to grab 'em, too, thought Bunter.

4. Leaving Bunter to bemoan his fate, Quelchy faded away. Where could he hide those vulgar-sounding sweets? Ah! The Christmas decorations! Bunter would never look for them there.

5. Meanwhile, Billy was doing a spot of Sexton Blake sleuthing after his bullseyes. He thought he was on the target when he saw Quelchy slip into his study and hide something in a drawer.

6. Billy parked his person round a corner of the corridor until Quelchy came out again. Then the fat lad slipped into the study. Old Quelchy couldn't slip one over on him.

7. Billy looked round. In fact, he was so fat that he always looked round. But this time he looked round Quelchy's room. Ahahaha! There was a key in the top drawer.

8. But there was more in there than met the eye. Bonk! A wooden ball on a spring suddenly shot out and met Bunter on his nose. Instead of sweets, he got a smack.

9. But somebody was enjoying the joke— Old Quelchy! The master shook with mirth at the way his outsize scholar had been poked on the smeller. He was tickled with his trick.

13. Billy howled with pain. He'd been diddled, he'd been done. The master gurgled with glee. He'd put two across the wily William George. But the frivolities were finished. There was a job of work to be jobbed.

14. The Christmas decorations had to be hung, but they could go to hang for all Billy cared. After all, a chap can't chew decorations, can he? But the headmaster meant it, and so Billy was put on the job with Jones Minor.

15. At least, Jonesy did the job while Billy bemoaned his lost sweets. Oh where, oh where could his bullseyes be? Billy sat down on the steps to think things over—and that's where more trouble stepped in.

16. The great Bunter brain was going nineteen to the dozen. Suddenly, a bright think ticked over. The bullseyes were bound to be in Quelchy's bed-room. The greedy rotter must have hidden them under the pillow!

17. That thought was good enough for William George Bunter. The fat lad was up in a flash. He was still wrapped in his thoughts, but didn't know that he was also wrapped up in the decorations. He soon knew!

18. Crash! Something hit Bunter on the back of the neck. It was Jones Minor! Billy thought that he was after the sweets, too, but Jonesy hadn't meant to follow his fat friend. It was Billy's sudden rising that did it.

19. Gosh, what a mix-up there was as Billy yanked the decorations and Jonesy did a high dive from the top of the steps. But they were soon sorted out when other boys arrived to say that Quelchy was coming.

20. Everybody piled in to lend a hand. Billy Bunter never lent anything in his life, but he tried to show willing. Soon, Quelchy arrived and gave the decorations a good dekko-over.

21. Talk about the sergeant-major on parade! Quelchy didn't miss much as he inspected the decorations . . . his optics were as keen as Bunter's after his bullseyes. But the master was pleased except for . . . .

BILLY BUNTER
THE FATTEST SCHOOLBOY ON EARTH!

1. It was Christmas Day and Billy was broke. He was stonier than a pound of cherries! But Billy brightened when he saw a big drum. He had a wheeze to beat the band. He'd go carol singing for an early dinner!

2. No sooner had the wheeze wheezled than William Geo. went into action. He collared Jones Minor to beat the big drum as he would need all his own strength to eat later, Off they went to Colonel Bracebutton's house.

3. Have you ever heard a ship's siren in a fog? Billy's voice sounded just like that. He was the weightiest wait that ever warbled, and he did sound weird. Jonesy beefed away at the big drum to drown that awful noise.

4. But, suddenly, both were drowned in a heavy shower of snowballs! A few of Courtfield's best brand of bad boys had been attracted by Bunter's bleatings. They were attacking.

5. Whizz! Wallop! The snowballs sizzled through the air. Billy and Jonesy didn't have a chance, so down they dodged behind the big drum. This certainly changed Bunter's tune.

6. Meanwhile, Mr. Quelch was having a quiet meander. Suddenly his face twisted in agony as he heard Bunter begin to sing. Then the Head hurried forward as sounds of battle followed.

7. Swoosh! Thud! Quelchy came to a full stop as a snowball hit him full in the face. That put an icy glitter in his eyes and he dashed forward angrily. Then came another. . . .

8. But Quelchy was ready. With a nifty move of his mortar-board the master made that snowball miss. Then Bunter blinked as he saw Quelchy grab a handful of snow.

9. Quelchy was far from being the foozly old fossil that he looked. Those sizzling missiles brought back memories, and he began slinging snowballs. Billy and Jonesy joined in!

13. It certainly was the chance of a laugh-time! Quelchy was so busy slinging snowballs that he didn't see the Colonel coming up to carry out his rear attack. The next thing Quelchy knew was that the snow was down his neck.

14. But the master was in fine form. He also had a snowball in his hand and—whizz!—he slung it with the greatest of gusto. The Colonel's chortle changed to a gurgle. Quelchy had scored a bulls-eye on his optic!

15. Billy blinked at the master in amazement. This certainly was a new Mr. Quelch! But Billy was even more surprised when Quelchy grabbed him by the flipper and pulled him away. The master was up to more fun and games.

16. Quelchy's idea of a surprise attack was a nifty notion. It was an aerial attack from the roof! But, if the master was grinning, Bunter was groaning. Climbing on nasty, snow-covered roofs wasn't much fun for the fat lad.

17. What's more, all this exercise was making Billy more hungry than ever. Gosh, how he could do with a feed, he thought, as he watched Quelchy prepare for action. The master was piling up a heap of snow to drop on the Colonel.

18. Billy watched it grow bigger and bigger. He could just do with a Christmas pudding that size, he could. Then Bunter thought of a wheeze to get off—he offered to spy out for Colonel Bracebutton. That was a big slip!

19. It was, because Billy slipped as he tried to scramble up the roof. Swooooosh! Down came Bunter like an elephant in an avalanche and Quelchy, plus his huge pile of snow, went over the edge. But who was that below?

20. It was P.-c. Potts! The man in blue thought Quelchy was a bolt from the blue when the master landed on him. Thud! Down crashed the copper covered in snow, while Bunter came tumbling after.

21. Coo, what a to-do! P.-c. Potts thought that everybody had gone potty. Things were coming to a fine pass when master and pupil came popping down on a person from roof-tops. Something had to be done about this!

BILLY BUNTER

THE HEAVYWEIGHT CHUMP OF GREYFRIARS

ON CHRISTMAS MORNING, BUNTER SLEPT LATE, HAVING PLEASANT DREAMS!

WHILST MR. QUELCH WAS HAVING PROBLEMS..

TUT! NO LOGS OR FIREWOOD FOR CHRISTMAS!

WAKEY-WAKEY! HERE'S SOME WARM FRUIT JUICE, BOYS! DON'T HURRY TO GET UP—!

—OPEN THESE PARCELS FIRST!

COR! CHRISTMAS PRESENTS!

A SAW!

AN AXE!

NOW COME WITH ME INTO THE WOODS AND CHOP SOME FIREWOOD AND SAW DOWN A NICE YULE LOG!

BAH! WHAT A SWIZ!

THIS IS A GOOD SPOT! WE WON'T GO BACK UNTIL WE'VE GOT A LOT OF WOOD! SET TO WORK!

BRR! IT'S COLD OUT HERE!

I'LL CHOP DOWN THIS TREE SO THAT IT BONKS OLD QUELCHY! THEN WE'LL HAVE TO CARRY HIM BACK TO THE WARM SCHOOL!

WHOOPS! THE AXE-HEAD'S SLIPPED OFF!

I'D BETTER GET IT BACK!

CRASH

BUNTER SAW A CHANCE TO PRETEND HE'D DONE HIS SHARE OF CHOPPING...

I'LL TAKE THAT PILE OF LOGS!

TAKE THAT INSTEAD! THIS WAS MY FORESTER'S SHELTER BEFORE YOUR WHOPPING GREAT AXE-HEAD FELL ON IT!

OW!

STOP MOANING, BUNTER! YOU HAVEN'T DONE ANY WORK YET—SO DON'T PRETEND YOU'VE GOT BACKACHE!

I'M NOT PRETENDING! OW!

I'LL TAKE THE AXE— YOU TAKE THESE SNIPPERS AND COLLECT SOME HOLLY WITH NICE BERRIES FOR CHRISTMAS DECORATION!

I'LL MAKE QUELCHY GET WET, THEN HE'LL WANT TO GO BACK TO SCHOOL! IF I HIDE THE THIN POND ICE WITH LEAVES, AND THEN LURE HIM INTO STEPPING ON IT, HE'LL FALL THROUGH!

HI, SIR! MY ARMS AREN'T LONG ENOUGH TO REACH THOSE BERRIES! YOU COULD IF YOU STEPPED NEARER!

NO NEED TO! I CAN HOOK MY CANE ROUND IT FROM HERE—!

AND PULL THE BRANCH BACK— SO!

YAROO!

NOW WE'LL RETURN TO SCHOOL! I'LL CARRY THIS FIREWOOD AND HOLLY! YOU BOYS CAN BRING THE YULE LOG!

I'M NOT CARRYING THAT HEAVY THING! LET'S SIT ON IT AND SLIDE DOWNHILL TO SCHOOL!

GOOD IDEA, FAT MAN!

BUT.. EE! STOP! OLD QUELCHY IS IN THE WAY!

WE CAN'T, STUPID! THERE AREN'T ANY BRAKES!

BUT WE'VE GOT A NICE SOFT OLD BUFFER ON THE FRONT TO DEADEN THE IMPACT!

DINING ROOM

THUD

COO! A FEAST— AND GIFTS, TOO!

YES! IT WAS MR. QUELCH'S IDEA TO TEASE YOU THIS MORNING— THEN GIVE YOU THIS LOVELY SURPRISE!

POOR OLD QUELCHY'S GOT THE SURPRISE!

NUTS

THREE CHEERS FOR 'SIR'! FOR HE'S A JOLLY GOOD FELLOW..!

I'VE SAWN OUT A BIT OF THE TABLE, FAT MAN, TO ALLOW FOR SWELLING!

JOLLY GOOD IDEA! MERRY CHRISTMAS, ALL!

CHRISTMAS AT GREYFRIARS

There's mirth and mystery in this rollicking yarn of BILLY BUNTER, the famous fat school-boy, and Harry Wharton and Company of Greyfriars School - - - -

ALONZO TODD WAS CHOSEN TO PLAY THE PART.

I TRUST YOU WILL MAKE ME SUFFICIENTLY FEARSOME, MY DEAR FELLOWS!

YOU MAKE A FINE GHOST, LONZY! THIS LUMINOUS PAINT WILL SHINE LIKE ANYTHING IN THE DARK!

WE WANT TO LURE BUNTER DOWN TO THE CLOISTERS. HOW CAN WE WORK THAT?

LEAVE IT TO ME! IT'S SEVERAL HOURS SINCE BUNTER SCOFFED THAT TURKEY --- AND HE'S GETTING HUNGRY AGAIN!

I'VE GOT A BIG PARCEL OF TUCK THAT I HID IN THE CLOISTERS TO KEEP IT OUT OF BUNTER'S WAY! WE'LL HAVE A MIDNIGHT FEAST IN THE DORM WHEN HE'S ASLEEP!

WHAT-HO!

THE WHAT-HOFULNESS IS TERRIFIC!

AND IN THE COMMON ROOM, BILLY BUNTER'S FAT LITTLE EARS FAIRLY WAGGLED WITH EXCITEMENT!....

TEN MINUTES LATER ~~

FANCY THOSE SUSPICIOUS BEASTS THINKING I'D PINCH THAT TUCK! NOW -- I WONDER WHERE SMITHY HID IT!

THERE GOES THE GREEDY OLD BARREL!

AND ALONZO IS WAITING FOR HIM! IT SHOULD BE FUN!

BUNTER DIDN'T LOOK FOR LONG!

YAROOGH! A GHOST!

EEEE~~OOOWW!

WHATEVER ARE YOU BOYS UP TO? AND -- AND WHAT IS THE MATTER WITH BUNTER?

IT'S ALL RIGHT, SIR! WE'RE JUST PLAYING A JOKE ON BUNTER. HE THINKS HE HAS SEEN A GHOST!

MR. QUELCH WAS WALKING THROUGH THE CLOISTERS TO HIS ROOMS.

MR. QUELCH HID A SMILE. AND THEN A SECOND EAR-PIERCING YELL RANG FROM WITHIN THE CLOISTERS ~~~ AND LONZY HURTLED OUT!

WHOOPS!

OUT OF MY WAY EVERYBODY! TH-TH-THERE'S A REAL GHOST IN THE CLOISTERS!

YOU FATHEAD!

AND ALONZO TODD WAS NOT JOKING!

L-L-LOOK!

GOOD GRACIOUS! AN APPARITION!

A CLOAKED FIGURE SHIMMERING IN THE DARKNESS, SENT SUDDEN CHILLS UP AND DOWN THEIR SPINES!

281

PROFESSOR SEBASTIAN CREEP WAS ALLOWED IN, OF COURSE, AND IN THE HEAD'S STUDY LATER, HE DISCUSSED HIS BUSINESS WITH DR. LOCKE. HE WAS PROFUSE IN HIS THANKS AND SAID SO MANY TIMES, IN AN OILY SORT OF VOICE.....

SO KIND OF YOU TO LET ME STAY, DR. LOCKE. I HOPE TO MAKE A CLOSE STUDY OF THIS GHOST. THE NATIONAL GHOST SOCIETY WILL BE DELIGHTED!

ER - DO YOU? I MEAN, WILL THEY? OH DEAR! I AM REALLY QUITE AT SEA IN THIS MATTER!

NEXT MORNING, THE BOYS OF THE REMOVE WOKE BRIGHT AND EARLY. BOB CHERRY, FEELING FULL OF BEANS AS USUAL, DASHED TO THE WINDOW AND FLUNG IT WIDE OPEN WITH A YELL OF DELIGHT!.....

BRRR! IF YOU WOULD SHUTFULLY CLOSE THE WINDOW, THE OBLIGEFULNESS WOULD BE TERRIFIC, MY ESTEEMED BOB!

HALLO, HALLO, HALLO!, BAGS OF SNOW! WE'LL GO AND HAVE A SNOW FIGHT WITH THE FIFTH WHEN MARJORIE AND THE CLIFF HOUSE GIRLS ARRIVE!

HA-HA-HA!

AFTER BREAKFAST ---

GOOD IDEA! AFTER ALL, IT'S HOLIDAY TIME! I'LL GIVE YOU A HAND, BOB!

MY HAT! WHAT HAVE YOU BROUGHT YOUR NEW BIKE UP HERE FOR, BOB?

I THOUGHT I'D OIL IT AND CHECK IT OVER WHILE WE WAIT FOR THE SNOW TO STOP. IT'S TOO COLD DOWN IN THE SHED!

THE REMOVITES STARTED WITH THE BEST INTENTIONS ~~ BUT THEY HAD TIME ON THEIR HANDS, AND WERE FULL OF THE HOLIDAY SPIRIT. BEFORE LONG ---

I SAY, YOU FELLOWS, I'M SMASHING ON A BIKE!

SMASHING'S THE WORD, YOU FAT OWL!

MIND THE STAIRS, JOHNNY!

NEXT MOMENT ---

EEEEK!

LOOK OUT- OOOPS!

THE BIKE CAREERED WILDLY ON -- AND DOWN THE STAIRS!

AGH- UGH- OOGH!

YOU FAT-HEAD! OH -OOGH- OUCH!

CRUMBS! IT'S THAT GHOST- HUNTING CHAP!

MY BIKE!

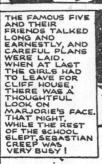

HE MUST HAVE BURIED IT IN OUR SOCCER PITCH -- AT ONE OF THE CORNERS, SO HE'D KNOW WHERE TO FIND IT AGAIN! BUT WE MARKED OUT THE PITCH AFRESH LAST SEPTEMBER! SO HE DUG FOR THE LOOT IN THE WRONG PLACE!

THEN CREEPS YOUR MAN! FIRST HE PLAYED THE GHOST, TO PUT YOU OFF THE SCENT. THEN HE BECAME GHOST-HUNTER, SO THAT HE COULD PROWL ROUND UNHINDERED AT ANY TIME OF NIGHT!

GOSH, I THINK YOU'RE RIGHT, MARJORIE!

SURE SHE IS, BOB! NOW ALL WE WANT IS A PLAN OF ACTION TO PROVE IT!

THE FAMOUS FIVE AND THEIR FRIENDS TALKED LONG AND EARNESTLY, AND CAREFUL PLANS WERE LAID. WHEN AT LAST THE GIRLS HAD TO LEAVE FOR CLIFF HOUSE, THERE WAS A THOUGHTFUL LOOK ON MARJORIE'S FACE. THAT NIGHT, WHILE THE REST OF THE SCHOOL SLEPT, SEBASTIAN CREEP WAS VERY BUSY!

EEEK!

A FUSILLADE FROM TWO WELL-HANDLED CATAPULTS SENT CREEP FLYING IN PANIC!

FRANK AND JOHNNY HAVE TICKLED HIM UP! NOW FOR IT!

GOT HIM!

WRAP HIM UP!

HE MUST HAVE FOUND OUT WHERE THE GOAL-POSTS USED TO BE LINED UP! HE KNEW WHERE TO DIG THIS TIME!

MARJORIE! WHAT--?

YOU DIDN'T THINK WE WERE GOING TO MISS THE FUN, DID YOU?

YOU LITTLE 'ORRORS, LET ME OUT!

IN THE EARLY HOURS OF THE MORNING -

BOYS! YOU SHOULD NOT HAVE TACKLED THIS ON YOUR OWN! HOWEVER --- I AM VERY PROUD OF YOU! NOW YOU MAY CONDUCT THESE YOUNG LADIES TO THEIR SCHOOL, AND THEN RETURN TO BED. OFF WITH YOU!

WELL, SIR! WE'VE GOT THE SILVER PLATE UP SAFELY, AND WE'VE GOT THE THIEF, THANKS TO THESE YOUNGSTERS!

OH -- THANK YOU, SIR!

GOODNIGHT, SIR!

SO ALL ENDED HAPPILY FOR THE BOYS OF GREYFRIARS, INCLUDING BILLY BUNTER!

BILLY BUNTER

THE FATTEST SCHOOLBOY ON EARTH!

HURRAH FOR CHRISTMAS! FATHER HAS SENT ME FIVE POUNDS!

HOW JOLLY!

JONES MINOR - I'M GOING TO MAKE THE BIGGEST CHRISTMAS PUDDING IN THE WORLD! AND YOU'RE GOING TO HELP ME!

TO THE SHOPS! I'LL NEED LOTS AND LOTS OF-ER-STUFF FOR MY BIG PUDDING - AND I CAN BUY IT ALL!

I'VE STILL LOTS OF CASH LEFT-SO HOLD ON TO THOSE WHILE I POP IN HERE FOR MORE CHRISTMAS GOODIES!

THAT'S ABOUT ALL I NEED! LET'S GET BACK AND MAKE MY PUDDING!

IN THE SCHOOL KITCHEN
TEE! HEE! YUM! LET'S GET STARTED!

PLEASE BUNTER - YOU FAILED TO BUY I FRUIT-

CORKS! FRUIT! WHY DIDN'T YOU SAY SO BEFORE, JONES MINOR -

WHERE ARE YOU GOING, BUNTER?

HOW LUCKY I CALLED IN TO SEE TODDY - I DON'T SUPPOSE HE WILL MISS THESE ORANGES AND BANANAS - I'LL BLAME JONES MINOR 'COS HE FORGOT THE FRUIT!

O JOY! I SPY CHOCOLATES AND A JAR OF JAM ON BOLSOVER'S TABLE! THEY WILL HELP TO MAKE MY PUDDING FRUITY AND RICH!

- AND BOB CHERRY'S BAG OF FRUIT DROPS WILL ADD TO THE TASTE! SMACK! YUM!

DON'T STAND IDLE, JONES MINOR - GET ALL THE BAGS OF YEAST READY!

BUT - OH! LISTEN - I MEAN - PEEL AND RAISINS-

HERE GOES THE YEAST-AND DON'T INTERFERE SO MUCH, JONES MINOR! NOW LEAVE IT ALL TO ME!

I WILL LEAVE BEFORE THE EXPLOSION!

COO! THAT LITTLE ROTTER HAS BUNKED! GOOD RIDDANCE! NOW I CAN ENJOY THE BIGGEST CHRISTMAS PUDDING IN THE WORLD ALL TO MYSELF!

IT WILL TAKE A JOLLY LONG TIME TO COOK - SO I'LL JUST SIT HERE AND WAIT FOR IT! HEE! HEE!

BUT BUNTER FELL ASLEEP
BUBBLE!
SNORE!

AND THE PUDDING BEGAN TO OOZE OUT OF THE OVEN AND ALL OVER THE FLOOR!

WHAT - OH! BUNTER!

OW! I'VE SLIPPED!

EH? WHASSAT? CRUMBS! QUELCHY!

O LOR! THAT'S DONE IT! I'M IN FOR A WHACKING NOW!

I SHOULD PUNISH YOU MOST SEVERELY, BUNTER - BUT AS IT IS CHRISTMAS - THE SPIRIT OF GOODWILL PREVAILS TOWARDS - ER - EVEN YOU! LET US TO OUR CHRISTMAS PARTY, DEAR BOY!

COO! A JOLLY CHRISTMAS, SIR!

A MERRY CHRISTMAS TO ALL MY GOOD PUPILS - AND THE BAD ONE!

HERE'S TO YOU - AND HERE'S TO ME! WHAT A JOLLY CHRISTMAS SPREE!